Web Offset Press Operating

by
GATF Staff

GATF*Press*
PITTSBURGH

Library of Congress Catalog Card Number: 95-82165
International Standard Book Number: 0-88362-181-9

Printed in the United States of America

GATF Catalog No. 1516
Fourth Edition
Reprinted 1998

Printed on 60-lb. Wove Offset from P.H. Glatfelter Company

GATF*Press*
Graphic Arts Technical Foundation
200 Deer Run Road
Sewickley, PA 15143-2600
Phone: 412/741-6860
Fax: 412/741-2311
Email: info@gatf.org
Internet: http://www.gatf.org

Orders to:
GATF Orders
P.O. Box 1020
Sewickley, PA 15143-1020
Phone (U.S. and Canada only): 800/662-3916
Phone (all other countries): 412/741-5733
Fax: 412/741-0609
Email: gatforders@abdintl.com

Contents

Foreword

The Graphic Arts Technical Foundation is pleased to introduce the fourth edition of *Web Offset Press Operating*. The chapter structure of the previous edition has been maintained, but the chapters have been updated and expanded by Dennis J. Cook, GATF consultant. The book now has information on waterless offset lithography as well as a comprehensive glossary of terms pertinent to the web offset press operator. Designed to supplement press operating manuals and formal apprenticeship programs, GATF's *Web Offset Press Operating* provides both novice and experienced press operators with valuable information to improve productivity and print quality. Theoretical and practical how-to information have been combined in a single volume.

The concepts presented in this book are applicable to most web offset presses. Actual press adjustments, however, must be made following the press manufacturer's recommendations.

Like the previous three editions (1974, 1984, and 1989), this edition was also developed by GATF staff members. Cook, the Foundation's web offset specialist, was primarily responsible for the update of this edition. Cook reviewed the third edition and provided us with his comments on what needed to be changed to make this book reflect current industry practices and technology. As a consultant, Cook has conducted technical plant assessments for countless web offset printers, helping them become more productive. In addition, he is a leader of GATF's workshops on web offset printing.

GATF editor in chief, Thomas M. Destree, assisted Cook with the update, wrote the glossary of terms, edited the manuscript, and performed many desktop publishing functions, including pagination and creating the line drawings.

Charles J. Lucas, GATF art director, designed the cover. Thomas A. Whiteman, senior prepress technologist, ensured that the photographs would have the proper tone reproduction and dot gain characteristics.

Frank S. Benevento
Director, GATF Technical Information Group

Acknowledgments

GATF would like to thank the following companies for contributing information, photographs, and/or line illustrations for the fourth edition of *Web Offset Press Operating:*

- **AEC, Inc.,** Wood Dale, Ill.
- **American Environmental International, Inc.,** Arlington Heights, Ill.
- **Applied Web Systems, Inc.,** Elgin, Ill.
- **Automation, Inc.,** Canton, Mass.
- **Baldwin Dampening Systems,** Naugatuck, Conn.
- **Baldwin Graphic Products,** Stamford, Conn.
- **Baldwin Web Controls,** Countryside, Ill.
- **Louis P. Batson Co.,** Greenville, S.C.
- **Bel-Art Products,** Pequannock, N.J.
- **Bilsom International, Inc.,** Sterling, Va.
- **Böttcher America Corp.,** Belcamp, Md.
- **Brandtjen & Kluge, Inc.,** St. Croix Falls, Wis.
- **Butler Automatic, Inc.,** Canton, Mass.
- **E. J. Cady & Co.,** Wheeling, Ill.
- **Cascade Corporation,** Portland, Oreg.
- **Catalytic Products International,** Lake Zurich, Ill.
- **Chemgrate Corporation,** Woodinville, Wash.
- **Converter Accessory Corp.,** Wind Gap, Pa.
- **Dahlgren USA, Inc.,** Carrollton, Tex.
- **DAY International Printing Products Co.,** Dayton, Ohio
- **Didde Web Press,** Emporia, Kans.
- **Double E Co., Inc.,** West Bridgewater, Mass.
- **J. E. Doyle Co., Inc.,** Akron, Ohio
- **Elsner Engineering Works, Inc.,** Hanover, Pa.
- **Epic Products International Corp.,** Arlington, Tex.
- **Flint Ink Corporation,** Detroit, Mich.
- **P. H. Glatfelter Co.,** Spring Grove, Pa.

- **Grace TEC Systems, Inc.,** De Pere, Wis.
- **Graphic Services Corp.,** Sandy Hook, Conn.
- **Graphics Microsystems, Inc.,** Sunnyvale, Calif.
- **Heidelberg Harris, Inc.,** Dover, N.H.
- **Herbert Static Control,** Hatfield, Pa.
- **Hurletron Incorporated,** Danville, Ill.
- **Institute of Paper Science and Technology,** Atlanta, Ga.
- **Jardis Industries, Inc.,** Bensenville, Ill.
- **Jomac, Inc.,** Warrington, Pa.
- **KBA-Motter Corp., Web Press Division,** York, Pa.
- **King Press Corporation,** Joplin, Mo.
- **Lithco, Inc.,** Culver City, Calif.
- **MAN Roland, Inc., Web Press Division,** Groton, Conn.
- **Martin Automatic, Inc.,** Rockford, Ill.
- **Maxson Automatic Machinery Co.,** Westerly, R.I.
- **Muller Martini Corp.,** Hauppauge, N.Y.
- **Myron L Company,** Carlsbad, Calif.
- **Network Industrial Services, Inc.,** Lake Zurich, Ill.
- **Pacific Transducer Corp.,** Los Angeles, Calif.
- **Print Systems Co.,** Northbrook, Ill.
- **Procam Controls, Inc.,** Plano, Tex.
- **Prodeco,** Kenmore, Wash.
- **Quad/Tech International,** Sussex, Wis.
- **Rockwell Graphic Systems, Rockwell International,** Westmont, Ill.
- **RTE,** Vista, Calif.
- **Smith R.P.M. Company,** Overland Park, Kans.
- **Solna Web USA, Inc.,** Lenexa, Kans.
- **SPEC, Division of Sequa Corporation,** Avon, Mass.
- **Stoesser Register Systems,** Mountain View, Calif.
- **Strachan Henshaw Machinery, Inc.,** Chicago, Ill.
- **Ternes Register System,** Roseville, Minn.
- **Tilt-Lock, Inc.,** Columbia Heights, Minn.
- **Tobias Associates, Inc.,** Ivyland, Pa.
- **Toray Marketing & Sales (America), Inc.,** New York, N.Y.
- **US Ink Corporation, a Sun Chemical Company,** Carlstadt, N.J.
- **Valco Cincinnati, Inc.,** Cincinnati, Ohio
- **Valmet Paper Machinery, Inc.,** Hollola, Finland
- **Vits-Blava Technologies Corp.,** Tappan, N.Y.
- **Warren Rupp, Inc.,** Mansfield, Ohio
- **Web Systems, Inc.,** Boulder, Colo.

1 History

Alois Senefelder, the inventor of lithography, came into his role as a technological innovator indirectly. He saw himself as a dramatist despite his preparation for a law career. Lacking sufficient personal funds, a sponsor, or a publisher, he set out to discover an inexpensive method for printing his own plays. Copperplate engraving was too costly; the copper could be used only once and the process was slow.

In 1796, he began experimenting with limestone. He produced a relief image by chemical etching. In 1798, as a result of discoveries made during the course of these experiments, he invented the lithographic process, a flat-surface rather than a relief system.

Copperplate engraving was a widely used printing technique at the time, but limestone was much cheaper and reusable. It provided stiff competition, and lithography ("stone printing") soon became popular. Overcoming the hazards of handling the heavy limestone blocks, Senefelder eventually came up with a press that employed a scraper operated by a lever. Before he died in 1834, he not only had suggested the use of metal instead of stone, but had invented the paper lithographic plate — ideas more than 100 years ahead of their time.

The early lithographer had to start from scratch, building presses and preparing limestone plates and oil-based inks. Printing became considerably easier when a steam-driven flatbed cylinder press was developed in the nineteenth century, and the rotary press in 1860.

Meanwhile, the increasing need for high-speed printing created by the booming newspaper industry had inspired the invention of the web *perfecting* press in 1856. This press printed on both sides of a continuous roll (web) of paper. By 1875, a folding service was introduced, making web printing even more efficient. The invention of the Linotype composing machine gave further impetus to printing's growth as a major industry.

In the nineteenth century, letterpress was the predominant printing process; lithography was confined largely to the reproduction of illustrations ranging from works of art to posters. The invention of the offset press in the early 1900s, coupled with the great strides in photography and photomechanical platemaking, made lithography much more competitive.

About 1904, Ira Rubel discovered that the rubber blanket covering the impression cylinder on a rotary press transferred images more effectively than the stone plate. Rubel persevered and developed a press using his discovery; offset lithography was born. This new press, and William Huebner's photocomposing machine invented several years later, took lithography out of the artisan category. From that time, it became a fast-growing segment of the printing industry.

In the mid-1930s, an increasing demand for profusely illustrated mass-market magazines had inspired the development of a heatset ink drying system for high-speed letterpress printing. Offset lithography was beset by technical problems and was not yet ready for high-speed, large-volume production. By the late 1940s, lithographic platemaking was perfected, and web offset could use the inks and drying systems developed for high-speed magazine letterpress printing — this about thirty-five years after the first web offset press had been built.

By 1950, web offset was ready for serious competition with letterpress, as well as with sheetfed lithography. The ability of the offset method to perfect was unique. Growth was slow during the 1950s while press engineers were improving their press designs, but the '60s saw rapid acceleration of web offset's growth in the graphic arts industry.

In the 1950s and early '60s, firms buying their first web offset presses accounted for most of the growth, while firms purchasing additional presses were eventually responsible for the continued increase in press sales. Web offset had not only come to stay, it was gathering for itself an ever larger share of the graphic communications market.

The continued growth of web offset has depended upon improvements in equipment and supplies. The quality of the paper, inks, plates, blankets, and other press supplies has constantly improved to meet the ever-increasing requirements of great speed and quality placed on web offset printing. Along with this, improvements in the basic press and its equipment including infeed, dryers, and folders have kept pace with the growing need for increased speed and quality production.

In the past, much of the growth of web offset printing was due to the economics involved. Savings alone motivated many printers to switch to web offset, regardless of other factors. Today, there are many products that depend upon the ability of heatset web offset to produce printing that is sharp and has high gloss and heavy coverage.

Newspapers began converting to web offset during the 1960s, when over half the weeklies and 20% of the dailies switched from letterpress to offset. The newspaper's switch to web offset has been influenced mainly by the size of each plant's operations. Most large daily newspaper operations have replaced letterpress equipment with web offset lithographic presses.

National and international newspaper production and distribution have been made possible by satellite transmission of information to printing plants in suburban areas, and even in branch plants separated by an entire continent. Lithography is well-suited to the copy transmission required in such an arrangement.

About 70–80% of all books are printed on web offset presses. During the 1960s, periodicals turned more and more to web offset, increasing from $50 million to $210 million in value of printed products. Similar to newspapers produced by way of satellite transmission, many large edition weekly magazines are printed in regional editions.

Business forms have long been printed on in-line web offset presses. These presses are generally smaller and less flexible; however, flexibility is not an important criterion in this unique and specialized application of web offset.

The bulk of web offset printing still includes promotional brochures, magazine inserts, catalogs, annual reports, and all of the miscellaneous items that are best printed by the lithographic process. Web offset printing experienced its most dramatic increase in the value of printed products during the '60s—from $60 million to $830 million.

There are three classifications of web offset presses in use today. Most business forms are printed on *in-line* presses. These are nonperfecting presses in which each unit contains an inking system, a dampening system, a plate cylinder, a blanket cylinder, and an impression cylinder. Such presses are generally small and equipped with auxiliary devices like imprinters, numbering devices, perforators, and punches.

Common-impression-cylinder (CIC) presses have one large impression cylinder running in contact with several blanket cylinders. The paper wraps around the surface of the impression cylinder. Large size and longer makereadies are disadvantages inherent in the design of CIC presses. Their speed, however, is higher than that of blanket-to-blanket presses.

The most common commercial web offset press in the United States is the *blanket-to-blanket* press. Each printing unit on a blanket-to-blanket press has two blanket cylinders simultaneously printing both sides of the web, each blanket cylinder serving as the other's impression cylinder. Each blanket cylinder is part of a printing couple that also has a dampening system, inking system, and plate cylinder.

The popularity of the blanket-to-blanket press is due to several factors:

- It is capable of producing a high-quality product.
- Makereadies are efficient.
- The press is flexible in terms of web configurations and the number of colors run in one pass.
- Paper passes through a dryer and cooling system once.

Color plays an important role in web offset printing. In the late 1980s, the average number of units per press purchased was five. This reflects the great amount of process color printing currently produced on web offset presses.

As problems with air pollution control and the effluent produced by heatset printing increase, more work is being printed by nonheatset web offset. As the demand for quality printing increases, improvements in paper and ink will complement the needs of nonheatset web offset printing.

Since the inception of web offset printing, the sixteen-page blanket-to-blanket press has been the standard of the industry. However, printers are employing an increasing number of eight-page and thirty-two-page presses. The eight-page press is continuing to put pressure on sheetfed lithographic markets, and the thirty-two-page press is moving into markets that are presently served by long-run sixteen-page web offset presses and by gravure presses. Both of these press configurations are expected to play a role in the continued expansion of the web offset segment of the printing industry.

Economic factors are responsible for the growth of web offset printing. In the past, web offset has been somewhat confined to its natural market: those products that because of their nature belong with web offset printing. Future expansion into existing markets will be at the expense of both sheetfed offset and gravure in areas where each has good economic leverage. To successfully expand into these areas, the web offset printer must operate with greater efficiency.

2 Overview: General Terminology

Over the years, several terms have come into common use in web offset pressrooms, some borrowed from sheetfed printing, others used only in web offset work.

Lithography is the printing process by which ink and water transfer an image from a level-surfaced plate onto another surface. Image and nonimage areas are chemically separated.

Offset describes image transfer from the image carrier to an intermediate surface, then to the paper or other substrate. Offset does not really mean lithography. It is common, however, to interchangeably use the two words.

A five-color, 57-in.-wide Heidelberg Harris M-850L web offset press
Courtesy Heidelberg Harris, Inc.

Offset lithography, then, is lithographic printing that uses the offset method to transfer images. Following are the basic steps involved in the most common form of offset lithography:

1. Plate with photochemically produced image and nonimage areas is mounted on a cylinder.
2. Plate is dampened with a mixture of chemical concentrates in a water-based solution, which adheres to the nonimage areas of the plate.
3. Plate surface is contacted by inked rollers, which apply ink only to the image areas of a properly dampened printing plate.
4. Right-reading inked image on the printing plate is transferred under pressure to a rubber-like blanket, on which it becomes reversed (wrong-reading).
5. Inked image on the blanket is transferred under pressure to a sheet of paper or other printing substrate, producing an impression of the inked image on the paper.

Transfer of the inked image from the blanket to the printing substrate

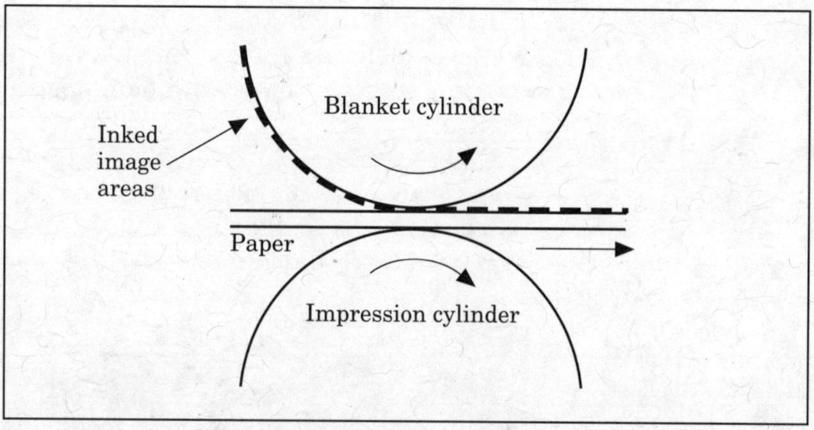

Waterless offset lithography is a variation of offset lithography that does not require the use of a water-based dampening solution. The process uses an offset press equipped with temperature-controlled inking systems. The process requires special inks and special waterless plates.

Web offset is the process by which presses print on continuous webs of paper. This is the basic difference between web and sheetfed presses. Compared to sheetfed presses, web presses have much smaller gaps on the plate and blanket cylinders, which means that ink and water flow much more continuously. Blanket-to-blanket offset presses lack a hard impression cylinder, which is inherent in sheetfed press designs. This manual deals with (to use the most accurate expression) lithographic web offset presses.

Direct lithography, or **direct print,** is the process of printing directly from a printing plate to a substrate. It is accomplished in web offset by running paper through a blanket-to-blanket unit so that the paper contacts one plate and takes ink from it. In this case, the blanket cylinder of the couple acts as an impression cylinder.

A blanket-to-blanket offset press unit that has been so threaded that the web comes in direct contact with one plate and takes ink from it

Two colors are printed on the same side of the web, one by offset lithography and one by direct lithography.

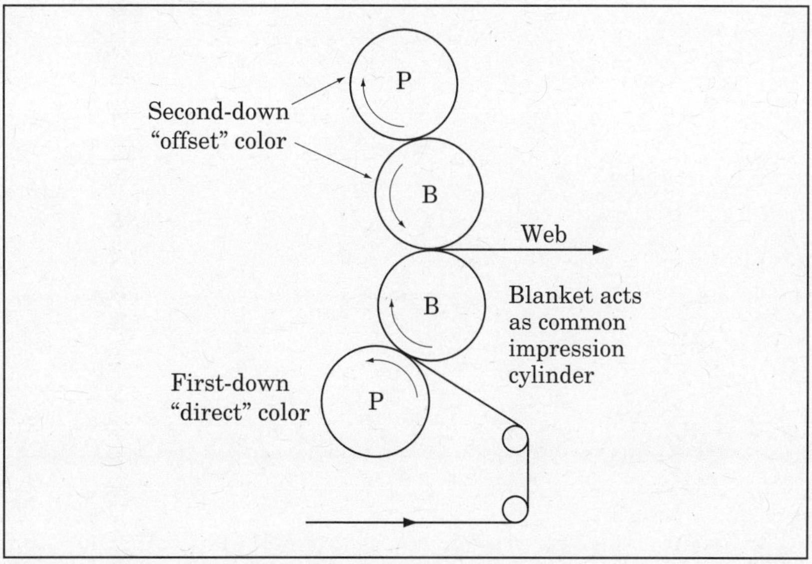

For the purposes of this book, think of the press as consisting of several sections. The **infeed** of the press is where the unprinted rolls of paper are mounted. The **delivery** is where the final printed material comes out. Going from the infeed to the delivery, the elements of a heatset web offset press are, in order, *infeed, printing units* (press), *dryer, chill rolls,* and *delivery* (either a *folder, sheeter,* or *rewinder).* A non-heatset web press does not have a dryer or chill rolls.

A Solna web offset press
Courtesy Solna Web USA, Inc.

A four-unit blanket-to-blanket web offset press with optional delivery to a folder or sheeter

The press configuration shown here is the most common, but variations are possible. For example, with some presses having more than six units, the folder(s) is placed in the middle of the total press configuration and the infeeds are placed at each end.

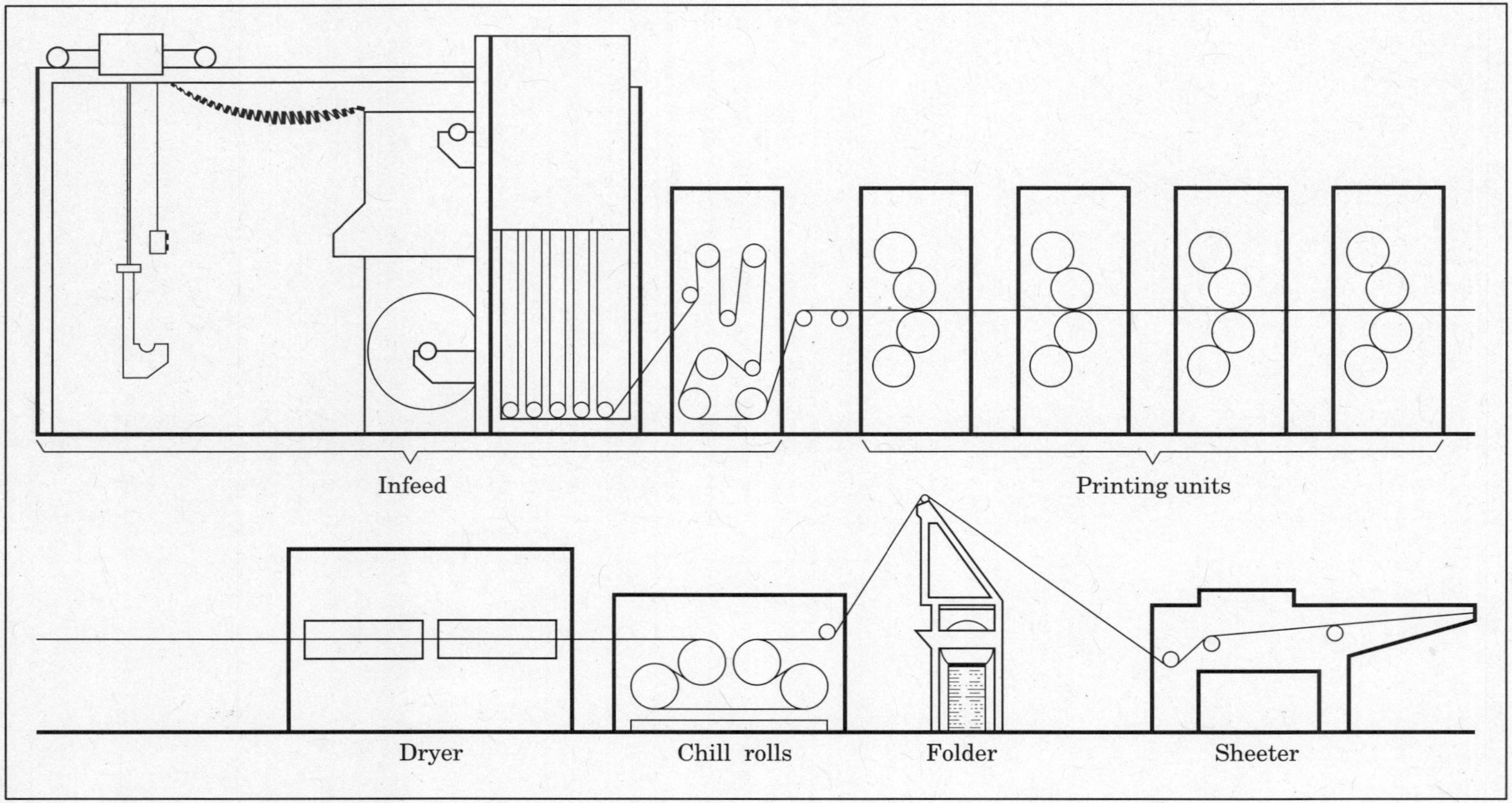

Goss Universal web offset press
Courtesy Rockwell Graphic Systems

A **folder** delivers folded signatures ready for mailing or for binding with other signatures to form a magazine or book. A **sheeter** cuts the web and delivers flat, printed sheets. A **rewinder,** as the name implies, rewinds the printed web back into roll form. A folder produces signatures; a rewinder produces rolls. The bulk of web offset work involves folding and producing signatures.

The ends of the press are referred to as the **infeed** and **delivery.** The sides also have specific designations. One side of the press houses the driveshaft and gears that power the press. This side of the press is called the **gear side.** The crew always works on the other side, because this is where all of the press controls are located. This is called the **operator side** of the press.

Web offset presses are available in a variety of special configurations or arrangements of printing couples within the printing units. A **printing couple** is an assembly that includes an inking system, a dampening system, a plate cylinder, a blanket cylinder, and an impression cylinder, all of which are required to apply one color of ink to one side of a substrate. If another color is to be printed, the paper has to go through another printing couple.

A **printing unit** is a single physical structure in which a number of printing couples are mounted. The exact definition of the term, however, depends on the press.

Perfecting is the process by which a sheet or web is printed on both sides during one run through the press or unit. A blanket-to-blanket unit is therefore a perfecting unit, while a forms press may or may not be a perfecting press.

In-line describes a press with printing units that consist of a single printing couple: an inking system, a dampening system, a plate cylinder, a blanket cylinder, and an impression cylinder. The printing units on an in-line press are **nonperfecting;** that is, they can print only one side of the web at a time.

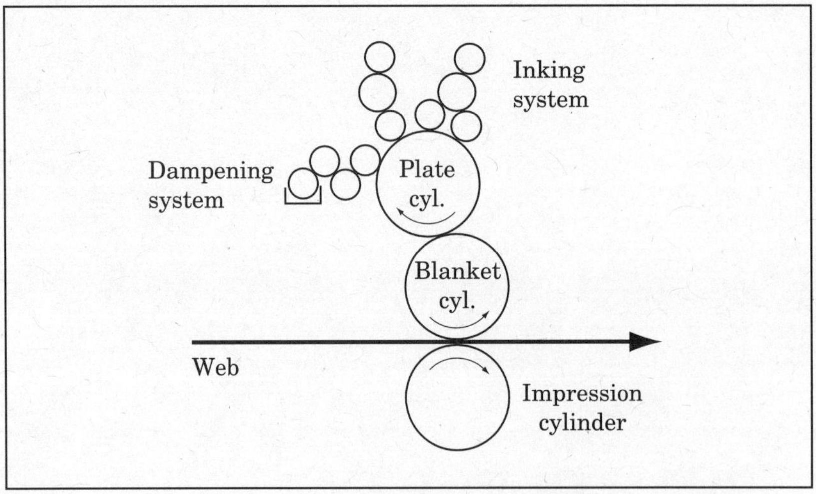

An in-line offset lithographic press unit that prints a single color on one side of a web

During offset printing, paper never comes in contact with the plate. Rather, the image is transferred from the plate to the paper by the blanket cylinder.

A two-color business forms press
Courtesy Brandtjen & Kluge, Inc.

The **blanket-to-blanket press** consists of printing couples that are usually stacked in pairs, one on top of the other. The blanket of one couple is next to the blanket of the other couple and the web runs between them. In other words, these presses have no impression cylinders; the blanket cylinder of the top couple acts as the impression cylinder for the bottom couple, and vice versa. Since these units can print on both sides of the web of paper at once, a blanket-to-blanket press is perfecting.

A typical blanket-to-blanket printing unit (horizontal)

Each blanket cylinder acts as an impression cylinder for the other couple in the printing unit. Blanket-to-blanket units have two couples, arranged to simultaneously print both sides of the web.

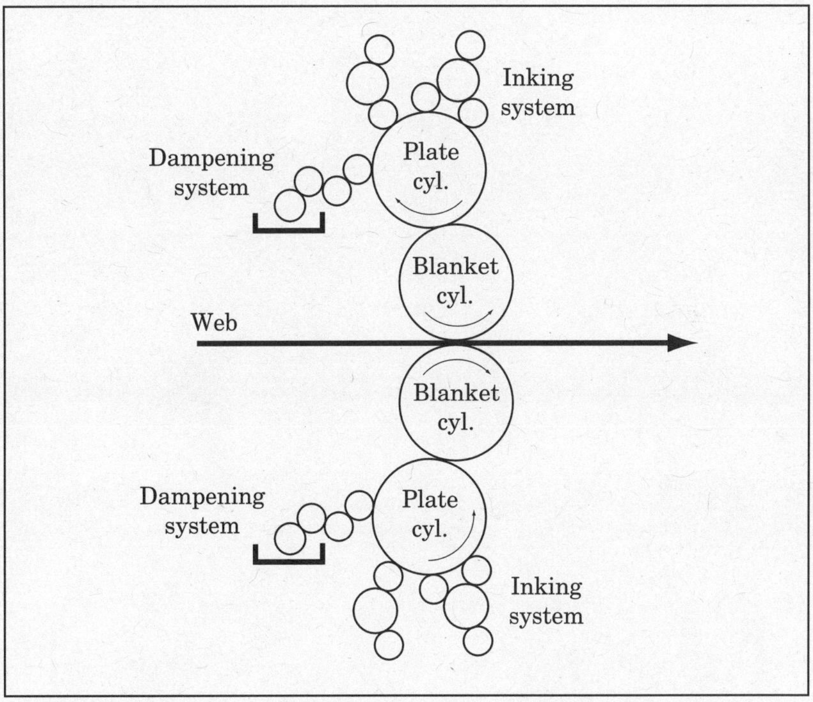

On a blanket-to-blanket press, the printing units are usually arranged one after the other, an arrangement that offers a great deal of flexibility. With four units, one web can be run and four colors printed on each side. Or the press can be set up so that four webs are run and only one color printed per side. Anything in between is possible. For example, one web runs through the first two units, getting two colors on each side, the second web runs through the third unit, getting one color per side, and a third web runs through the fourth, also getting one color per side. This flexibility combined with high speed is what accounts for web offset's popularity.

Blanket-to-blanket press units come in two basic configurations. The most common arrangement is horizontal, in which the web runs through the printing units in a horizontal plane; the printing unit cylinders are therefore stacked vertically, one on top of the other. Vertical blanket-to-blanket presses

Process King® web offset press with Kingtrol control console
Courtesy King Press Corporation

have the web running vertically between blankets, with the cylinders laid out horizontally. This arrangement allows for symmetrical design of the printing units and provides easier access to the printing couples.

A vertical web offset press

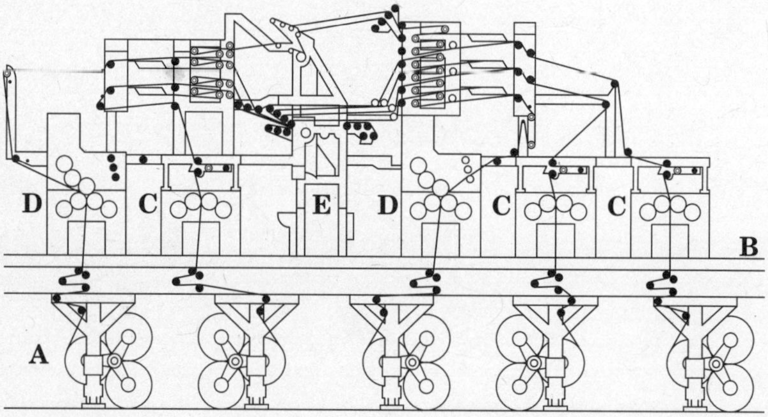

Rolls (A) are located on a level below the pressroom (B), a common arrangement in newspaper plants. Three units on this press are blanket-to-blanket units (C). Two of the units are semi-drum units (D), each with three couples. The folder (E) is located in the center of the press.

C450 vertical web offset press
Courtesy Rockwell Graphic Systems

Each printing unit of a **common-impression-cylinder** (CIC) press has one very large impression cylinder with four or five printing couples radially arranged around it. Because of the arrangement of the couples and the size of the impression cylinder, these presses are also called *satellite presses.*

A CIC press can be made to perfect in two ways. The most common means is to run the web through one unit, dry the

One unit of a semi-drum press

All three blankets of this nonperfecting unit contact a single impression cylinder.

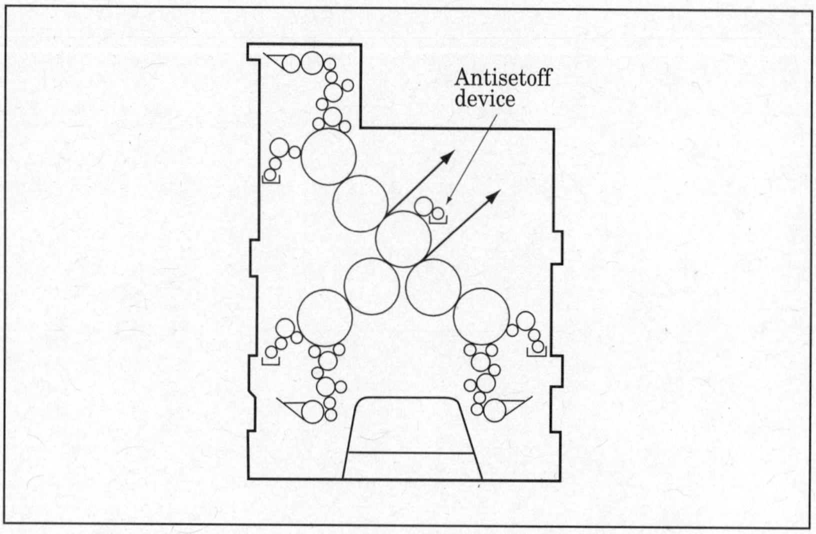

ink, flip the web over, and run it through a second unit to print the other side. The second method prints half-webs of paper; that is, the width of the web is only half the width of the plate cylinder. The web is threaded so that it runs along

A two-unit CIC press

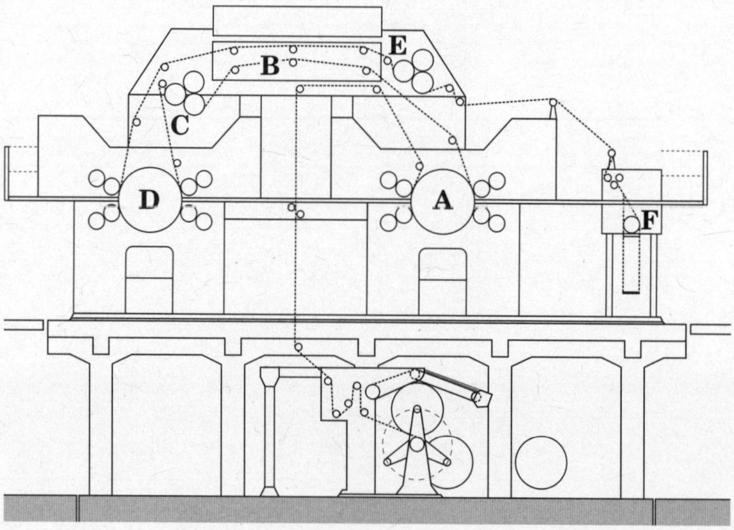

Each unit (A, D) has four printing couples. The web feeds into the first unit (A), which prints four colors on one side. It passes through a dryer (B) and over chill rolls (C), is turned over and enters the second unit (D), which prints four colors on the other side of the web. The web then reenters the dryer (B), is chilled (E), and finally is folded (F) and delivered.

one side of the printing unit, and the top of the web is printed. The web then travels through a dryer and chill rolls (on a heatset press), through a turning bay where it is flipped over, and returned to the printing unit, where it runs on the other side of the cylinder. On its second pass through the printing unit, the other side of the web is printed. During operation, paper runs continuously on both sides of the press. This is called *double-ending*.

3 The Blanket-to-Blanket Printing Unit

Each printing couple on a blanket-to-blanket web offset lithographic press consists of four basic elements:

- A dampening system, consisting of a fountain pan holding a supply of dampening solution, and a series of rollers that apply the solution to the plate.
- An inking system, consisting of a fountain trough holding a supply of ink, and a series of rollers that carry the ink from the fountain to the plate.
- A plate cylinder, on which the plate is mounted. The plate is a thin metal sheet that wraps around the cylinder surface and carries the image.
- A blanket cylinder, on which the blanket is mounted. The blanket is a sheet of fabric that is covered with synthetic rubber. It picks up the inked image from the plate and transfers it to the paper.

Because the blanket-to-blanket press uses rotating image-carrying cylinders, it is classified as a rotary press. Each revolution of the plate cylinder is called an impression; these nearly continuous impressions account for the efficiency of such presses. All cylinders must be timed relative to each other.

With properly made plates, water from the dampening system adheres to all the nonprinting, or nonimage, areas. This control is so selective that points as small as 0.0002 in. (0.005 mm), completely surrounded by nonimage areas, can be reproduced. As the plate cylinder turns, the inking system puts the ink on the plate. The greasy ink will not adhere to the dampened nonimage areas, but does adhere to the unwetted image areas of the plate.

There is one fundamentally important aspect of this system: no ink or water will transfer without proper pressure between the elements making the transfer. The plate cylinder and the blanket cylinder have to run with pressure between them to transfer ink; running contact is not enough. There must also be adequate pressure between the blanket and the paper. Pressure is critical in lithography. Tolerances in squeeze may be as low as 0.002 in. (0.05 mm). The procedure for setting cylinder pressures is called *packing*.

The Plate Cylinder

The basic features of all plate cylinders are the same. Almost all have **bearers:** smooth, flat metal rings at the extreme ends of the cylinder. Just inside each bearer (between bearer and cylinder body) is a narrow groove, called the **gutter.** Between the two gutters is the **body** — the main portion of the cylinder — on which the plate and packing are mounted.

A printing-unit cylinder with the major elements identified

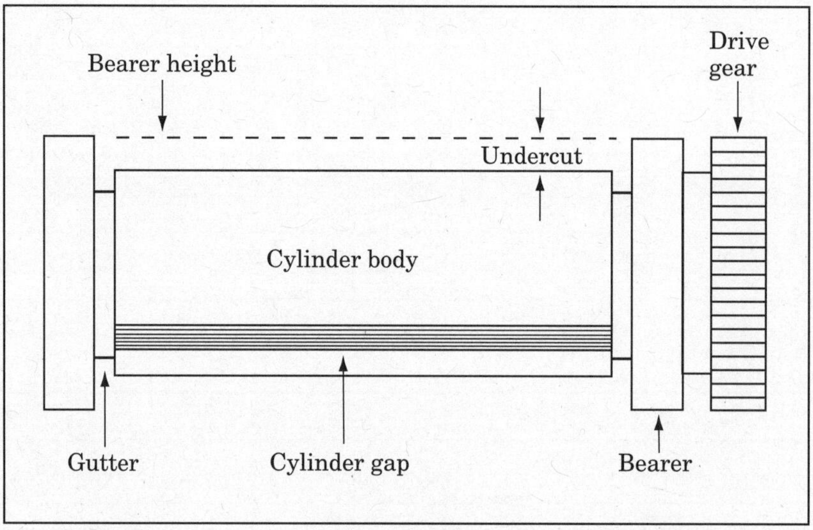

The body of the cylinder is always lower than the surface of the bearers; the exact difference in height — called the **cylinder undercut** — varies with the specifications agreed on by the manufacturer and the printing plant. Often, the amount of undercut is specified by the plant ordering the press. The exact amount of undercut on the plate cylinder must be known in order to set proper pressures in the printing unit.

The surface of the plate cylinder body does not extend all the way around the cylinder circumference. On nearly all presses, a gap runs from gutter to gutter across the cylinder. This gap contains clamping devices that hold the plate tightly onto the cylinder. These are the basic mechanisms of the plate lockup.

Cross section of a typical plate lockup mechanism, showing the printing plate fully tightened *Courtesy Heidelberg Harris, Inc.*

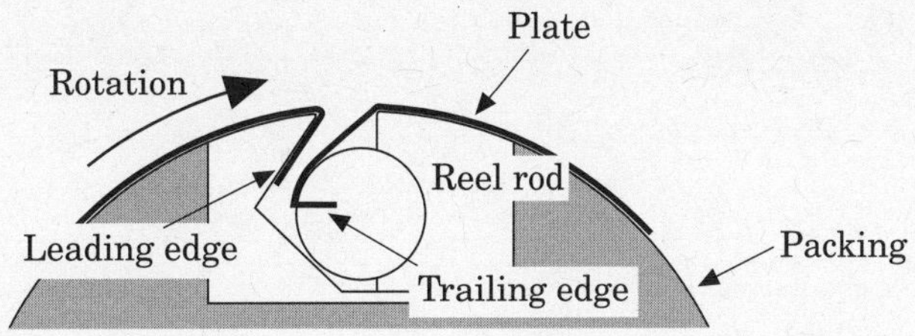

The reel rod is turned with a wrench and locked into position through a ratchet-trip arrangement. Although the drawing shows the plate lead edge hooked over the cylinder nose, the lead edge is actually wedged against the nose by the reel rod when the plate is fully tightened.

The leading edge of the plate cylinder is the edge along the gap that is followed by the cylinder body as the cylinder rotates in the running direction. The trailing edge is followed by the cylinder gap. The leading edge of the gap is machined at an acute angle to the surface of the cylinder body, and the leading edge of the plate is bent to this angle before mounting on the press. The plate is inserted in the slot at the lead edge and the lockup at the trailing edge, which provide the gripping force necessary to hold the plate tightly and smoothly against the cylinder.

The gap represents a nonprinting area. The white space left on the web by the cylinder gap is ultimately where the web is cut into sheets and subsequently folded into *signatures*. The cutoff length of a press is fixed in that it may measure any one of a number of specified sizes. When ordering a web offset press, the printer must know what work will be run, as the fixed cutoff on these presses presents some limitations.

The gap on the plate cylinder is usually about ⅛ in. (3 mm) narrower than that on the blanket cylinder. The reason for the wider blanket gap is that the blanket and its mounting bars are much thicker than the plate and require a wider lockup. If the cylinders are properly timed, the plate cylinder gap should fall between the blanket cylinder gap.

The undercut on a plate cylinder is usually much less than the undercut on a blanket cylinder, simply because plates are thinner than blankets. Plate thickness or gauge depends on the size of the plate, usually increasing with plate size. Gauges normally vary from about 0.012 in. (0.30 mm) for a 17×22-in. plate up to 0.015 in. (0.38 mm) on large plates.

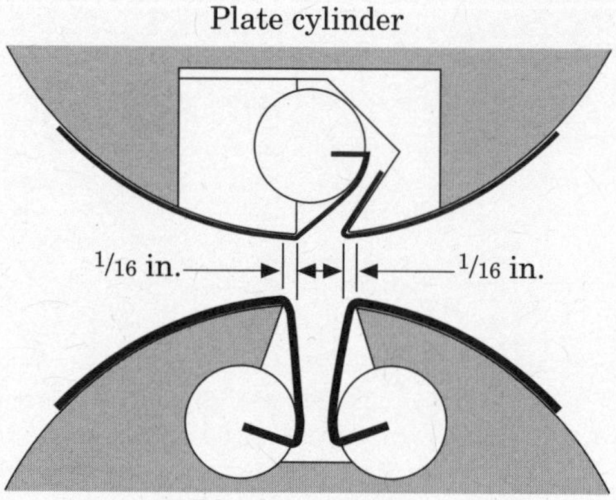

The plate cylinder gap falling inside the blanket cylinder gap, indicating proper timing
Courtesy Heidelberg Harris, Inc.

On this press, the blanket cylinder gap is about ⅛ in. (3 mm) wider than the plate cylinder gap. The cylinders are shown spread apart for easier visualization.

The Blanket Cylinder

The basic design of the blanket cylinder is the same as that of the plate cylinder. Almost all blanket cylinders have bearers that run in firm continuous contact with the plate cylinder bearers. The blanket cylinder gutters help to prevent chemicals from working in under the blanket, and they keep foreign matter picked up by the bearers from moving onto the blanket surface. The body of the cylinder is the area around which the blanket and its packing are mounted.

Usually, the blanket cylinder body also has a gap containing the lockup that holds the blanket at the leading and trailing edges. The gap on the blanket cylinder is wider than that on the plate cylinder, usually by ⅛ in. (3 mm), in order to accommodate the thicker blanket and mounting bars.

Three-ply blankets are generally used on blanket cylinders with undercuts of 0.075 in. (1.9 mm) or less. Four-ply blankets are used on presses with undercuts of more than 0.075 in.

Cylinder Pressures and Timing

A printing unit of a blanket-to-blanket press has two printing couples that run with their blankets in contact. Often, problems involve only one couple in the unit, and the press operator need deal only with the offending couple. Other problems involve the entire unit. In this light, the printing unit is a single, dynamic system. Changes in one part of the system affect every other part. This is most true when cylinder pressure and cylinder timing are involved.

Pressures on a printing press are not measured in pounds per square inch; rather, such pressures are inferred by measuring the amount of squeeze — in thousandths of an inch — established at the printing nip.

A blanket lockup

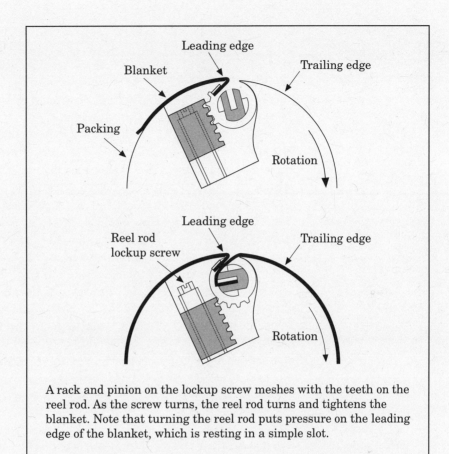

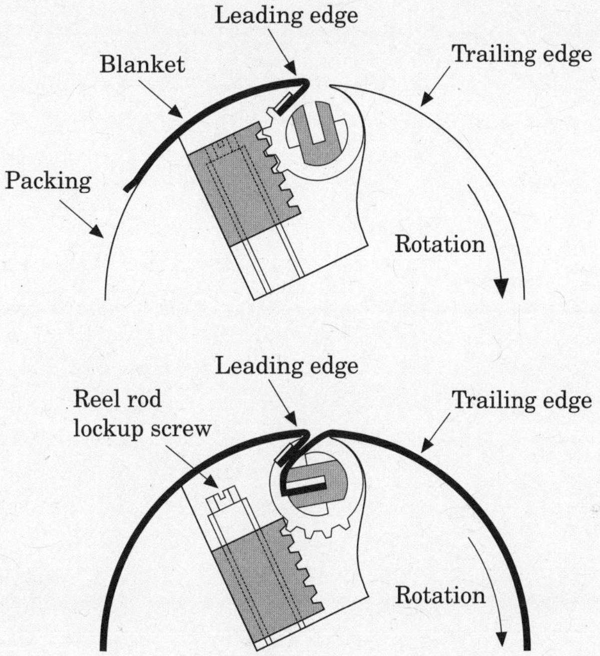

A rack and pinion on the lockup screw meshes with the teeth on the reel rod. As the screw turns, the reel rod turns and tightens the blanket. Note that turning the reel rod puts pressure on the leading edge of the blanket, which is resting in a simple slot.

Unpacked plate and blanket cylinders turning together with their bearers in firm contact with one another exert no pressure between the cylinder bodies, because there is a space between them. The dimension of this space is the amount of undercut on the plate cylinder plus the amount of undercut on the blanket cylinder.

To develop squeeze in the nip — the area where the cylinders meet — the press operator raises the height (increases the diameter) of the cylinder bodies by inserting packing under the plate and blanket. The total thickness of plate, blanket, and packing sheets on both cylinders determines the amount of squeeze.

Packing the cylinders so that the plate and the blanket are exactly even with the surface of their respective cylinder bearers theoretically creates no squeeze. The cylinders are only touching, and there is no pressure between them. Adding just one more sheet of packing 0.001 in. (0.025 mm) thick under the plate creates 0.001-in. (0.025-mm) squeeze.

Adding a similar sheet to the blanket cylinder results in squeeze pressure of 0.002 in. (0.05 mm). The effective surface of each cylinder body will run at 0.001 in. (0.025 mm) over its respective cylinder bearers for a total of 0.002 in. (0.05 mm).

The pressure created by squeeze is difficult to measure, because pressure does not vary directly with squeeze.

There is no pressure between the working surfaces until the packed plate and blanket exceed the total undercut of their respective cylinders when running. Since pressure cannot be determined in pounds per square inch, it is simply expressed in thousandths of an inch. Assume that the plate is to be packed 0.001 in. (0.025 mm) over its bearers and the blanket 0.004 in. (0.102 mm) over its bearers. Assume also that the plate cylinder undercut is 0.015 in. (0.38 mm) and that the blanket cylinder undercut is 0.071 in. (1.803 mm). The plate and its packing will have to equal 0.016 in. (0.41 mm) in thickness if the plate is to run 0.001 in. (0.025 mm) over bearers. Likewise, the thickness of the blanket and its packing will have to equal 0.075 in. (1.91 mm) to exceed bearer height by 0.004 in. (0.102 mm).

Packing the blanket accurately is more difficult than accurately packing the plate. Mounting tension and running compaction decrease the blanket's original thickness. This is especially true of a new or well-reconditioned blanket.

Packed cylinders should be measured with a packing gauge after the press operator has torqued the blankets to

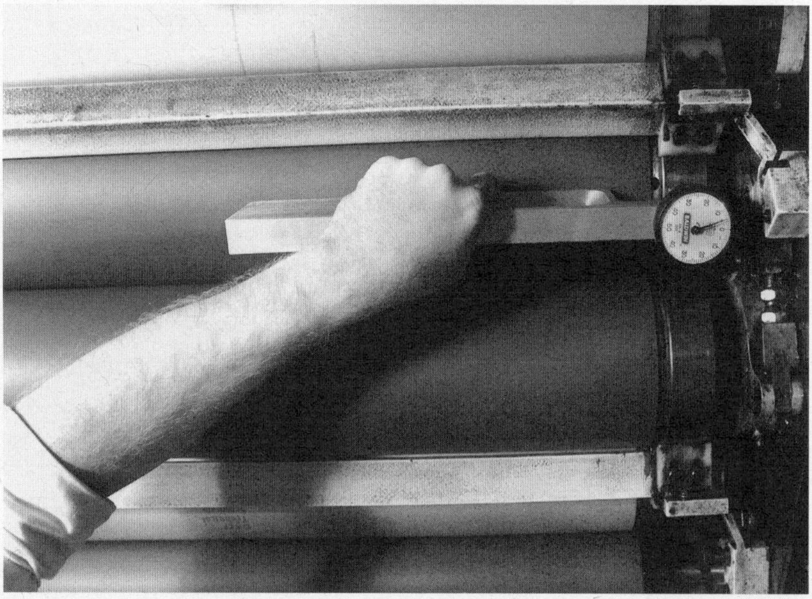

A packing gauge designed for achieving consistent and controlled results in cylinder packing

The arithmetic of packing

This method for calculating packing assumes that (1) the bearers are set according to the method recommended by the press manufacturer, (2) the height of the plate and blanket relative to bearer height is derived from a test (described later in this chapter) in which the press is underpacked and minimal amounts of packing are added until a full-strength solid is printed, and (3) the results from this test are corrected for any significant changes in the caliper or type of stock being run.

Squeeze desired: blanket-to-blanket*	0.011	Squeeze desired: plate-to-blanket*	0.005
Paper thickness	–0.003	Required squeeze per blanket	–0.004
(Divide by 2)	0.008		
Required squeeze per blanket†	0.004	Required squeeze per plate	0.001
Blanket cylinder undercut	+0.071	Plate cylinder undercut	+0.015
Total blanket interference required	0.075	Total plate interference required	0.016
Blanket thickness‡	–0.067	Plate thickness‡	–0.012
Required blanket packing‡	0.008	Required plate packing‡	0.004

------

*All dimensions are given in inches.

†These figures should be checked with a packing gauge after the press is fully packed.

‡These figures should be checked with a deadweight bench micrometer *before* the respective materials are mounted on press.

manufacturer's specifications. The press operator should measure all materials used in packing the cylinders, no matter how many times a particular brand of plate or blanket is used. This is especially true for blankets. Each blanket should be checked with a bench micrometer and its thickness marked on each corner.

In the earlier example, the plates were packed 0.001 in. (0.025 mm) and blankets 0.004 in. (0.102 mm) over the bearers of their respective cylinders. This amounted to a squeeze between plate and blanket of 0.005 in. (0.127 mm). The thickness of the paper that will run between the two blankets must be added to the amount of packing over bearers on both blankets in calculating squeeze at the printing nip.

A deadweight bench micrometer, manufactured by E. J. Cady & Co., which is used for measuring the thickness of plates, blankets, and packing

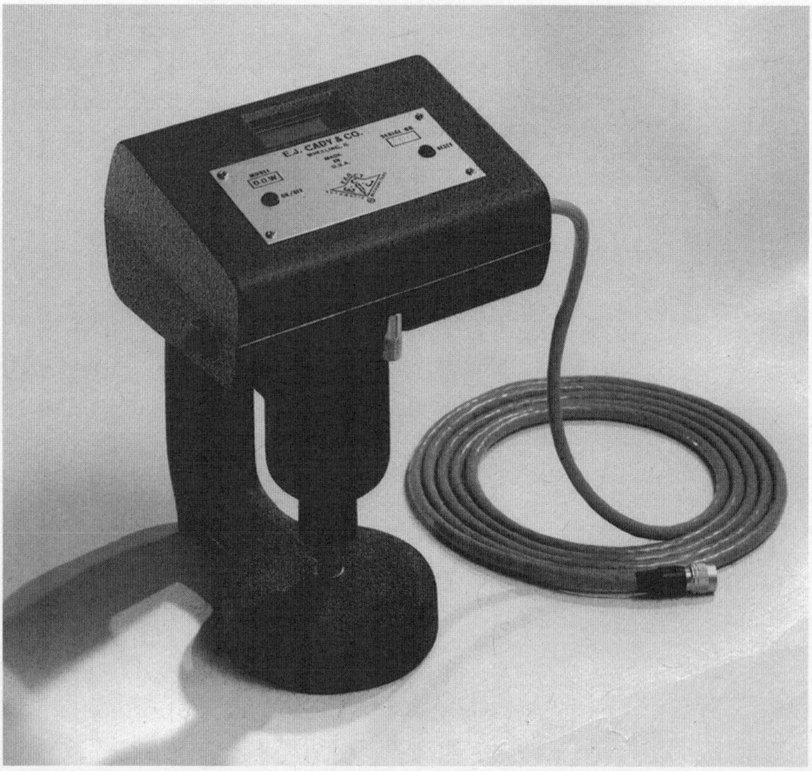

Digital bench micrometer
Courtesy E. J. Cady & Co.

Most web offset papers caliper between 0.002 in. (0.05 mm) and 0.004 in. (0.102 mm). Assume that the paper is 0.003 in. (0.076 mm) thick. To get a total squeeze at the printing nip of 0.011 in. (0.15 mm), each blanket needs to be packed 0.004 in. (0.102 mm) over its bearers. It is not necessary to repack cylinders every time the caliper of the stock changes, especially for a 0.001-in. (0.025-mm) or 0.002-in. (0.05-mm) change in paper thickness.

Minute variations in the surface contour of the paper can make the achievement of a uniform and continuous solid a little more difficult than it would be otherwise. A high degree of variation — rough texture — requires more pressure than a smooth-textured paper. For example, coated papers require less pressure than do pebble-finish or embossed stocks.

A change in paper thickness requires a change in the packing of all the cylinders in both couples. On a blanket-to-blanket printing unit, a change in the packing of one couple must match changes in the cylinder packing of the other couple.

The pressure between plate and blanket exceeds that between the two blankets with the same amount of squeeze. At the plate-to-blanket nip, a rigid surface (the plate) and a resilient surface are squeezed together. A given amount of squeeze at the plate-to-blanket nip creates more pressure than the same amount of squeeze applied between two resilient surfaces, as in the case of the printing nip. Thus, for a given amount of squeeze, pressure at the printing nip is about half that at the plate-to-blanket nip.

To determine the effective cylinder undercut when the press is running under pressure, pack the press in normal fashion and mount a plate that prints solids and screens. Print until ink and water are balanced. Then, remove packing (starting under the plate), until the solids no longer print. At this point, reinsert packing, 0.001 in. (0.025 mm) at a time, until solids print full strength. The press is now properly packed with minimum pressure.

Measure packed cylinder height with a packing gauge. The gauge indicates the minimum squeeze for printing with the paper, ink, and blanket combination, on the press in question. This figure automatically accounts for any bearer deformation occurring on the press.

The bearers on any press will deform; the amount depends on the construction of the press cylinders. This change in the radii of the bearers is important, because it increases the amount of squeeze generated in the printing nip as explained earlier. The previously prescribed procedure for determining squeeze automatically remedies this problem.

The objective of the procedure is to adjust press packing until a visible standard of performance is achieved: a full-strength solid. The packing gauge measures the conditions on press that will yield this standard of performance. Identical packing conditions can now be recreated.

Setting bearer pressure. One of the more popular bearer pressure setting procedures is known as the "light method." This method requires that two lights be placed on the far side of the unit, one light behind each bearer nip. **Caution:** The press operator must follow the proper safety precautions when setting bearer pressures.

Prior to setting the bearer pressure, the press operator or a maintenance worker must check the cylinders and bearers for run-out to make sure that the cylinders or bearers are not out of round. To check for run-out, a magnetic-base dial indicator is attached to a frame member, the press is inched a couple of inches, and a reading is taken. The press is again inched, and another reading is taken. This procedure is repeated until the cylinder has made one complete revolution. The readings on the dial indicator are recorded, and the difference between the highest and lowest readings is compared to the manufacturer's specifications for maximum allowable run-out. If run-out is within specifications, the bearer setting procedure can proceed. If run-out exceeds specifications, the cylinder may have to be repaired or replaced.

To conduct the light method of bearer pressure setting, the press operator first packs the plate and blanket cylinders according to manufacturer's specifications and cleans the bearers.

Setting bearer pressure requires the use of 0.003-, 0.004-, and 0.005-in.-thick (0.08-, 0.10- and 0.13-mm-thick) sheets of polyester (e.g., Mylar). The Mylar sheets should be the width of the plate and blanket.

As an example, to set the bearers on the horizontal blanket-to-blanket web press at GATF's training facility, the press manufacturer recommends placing a 0.003-in. Mylar sheet between each plate and blanket and placing a 0.005-in. Mylar sheet between the two blankets. The press manufacturer also recommends that the plate be packed 0.001 in. over bearer height and that the blanket be packed 0.003–0.005 in. over bearer height, which results in a squeeze of 0.005 in. between plate and blanket and 0.008 in. between the blankets.

If these cylinders are not preloaded during the bearer pressure setting procedure, the bearers will separate at high speeds. When the bearers are not running in contact, the plate and blanket cylinders can bounce as the gaps come in contact. This bounce may cause slurring, and eventually streaks will begin to appear.

Using the web press at GATF's training facility as an example, a sheet of 0.005-in. Mylar is placed between the two blankets, and a pair of strong bright lights are placed behind the nips of the bearers on both the operator and gear side, and the impression is put on. If the bearers are properly set, no light should be visible between the bearers. If light is visible, the bearers are too loose and need to be reset. Next, 0.003-in. Mylar is placed between each plate and blanket, and the same procedure is followed as with the two blankets. Once the bearers are touching and parallel, the sheets of Mylar are removed. Then a 0.008-in. thickness of Mylar (two 0.004-in. pieces) is placed between the blankets. With the impression on, a thin crack of light should appear between the blanket cylinder bearers. If no light appears, the blanket cylinder bearers are set too tight. To repeat, no light should be visible when 0.005-in. Mylar is placed between the blankets, but a crack of light should be visible when 0.008-in. Mylar is placed between the blankets.

Once the bearers of the two blanket cylinders are properly set using the above procedure, the bearer pressure between the lower plate cylinder and blanket cylinder is checked. After the press operator inserts a sheet of 0.006-in. Mylar between the lower plate and lower blanket, a parallel crack of light should be visible on both operator and gear side of the bearers. If no light is visible, the plate cylinder bearers need to be reset. To repeat, if the bearers between the plate and blanket cylinders are properly set, there should be no light visible with 0.003-in. Mylar between plate and blanket bearers, but a crack of light should be visible with 0.006-in. Mylar. This same procedure is repeated for the bearers of the upper plate and blanket cylinders.

To obtain a "picture" of the bearer setting, use a thin strip of aluminum foil less than 0.001 in. thick and wider than the bearers. Place the aluminum foil between the bearers and put the impression on and off, and then measure the width of the stripe using a 20–30× magnifier with built-in measuring reticle. This measurement is recorded and is then used as a standard against which future measurements are compared. It is recommended that this bearer pressure stripe procedure be performed monthly to determine if any setting changes have occurred. If the width of the stripe on subsequent measurements is narrower than the width of the original stripe, the bearer pressure has decreased and needs to be reset. If changes occur over a predictable length of time, this time frame should become part of a plant's preventive maintenance program. For example, if the stripe width changes in three months, the light method of bearer setting should be repeated every three months as a part of preventive maintenance.

Cylinder timing. For accurate cylinder timing on a web press, one of the most effective ways of registering plate cylinders circumferentially to one another and then timing the blankets cylinders to the plate cylinders can be achieved with a GATF Register Test Grid.

First, plates for all the top and bottom units of the press are made from the same GATF Register Test Grid. The plates are then mounted on the plate cylinders according to the press manufacturer's recommendations. Next, all the plate cylinders are centered circumferentially from the press register console. Once the plates have been circumferentially centered, the printing units are inked and the press is run until the ink laydown is satisfactory for all the colors on the top and bottom of the sheet. The press is stopped, and the press operator evaluates the placement of the GATF Register Test Grid on the press sheet.

At least one set of cylinders for the same color of ink should be backing themselves up on the top and bottom side of the press. The cylinders that are backing up will remain in the locked position. The other cylinders, however, need to be adjusted. To do this, the press operator puts the press on safe and opens the press housing on the gear side of the press. Next the press operator unlocks (loosens) the bolts on the gears of the plate cylinders that need to be adjusted, and then circumferentially advances or retards those plate cylinders by the distance required to get the units to register and back up top and bottom — as indicated by the printed GATF Register Test Grid.

Once the cylinders are moved the required distance, the press operator locks the plate cylinder gears, closes the frame housing, and starts printing again. The newly printed Register

Test Grid is evaluated to determine how close the units come to backing up circumferentially. If circumferential register is still off, the press operator repeats the above procedure on the offending plate cylinder(s) until circumferential register is accurate.

The next step in timing cylinders is to align all of the blanket cylinder gaps with their respective plate cylinder gaps. With the plate and blanket cylinders packed according to manufacturer's specifications, the press operator tapes the narrow edge of a piece of 2×18-in. (51×457-mm) clear Mylar to the plate (in-running side) of the first unit being timed; for example, the press operator might start with the top plate on the first printing unit. The long dimension of the Mylar should be parallel to the direction of web travel. The press operator then inches the press until the plate cylinder gap of that unit is easily accessible. With the press on safe, the press operator manually rubs some ink on both sides of the plate cylinder gap.

With the impression and safe both on, the press operator positions the Mylar against the plate cylinder gap and transfers some ink onto it. The resulting ink smudges represent the edges of the plate gap. Then, the press operator positions the Mylar against the blanket. The ink smudges on the Mylar allow the operator to evaluate the location of the blanket cylinder gap with respect to the plate cylinder gap. If the blanket cylinder must be adjusted, the press operator loosens the bolts on the blanket cylinder gear, takes the press off impression, and advances or retards that blanket cylinder so that its gap will align with the ink smudges on the piece of Mylar. This procedure should be repeated once or twice to make sure that the gaps are perfectly aligned. With the impression on, the press operator locks up the bolts on the blanket cylinders and moves to the next printing unit.

After all units have been adjusted, the plate cylinders should all be in circumferential register since they were adjusted using the printed GATF Register Test Grid, and all the blanket gaps will be timed to match up with the plate cylinder gaps. This means that at the end of a job, the operator will be able to put the plate cylinders back to their circumferentially centered "zero" position. When the press operators mount the plates on the press for the next job, the very first series of sheets should be in circumferential register.

4 The Inking System

The inking system of a lithographic press consists of a series of rollers that carries the ink from the fountain to the plate. Blanket-to-blanket web offset presses contain two inking systems per unit: one supplies ink to the top plate, and another to the bottom.

The inking system serves several important functions. Primarily, it delivers an even, controlled ink film to the plate. The thick film entering the system on each ductor stroke splits among many rollers, so that the intermittent ink feed from the ductor changes into the continuous feed required by the plate.

Second, the inking system deposits the ink film as needed on the plate. To accomplish this, the system must control the amount of ink flowing to the plate around and across the cylinder.

The inking system also acts as a reservoir to maintain consistent color between ductor cycles and from impression to impression.

It also helps to control dampening on the plate by picking up some water as the press runs. Some of the water mixes with the ink, forming an emulsion. Too much emulsification prevents image areas from accepting ink; however, controlled emulsification is essential to the lithographic process. Some water is also picked up by the blanket and transferred to the sheet. The rest of the water evaporates.

Additionally, the inking system also helps to clean the plate by picking up foreign matter that may collect on the plate. A roller specifically designed for this purpose is often used in one of the form roller positions.

An inking system consists of (a) a **fountain** that holds a supply of ink, (b) a **ductor** or **transfer roller** that carries the ink from the fountain to the roller train, (c) a **roller**

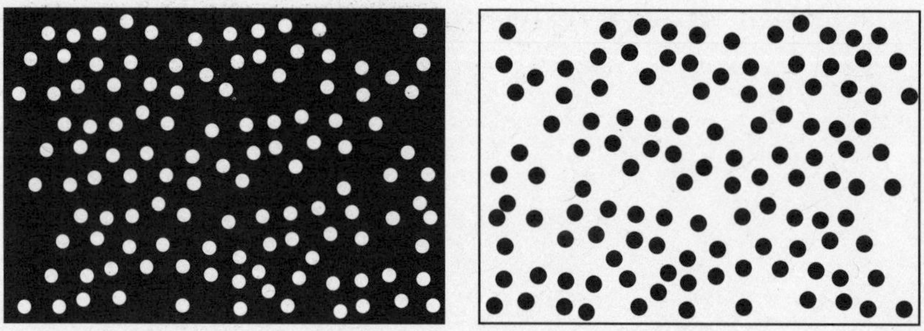

A water-in-ink emulsion *(left)* and an ink-in-water emulsion

On press, water-in-ink emulsification is usually more significant of the two in its effect on the process.

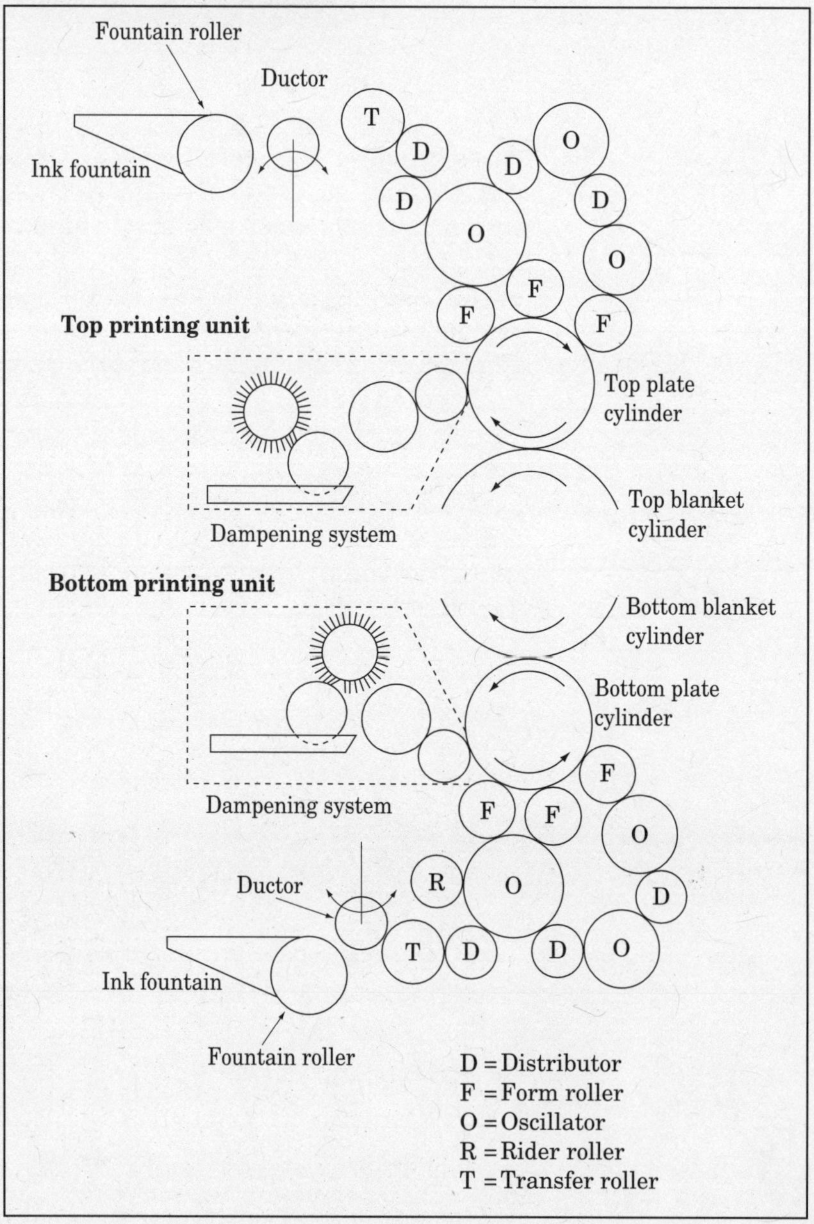

The upper and lower inking systems on a typical commercial web offset press *Courtesy MAN Roland, Inc., Web Press Division*

train that works and distributes the ink, and (d) **form rollers** that deposit the ink onto the plate.

The ink fountain is a trough that is shaped like a V tipped on its side. The bottom of the fountain is a flexible steel strip, called a **fountain blade.** The **fountain roller** is an ink-transporting cylinder, which forms one side of the fountain. It is fixed into the fountain assembly and rotates in place. With most fountain rollers, the amount of roller rotation per cycle of the ductor can be adjusted. Some fountain rollers are driven by their own variable-speed motors; others cannot be adjusted at all but rotate at a constant speed.

To avoid roller wear, the fountain blade should not touch the fountain roller; instead, there should be a narrow gap between the two, the width of which determines how much ink will be carried by the fountain roller as it rotates. Underneath the fountain blade on most presses is a row of thumbscrews or motor-driven screws called fountain keys, evenly spaced along the entire width of the blade. The keys are adjusted to move the blade closer to or farther away from the fountain roller, controlling the thickness of the ink film across the roller.

Alternatively, the fountain blade's position may be adjusted by an eccentric roller or cam that is controlled by a lever. This mechanical design has been used on some newspaper web offset presses. One of its advantages is the ease and rapidity of adjustments. Another advantage is that the position of the various control handles across the ink fountain automatically indicates the setting of the fountain blade across the press. The major disadvantage is that the precision of adjustment available from either the conventional or remote control ink fountain is not attainable.

Lever- or cam-operated ink fountain

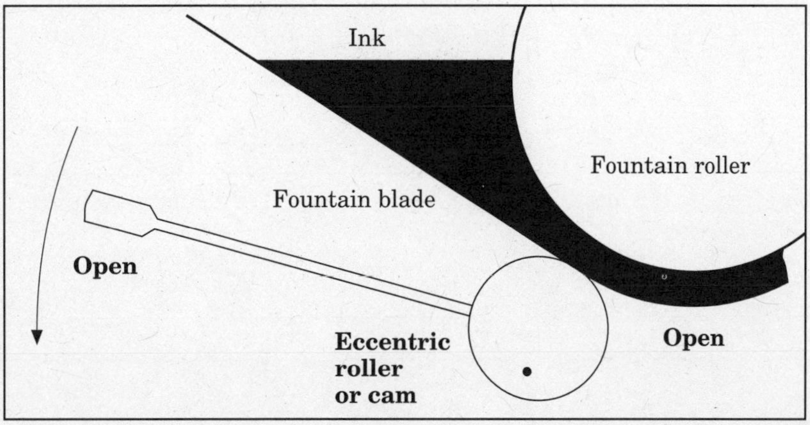

An alternative to the conventional inking system is the **anilox** inking system. This ink-metering system transfers ink from the fountain using an engraved fountain roller. A finely engraved pattern — usually of cells — in the roller surface picks up and holds ink, which continuously transfers to a short series of rollers or directly to an ink form roller.

Fountain rollers for anilox offset have either chrome-plated surfaces that are engraved by electronically controlled cutting mechanisms or ceramic surfaces, which are engraved by lasers. *Ceramic* rollers are actually composed of various

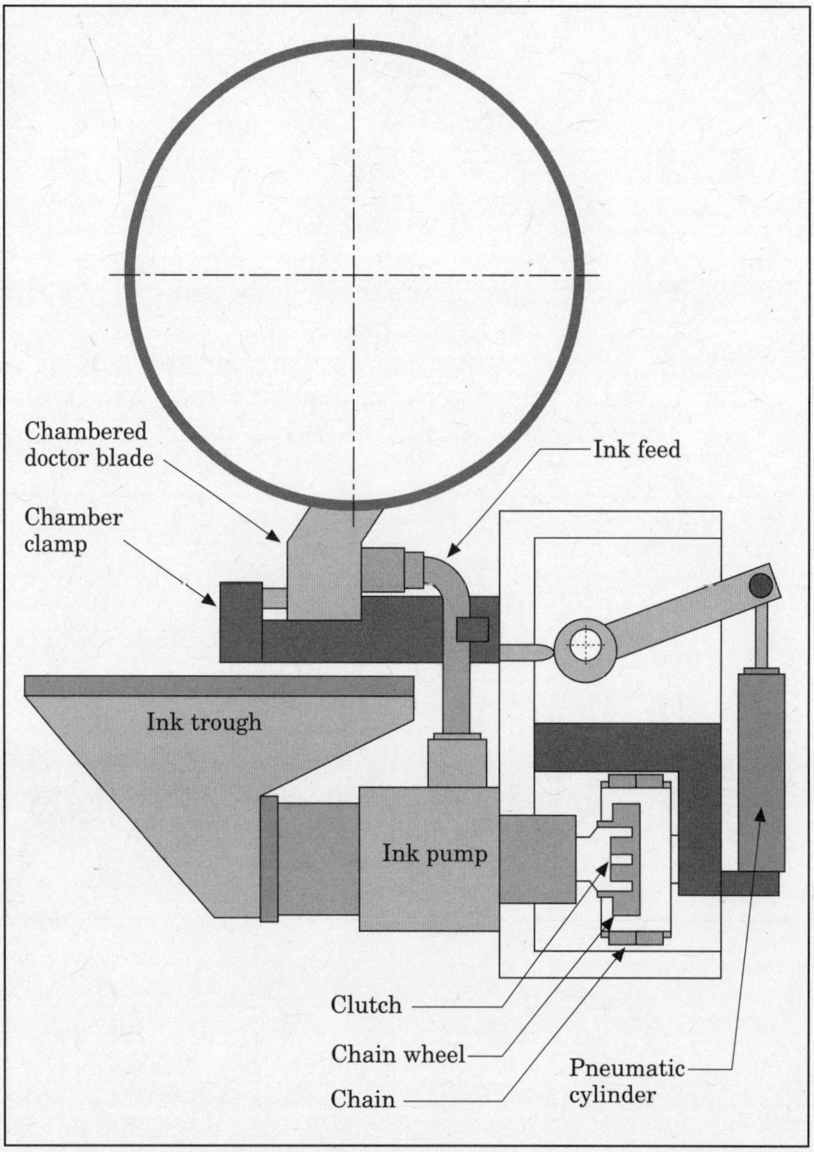

An anilox-offset inking unit with pneumatic loading
Courtesy KBA-Motter Corp., Web Press Division

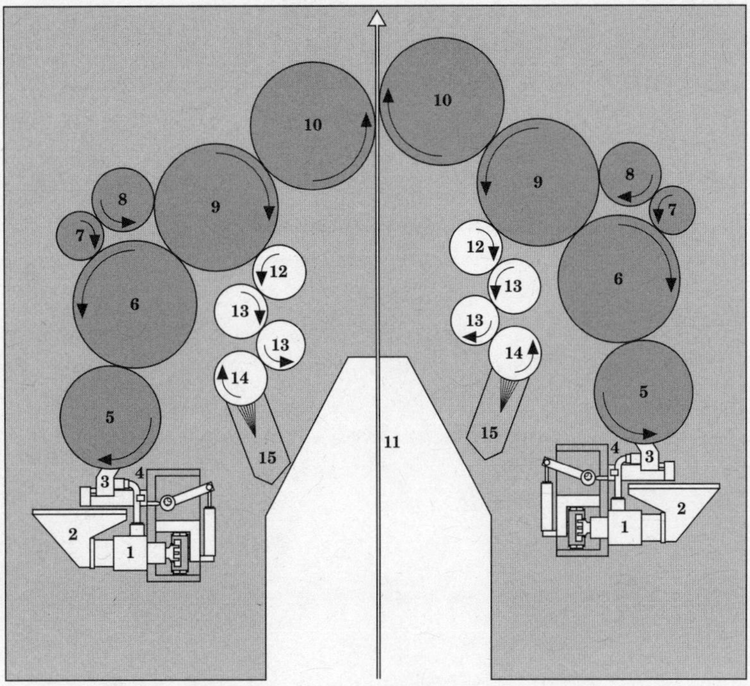

1 Ink pumps
2 Ink troughs
3 Doctor-blade holders
4 Ink feed
5 Screen rollers
6 Ink form rollers
7 Rider rollers
8 Ink form rollers
9 Plate cylinders
10 Blanket cylinders
11 Paper web
12 Dampening form rollers
13 Dampening rollers
14 Dampening chrome rollers
15 Spray bars

An arch-type printing unit that has an anilox inking system
Courtesy KBA-Motter Corp., Web Press Division

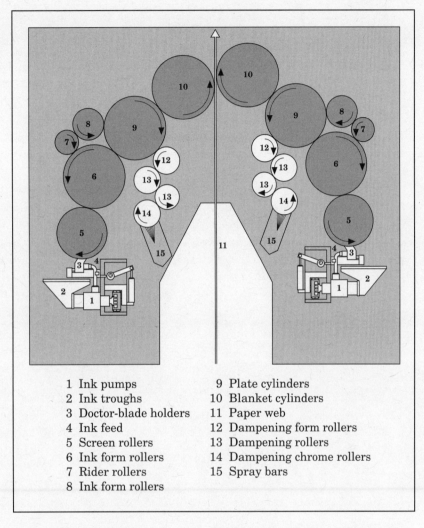

combinations of aluminum oxide, chrome oxide, and titanium oxide.

A **doctor blade** squeegees the surface of the rotating fountain roller, leaving ink in the cells. There is no fountain blade or ink keys for locally adjusting the amount of ink transfer.

The primary application of anilox systems is in newspaper printing, because the designs of these inking systems and the minute depth of the fountain roller cells requires the use of fairly fluid inks such as news inks. Since conventional intermittently fed inking systems supply surges of ink to the roller train (usually by way of a ductor roller), the ink film must be split numerous times between many rollers before it reaches the plate. This ensures smooth coverage on the plate. Anilox systems, however, continuously feed a smooth, metered ink film directly from the fountain roller; therefore, the ink train is much shorter. Furthermore, continuously fed inking systems eliminate ink starvation, which causes ghosting.

In conventional systems, a ductor roller that oscillates every few revolutions of the blanket cylinder takes ink from the fountain roller and deposits it on the first roller in the inking train. The amount of ink put on the ductor and fed into the inking train depends on two things: (a) the thickness of the ink film on the fountain roller, determined by the gap between the fountain blade and fountain roller, and (b) the rate of fountain roller rotation while in contact with the ductor.

The ductor roller dwells against the fountain roller for a time, picking up ink, then swings over to the first driven roller in the inking train and dwells against it, depositing ink. This cycle is repeated periodically, and fresh ink feeds into the inking train as the press runs. The ductor is the only roller in the inking system that oscillates in this way.

The ductor feeds fresh ink into the inking train intermittently, not continuously. The different diameters and rotation periods of the rollers help to smooth out the feed, unifying the ink flow to the plate.

Several inking systems employ other means of ink transfer. One ductorless design replaces the ductor with a brush roller that rotates from a fixed position between the fountain and a receiving drum. Ink is picked up and deposited by the bristles. Other systems use metal rollers rotating in place. Generally, the surfaces of these rollers have raised patterns, such as a spiral or diamond-shaped grid, so that only a fraction of the full roller surface carries ink. This prevents a continuously rotating fountain roller from supplying too much ink. Both of these systems are incapable of obtaining the precise lateral control that is obtained by conventional inking systems.

The exact layout of the inking train varies from press to press. Inking systems generally contain the same basic elements. All systems contain a number of hard rollers, driven directly off the press drive, called **oscillators, vibrators,** or **drums.** Some of these rollers rotate and oscillate from side to side. This motion smooths out and distributes the ink laterally across the press. Oscillators are usually steel, often copperplated or coated with synthetic materials like ebonite and nylon. These rollers are fixed in the press frame and cannot be adjusted in relation to the soft rollers that they contact. The side-to-side oscillation, however, is adjustable. The larger oscillators perform the additional job of effectively increasing the storage of the inking system.

Other rollers in the inking system between the ductor and form rollers are nondriven. Some of these are distributors and others are riders. **Distributors** transfer ink and help to condition it. They have mountings in the press frame, by which they can be adjusted against adjacent rollers. Distributors are composed of an elastomeric material containing mixtures of plastics, pigments, and several other ingredients.

Riders are rollers that run against only one other roller. A rider roller enlarges the inking system and further works the ink before it reaches the plate. Riders also effectively collect unwanted foreign particles from the ink. By holding these particles on their surfaces, the riders keep them out of the main path of the ink flow. Soft riders are usually set against hard rollers, while steel riders are set against soft rollers. Usually, a rider roller is one-half the diameter of the roller that it contacts. Consequently, the rider runs twice as fast, thus stripping and holding many foreign particles such as hickeys.

The inking system rollers that contact the plate are called **ink form rollers** or, more simply, **form rollers.** Some presses have four form rollers while others have only two or three.

Some presses have **oscillating form rollers,** which are substituted for the first and, sometimes, fourth (last) form rollers to reduce ghosting. This form roller oscillates (moves laterally, or side to side) at a rate sometimes different than the adjacent oscillator to smooth the ink film. The oscillation of the form roller can be turned on or off by the press operator.

An oscillating form roller

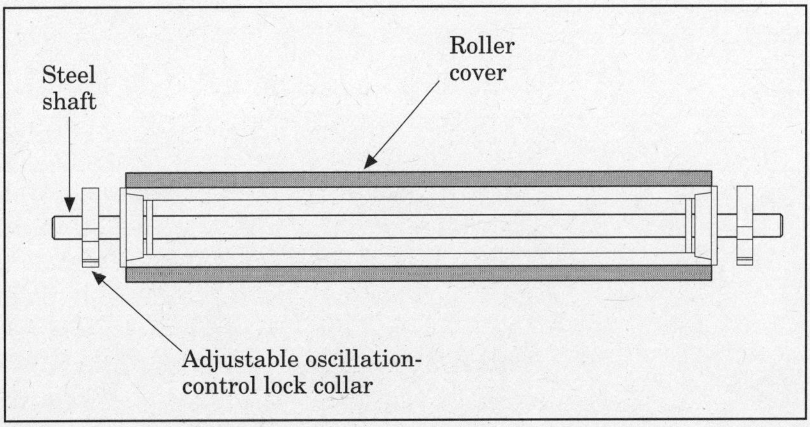

The roller train is comprised of a series of alternating hard and soft rollers. The hard rollers are usually steel covered with copper, ebonite, or nylon. The resilient rollers (ductor, intermediate, and form rollers) are often made of a synthetic rubber such as PVC (polyvinyl chloride), Buna-N (a copolymer of butadiene and acrylonitrile), or polyurethane. These substances are applied to a steel shaft.

Inking systems for waterless lithography. Waterless lithography requires a printing press that is equipped with a temperature control system. Two types of press temperature control systems are used: an ink oscillator cooling system and a plate cylinder cooling system. With the ink oscillator cooling system, a standard inking system is used with the exception that chilled or *heated* water solution flows through hollow vibrator rollers on the press. These temperature control systems allow the press operator to maintain ink temperature within a narrow range of only a couple of degrees Fahrenheit.

The ink roller cooling system used for waterless lithography
Courtesy Toray Marketing & Sales (America), Inc.

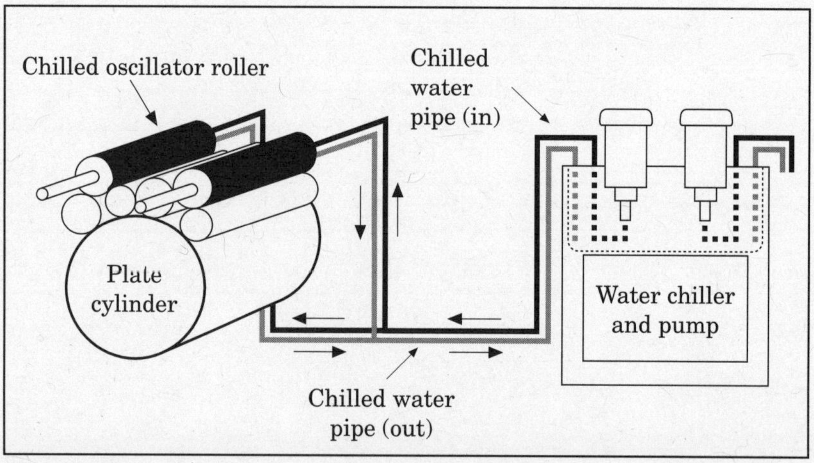

It is not unusual for each of the inks on the press to perform best at a slightly different temperature. For example, a black ink might operate best at, say, 72–74°F (22.2–23.3°C), while a cyan might operate best at, say, 68–70°F (20–21.1°C). Therefore, the temperature of each inking system on the press is independently controlled by using a zone control unit that blends hot and cold water to the proper temperature for the ink being used. In addition, infrared sensors monitor the temperature of each printing unit, providing immediate feedback to maintain the proper temperature level.

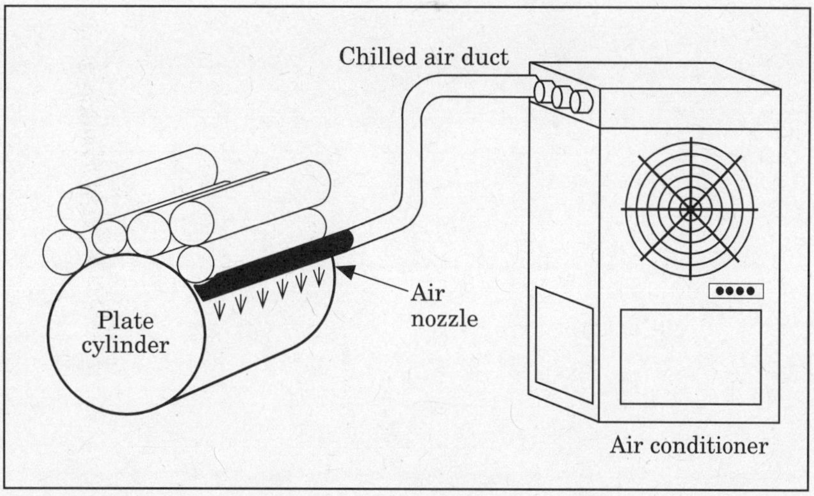

The plate cylinder cooling system used for waterless lithography
Courtesy Toray Marketing & Sales (America), Inc.

Setting the Ink Rollers

Proper ink roller settings assure good ink transfer and allow the rollers to ride and drive properly. Heavy or uneven settings can cause ink distribution problems, increased roller wear, and, through excess heat, setting of the ink on the rollers. About one-half of the power used to drive a sixteen-page blanket-to-blanket press goes into driving the inking train.

The proper setting of rollers is simple, but the task requires time and care. All rollers in the inking system are set parallel to one another and to the oscillators. The oscillators should always be parallel to one another, because they are fixed in the press frame. Undue roller wear on only one side of the press or the inability to get equal settings are indicators that the oscillators are out of parallel. Worn oscillator bushings or bearings can be one cause. Accidentally running an object like a sponge or rag through the system is another. For a major malfunction like this, the press operator should call in the manufacturer. All rollers should be checked in this way every time a roller is changed in the inking system. A new roller has a greater diameter than a worn old one. The difference in diameter can be enough to change the roller setting.

Setting the ductor roller involves three different adjustments:

- **Setting the ductor to the fountain roller.**
- **Setting the ductor to the transfer roller.** Accurate setting is critical. If the ductor roller is set too hard against the transfer roller, the adhesion supplied by the ink slows the transfer roller, which is running at press speed. GATF has conducted tests on instrumented

presses with the ductor roller set too hard against the transfer roller. The load created by the friction between the ductor and transfer roller was enough to slow the unit and vary web tension before and after the printing unit. Such a load also contributes to gear wear. Printing problems associated with this *ductor shock* include doubling and slurring.

- **Rechecking the ductor-to-fountain roller setting.** The second adjustment — setting the ductor to the transfer roller — may change the setting between the ductor and the fountain roller; therefore, the press operator should recheck the ductor-to-fountain roller setting.

The settings of the distributors and rider rollers are usually less critical than those of the ductor. This can best be shown by an example. If the distributor roller marked "X" in the illustration below were removed from the inking system, enough ink could be forced down the left side of the roller train to meet the needs of the form. However, this transfers more ink over these rollers than they were designed to carry, which reduces control of ink application to the plate.

Typical ink system

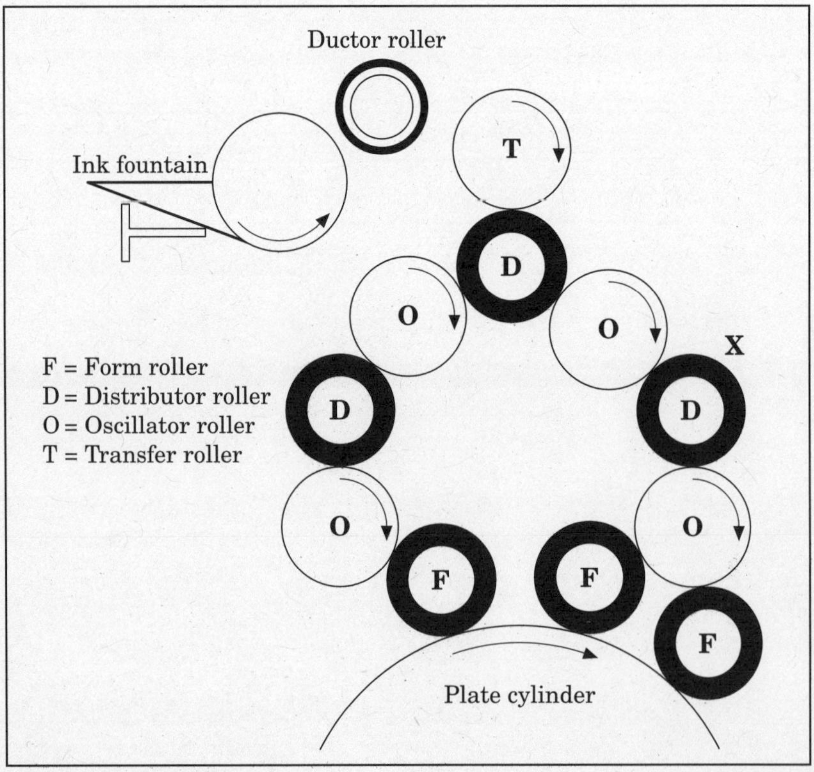

Inking systems should not be run with rollers missing; however, a press running with a distributor roller that inadequately contacts either the oscillator above or below it may exhibit the same effect. For example, assume that the distributor marked "X" is not in good contact with the oscillator above it. This means that all of the ink required by the form has to run through the left side of the inking system, as shown. This creates problems during makeready and while running. Too light a setting on the distributor causes little or no ink to transfer. The ink moves erratically down through the train from roller to roller or stops altogether at the poorly set distributor. In addition, proper washup becomes extremely difficult. On the other hand, too heavy a setting excessively wears rollers and roller bearings. Also, excessive heat will build up in the roller train, causing ink problems. In setting the distributors, the press operator strives to equalize pressure at all transfer points. This condition automatically assures that the rollers are parallel to the oscillators. Some distributors have spring-loaded mountings or simple sockets.

Durometer and roller settings

A roller's durometer is a measure of its hardness or softness. Durometer strongly affects roller settings when the ink-stripe roller-setting method is used. As an extreme example, the amount of pressure required to get a 1/8-in. (3-mm) stripe between two solid steel rollers is many times greater than that required to get the same stripe between two rubber rollers of the same diameter. The harder the rollers, the more pressure required to get a stripe of a particular width.

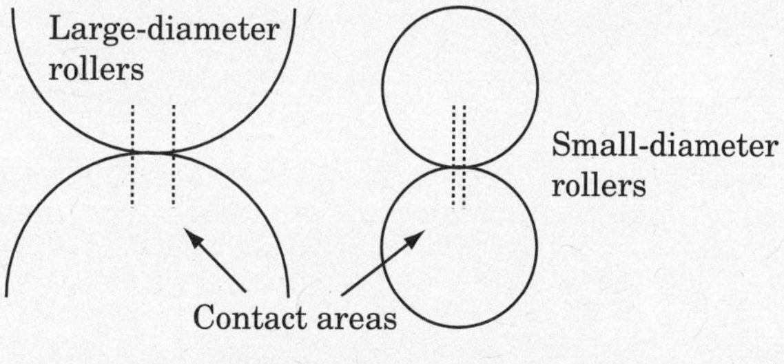

Another factor affecting roller settings with the ink stripe method is the diameter of the rollers. For a given pressure, large rollers will produce a wider stripe (contact area) than will small rollers. These are two major reasons why there is no single standard for durometer and for the size of roller stripes for all presses. Roller composition and size vary from press to press as does durometer and, therefore, the proper size of the stripe when setting ink rollers. Consequently, the press manufacturer's recommendations for roller settings should be followed.

On such rollers, well-maintained mountings and adequate lubrication are critical to proper functioning.

The form rollers contact the plate and the oscillators. These rollers are not driven but derive their rotation from the adjacent oscillators. Ink form rollers should be set heavy enough against the oscillators so that they are properly driven, and as light as possible against the plate, while still able to transfer a full charge of ink. All form rollers have adjustable mounting sockets to simplify their settings against the plate and oscillator. The design of the sockets permits the press operator to adjust the forms to the plate without disturbing the setting between form roller and oscillator.

Form roller settings should be checked frequently. First, ink up the press. After all rollers have been covered with a normal ink film, stop the press. Drop the form rollers onto the properly packed and gummed plate. Each form roller will

Roller stripes

Ink band swollen at ends: Setting roller too tightly against the oscillator causes rubber to break loose from the roller shaft. This allows solvent to swell rubber at the roller ends. Grind rollers or replace.

Too heavy at one end, too light at the other end: Uneven setting. Reset rollers to obtain uniform band.

Heavy in the center, light at the ends: Roller bowed or worn at ends. Caused by form roller being set too tightly against the oscillator. Correct by resetting rollers. Regrind or replace rollers if it is no longer possible to obtain the desired setting.

Light areas in ink band: Indicates improper grinding or manufacture of roller. Regrind or replace.

Ideal setting: Uniform, parallel bands.

stripe the plate. The width of each stripe is related to the pressure between each form roller and the plate. Some press operators use a rule of thumb and set the stripes at 1⁄16 in. (1.6 mm) for every 1 in. (25 mm) of form roller diameter, with the stripe of the last form over the plate always set narrowest, regardless of its diameter. Other press operators set the first form roller over the plate heaviest. Each form roller after the first is then set to lay down a narrower stripe than the one before it.

To roughly check the setting of a new roller, insert paper sandwiches at the center and at both ends of each roller. Take three strips of paper, 0.004–0.005 in. (0.10–0.13 mm) thick and about 12 in. (300 mm) long. Two of the strips should be about 2 in. (50 mm) wide and the third about 1 in. (25 mm) wide. The narrow strip should be sandwiched in between the two wider ones.

The use of a paper sandwich for setting rollers

The three-strip sandwich is inserted between the rollers being set. When the narrower middle strip is pulled, the press operator feels drag on the strip, which indicates approximately how much pressure there is between the two rollers. The pull in all three positions should be the same. A roller-setting gauge provides accurate measurable results. The metal tongue of the gauge is inserted between two paper strips. When the tongue is pulled out, the gauge gives a reading that indicates the maximum amount of drag on the tongue.

The use of a roller setting gauge
Courtesy J. E. Doyle Co., Inc.

Operating Procedures

In the day-to-day operation of an inking system, the press operator performs three different operations: setting the ink fountain at the start of a job, filling and adjusting the ink fountain during running, and washing up.

After putting ink in the ink fountain, the press operator sets the ink fountain for the job to be run. The keys are set to provide a uniform film thickness on the ink fountain roller. The keys are adjusted to meet the requirements of the form. In areas of heavy coverage, the fountain keys are opened. For lighter coverage, the blade should be set closer to the ink fountain roller. In other words, the ink film thickness on the fountain roller is set according to the estimated amounts of ink required by the form. Alternatively, ink transfer can be regulated by using ink fountain dividers that allow the ink to lie in only part of the fountain. The section with no ink demand should be lubricated. Special compounds known as *open-pocket compounds* are available for this purpose.

An ink fountain blade can last almost forever on a press or it may need to be replaced in a relatively short time, depending on the press operator's habits in setting the fountain. When opening the blade across the fountain, the press operator should always start with the fountain keys at each end and work alternately toward the center. In setting the blade closer to the fountain roller, the press operator should always start at the center and work alternately between each end. These procedures prevent a buckle from forming in the blade, which complicates setting the fountain blade thereafter.

The ink fountain blade should *never* be set so tight that it actually scrapes the fountain roller surface clean at any point. Such a setting damages or wears the roller and the blade, leading to expensive repairs.

Setting the fountain blade of the inking system

To open fountain keys *(top illustration),* start at the ends and work toward the center.
To close fountain keys *(bottom illustration),* start at the center and work towards the ends

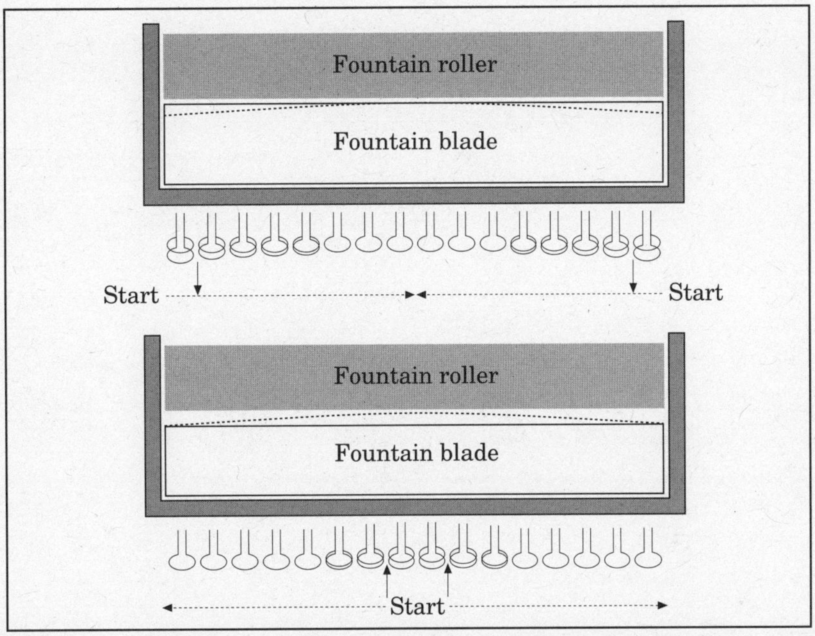

A fountain blade that has buckled because the keys were opened in the incorrect order

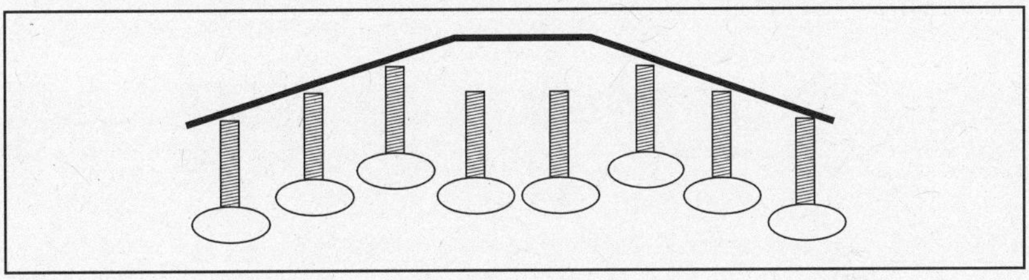

The setting of the fountain keys and blade determines the *variations* of ink from side to side due to the form. The amount of ink fountain roller rotation determines the *volume* of ink fed into the inking train. The amount of rotation can be adjusted by the press operator. Once the press is printing, the press operator visually evaluates the original settings by inspecting the first makeready signatures coming off the press and adjusting the keys as required. It is far easier to control ink flow starting with too little ink on the rollers; therefore, initial ink settings should be *light.*

In washup, a solvent that meets EPA and OSHA regulations is used to cut the ink, thin it out, and simplify its removal from the rollers. Washup solvents must be compatible with the ink. In addition, the solvents should be approved by the blanket and roller manufacturers. This is necessary to prevent premature aging of blankets and rollers.

It is important that the rollers be completely free of ink and solvent after washup is completed. If allowed to set, any solvent/ink combination left on the rollers can complicate the subsequent startup and damage the soft inking rollers.

The use of a washup device (washup machine) and solvents reduces washup time and helps greatly in keeping rollers in good condition. A washup device usually consists of a Teflon or molded rubber blade with a drip pan attached below it. Thumbscrews at each end of the blade allow for pressure adjustment between the blade and the oscillator. Minimal pressure between the blade and roller allows the blade to skim solvent and ink off the roller. As ink is removed from the roller, more ink from other rollers replaces it, and the whole inking train is cleaned in a short time. Both sides of the blade and the drip pan of the washup device should be thoroughly cleaned as soon as possible after use. Place rags in the bottom of the drip pan to catch the ink.

A washup device

The device's blade skims ink from the oscillator. The ink and solvent collect in a drip pan mounted beneath the blade.

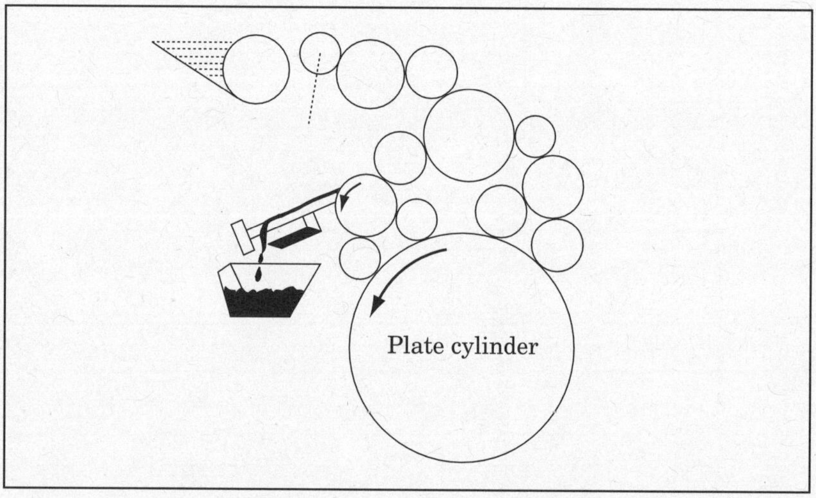

It is common practice to leave press plates mounted while the inking system is being cleaned; however, it is necessary to gum the plates to prevent the washup solvents from sensitizing them. Multistep washup or roller conditioning rinses usually dissolve gum. In this case, extra care must be taken to prevent dripping onto the plates. Otherwise, the plates must be removed before starting the washup or rinse operation.

The ink fountain blade, ink fountain roller, and ink ductor roller must also be thoroughly cleaned. The fountain blade should be removed or swung away for washup so that its underside can be cleaned. This also improves access to the fountain roller, especially the fountain roller ends.

Maintenance

A clean, properly adjusted inking system in good mechanical condition operates efficiently at maximum speed. An improperly maintained inking system that is either dirty or improperly set can produce a variety of ink distribution problems, which result in unsatisfactory print quality and increased roller and plate wear.

In washing up the inking system, solvents dissolve the ink and remove it from the rollers. Today, solvents are usually classified as one-step or multistep, depending on the number of distinct cleaning stages their application requires. Multistep solvents involve the use of two or three separate solutions. When using them, the press operator should never substitute one solution for another and should always use them in their proper sequence. One-step solvents are typically used for daily washups; multistep cleaners are more often used for thorough cleaning on a weekly basis.

The roller manufacturer should always be consulted for instructions as to the choice and frequency of use of any solvents. Regardless of which solvent is used, the press operator must ensure that the press is run until no solvent remains on the rollers after washup is completed.

The roller material determines the maintenance requirements. Rollers are subject to surface buildup of dried ink, gum, and, sometimes, paper coating material. This condition is known as **glazing.** When glazing occurs, the roller loses its ability to properly carry and transfer ink. Periodic washup with multistep solvents is usually enough to prevent glazing on the press. In extreme cases, the rollers have to be removed from the press and scrubbed by hand.

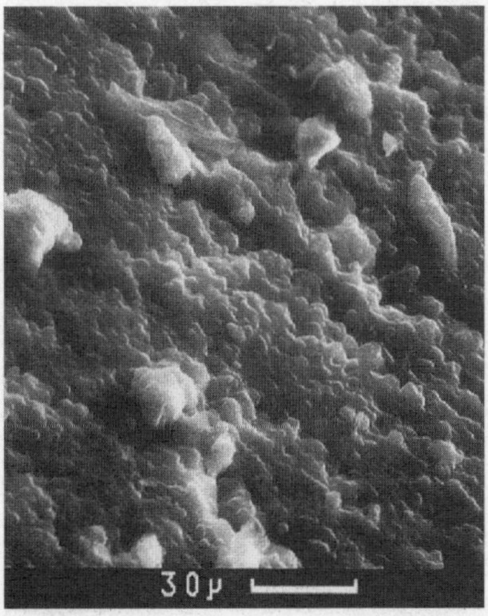

Photomicrographs of the surface of a new roller *(left)* and a glazed roller *(right)* *Courtesy Böttcher America Corp.*

The importance of roller care

(A) The surface of a properly maintained roller should look and feel velvety.
(B) Residual ink or solvent left on the roller overnight can cause the roller to pick apart when the press is started.
(C) Ink buildup on the roller ends can get rock-hard, in time cracking and splitting the roller ends and generating hickeys.
(D) Buildup of dried ink and varnish can create minute cracks and wrinkles in the roller surface.
(E) End-picking can be caused by ink buildup and by running narrow webs without lubricating the roller ends.
(F) A roller in as poor condition as this one will have to be recovered.
(G) The minimal time needed to keep roller ends clean is more than paid back in increased roller life, press productivity, and improved print quality.
(H) Periodic hand cleaning of rollers is an essential part of roller care.

A

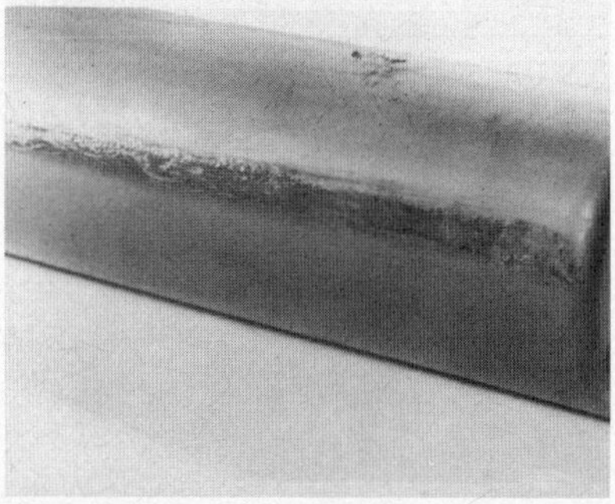

B

C

D

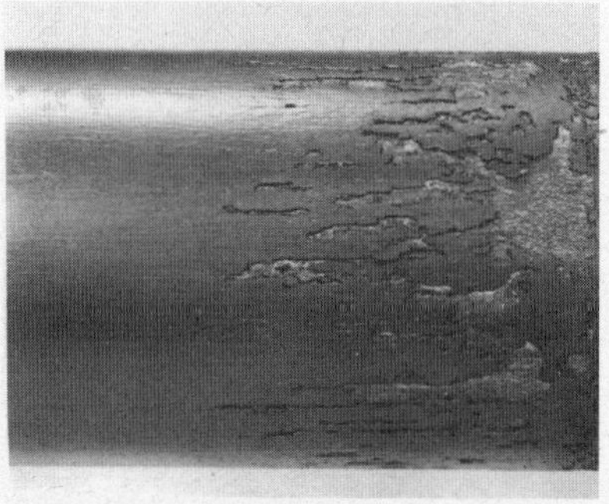

E

F

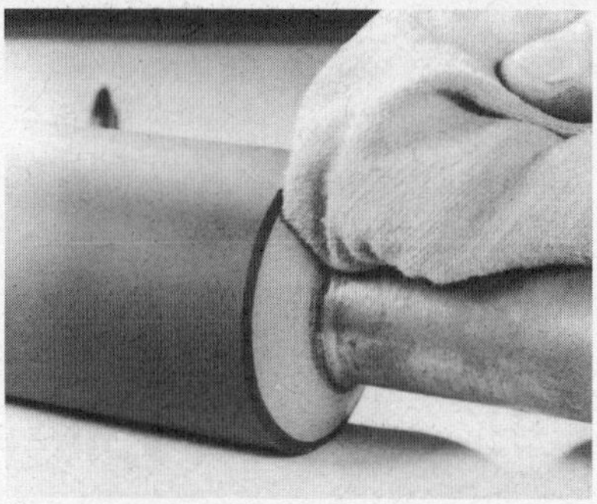

G

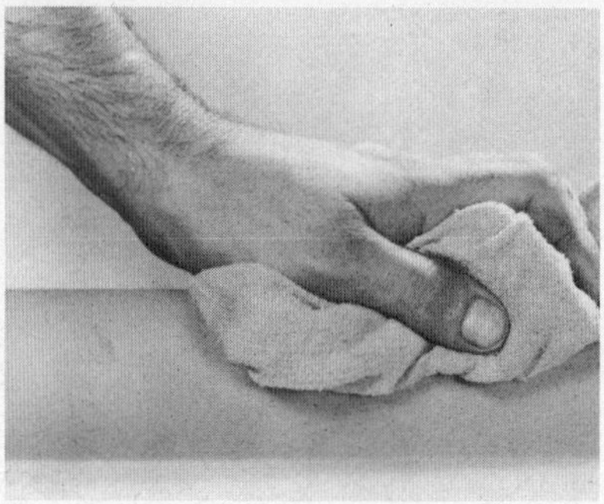

H

Because of the lateral movement of the oscillators, ink rollers invariably develop ink buildup on the ends, especially after the washup. If these *ink cuffs* are not removed during every washup, the ink dries and then has to be chipped away. If they are not removed, dried ink cuffs may chip during running. This debris can be a major cause of hickeys.

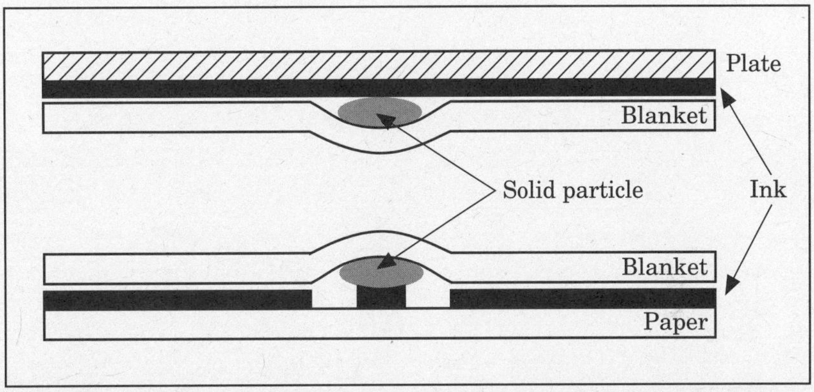

A solid particle (such as dried ink), enlarged, on the blanket, producing a hickey on the printed sheet

Oscillator rollers are subject to **stripping;** the roller becomes water-receptive because gum is adhering to its surface. The usual cause of roller stripping is too much gum in the dampening solution. If the dampening solution pH is too low, roller stripping increases greatly because acid improves gum's ability to stick to the roller surface. The cure for a

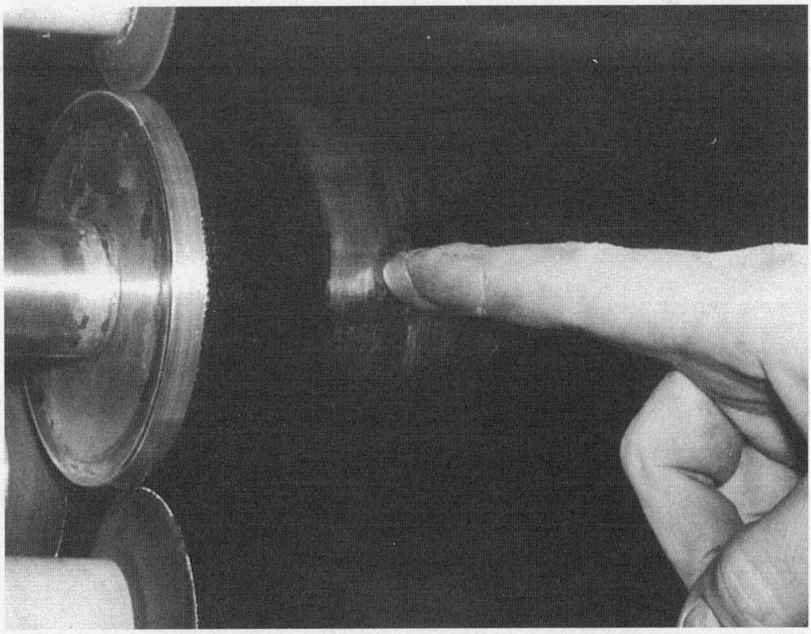

A roller that is stripping

stripped roller is to vigorously rub the roller with pumice and water, and then go over it with an etch. The etch should be recommended by the roller manufacturer and must comply with EPA and OSHA regulations. Most oscillators are made of steel tubing covered with copper, ebonite, nylon, or some other ink-receptive material that is resistant to roller stripping caused by dampening solution chemicals. Although this reduces roller stripping, the press operator should not run excess gum or acid in the dampening solution.

Clean roller surfaces do not indicate that the entire inking system is adequately clean. There are many remote places in the system where ink, dirt, paper lint, and other foreign matter can collect. Eventually, these accumulations fall onto the rollers if the press operator doesn't remove them. The fountain frame (the heavy metal block in which the ink fountain blade and keys are mounted) is one of these places; ink builds up on the underside and should be removed regularly. Ink also collects on the tie bars near the roller train that connect the two sides of the press frame. These bars should be cleaned regularly.

The ink fountain keys can become difficult to adjust because of dried ink. They should be removed and soaked in solvent while the metal block is cleaned. Ideally, the cleaned keys should then be returned to the same holes from which they were taken.

Roller storage is also an important part of maintenance. Always store rollers vertically. Storing them horizontally causes them to bow. Rubber rollers, especially, should be cleaned before storage, and care should be taken to prevent exposure to sunlight, because sunlight prematurely ages the rubber. Rollers should not be stored near a source of heat or ozone. Ozone (a form of oxygen and a powerful oxidizing agent) is usually found around a source of electrical discharge such as a motor armature. Ozone can cause fine cracks to develop on the rubber surface.

5 Dampening Systems

The dampening system on a lithographic press applies **dampening,** or **fountain, solution** to the plate. Dampening systems vary more widely in design than do inking systems. This chapter describes the characteristics of dampening solutions and examines the major options in dampening systems along with common operating features.

Dampening Solution

Dampening solution must desensitize nonimage areas of the printing plate without desensitizing the image areas. Since the dampening solution also mixes with ink, it must not excessively emulsify the ink or prevent proper ink drying. The dampening solution also helps keep the plate, rollers, and blanket cool and washes away much of the dirt and debris on the plate or blanket that might otherwise build up as *piling*.

Dampening Solution Ingredients

Dampening solutions are usually sold as concentrated solutions that are diluted with water to the proper concentration. The major ingredients in dampening solution are water, gum, acid, buffers, inorganic salts, sequestering or chelating agents, inhibitors to protect the plate, and surfactants. Isopropyl alcohol was once frequently used to reduce surface tension and increase viscosity so that the plate would stay clean with less water, but its use has been greatly reduced due to environmental regulations.

pH and Conductivity

The degree of acidity or alkalinity of a substance is measured on the pH scale in increments from 0 (highest acidity) to 14 (highest alkalinity), with 7 being neutral.

Conductivity is the ability of a substance to transmit electricity. In the case of dampening solution, conductivity is determined by the number of ions present, which is based upon mineral content.

The pH scale

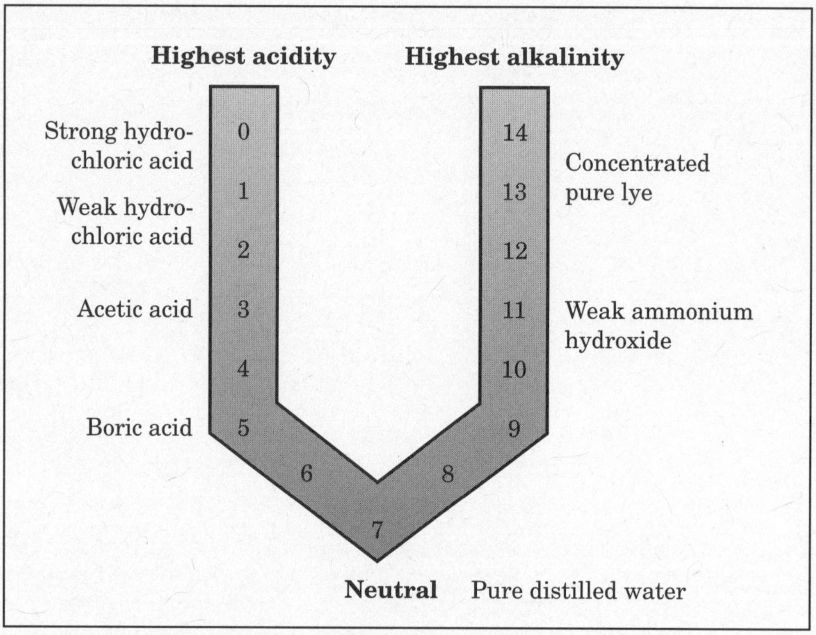

Dampening solution pH may range from 3.5 to 4.5, depending upon the plate etch. Dampening solutions will desensitize plates at much lower pH values; however, the higher acid content may desensitize plate images and attack

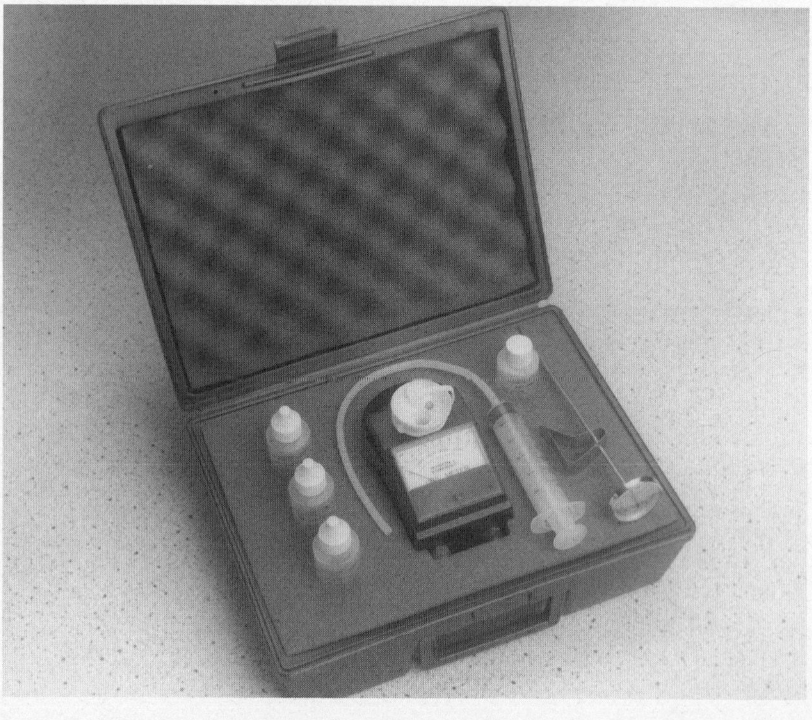

A combination conductivity/pH meter, Model M6/pH, with Model PLK Litho-Kit™
Courtesy Myron L Company

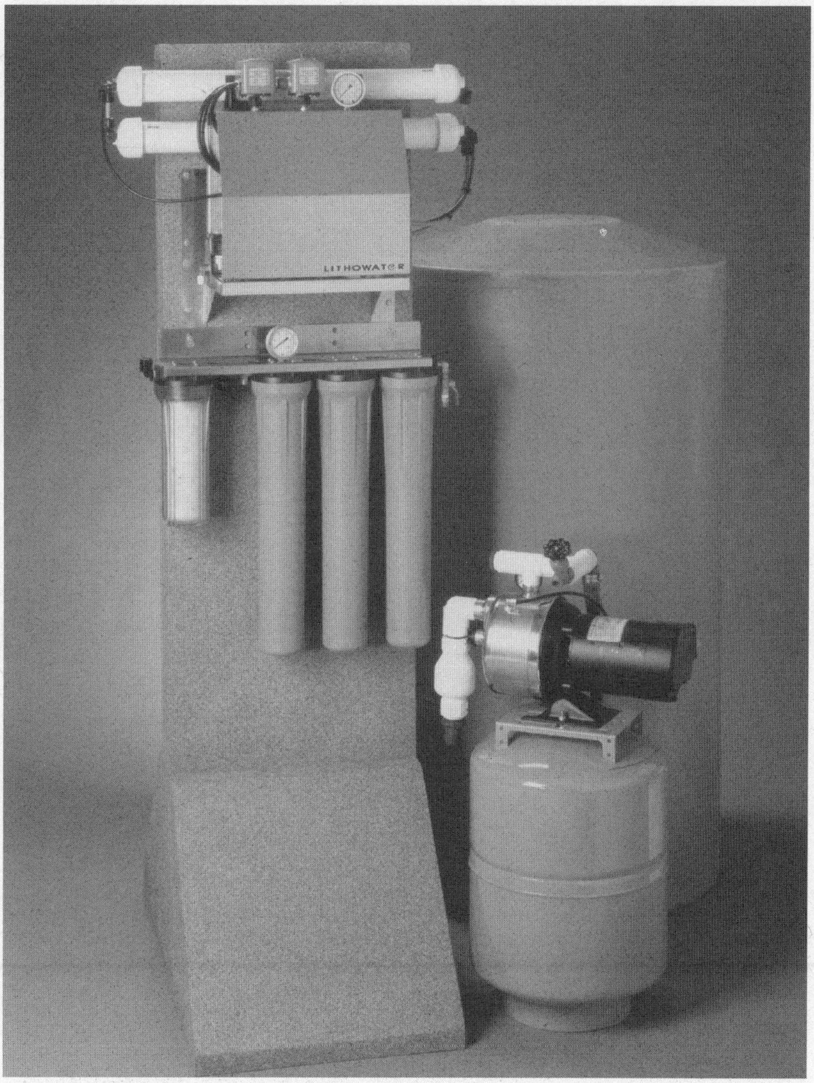

LithoWater water processing system: LW 2600 water processor, RP-2 storage tank, and automatic pump system
Courtesy Procam Controls, Inc.

the ink, causing poor ink drying and/or emulsification of the ink in the dampening solution. Unfortunately, pH readings do not accurately indicate if the dampening solution has been mixed in the correct concentration. The pH of dampening solution decreases when buffered acids are added; however, the pH reading will plateau at a certain level and remain relatively unchanged when more acid is introduced.

Conductivity proportionally increases as the amount of fountain concentrate is increased; therefore, solutions may be mixed to exact proportions. Conductivity readings also indicate the concentration of a *neutral* solution, which pH readings do not.

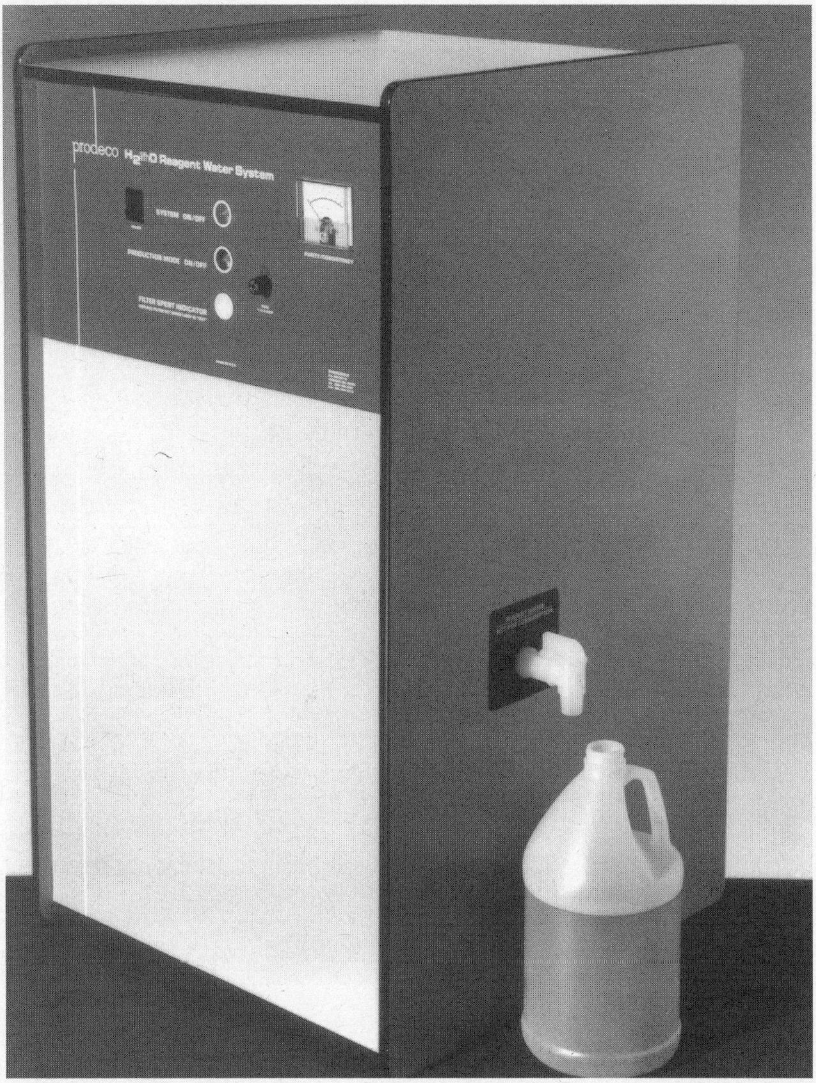

The H_2LithO system, a multi-stage filtering system that uses a combination of ultrafiltration (UF), reverse osmosis (RO), and deionization to produce ASTM Type III grade water for use in mixing fountain solutions
Courtesy Prodeco

Additions of isopropyl alcohol have little effect on pH but significantly reduce conductivity. Therefore, conductivity should be measured before adding alcohol. **Note:** Environmental regulations limit the percentage of alcohol permissible in dampening solution; check with your local and state environmental agencies for permissible amounts of alcohol in the dampening solution.

Conductivity of a dampening solution. The consistency of the water used in the dampening solution is important. Although the hardness of raw water is sufficient to change the pH of dampening solution by one to three units, the

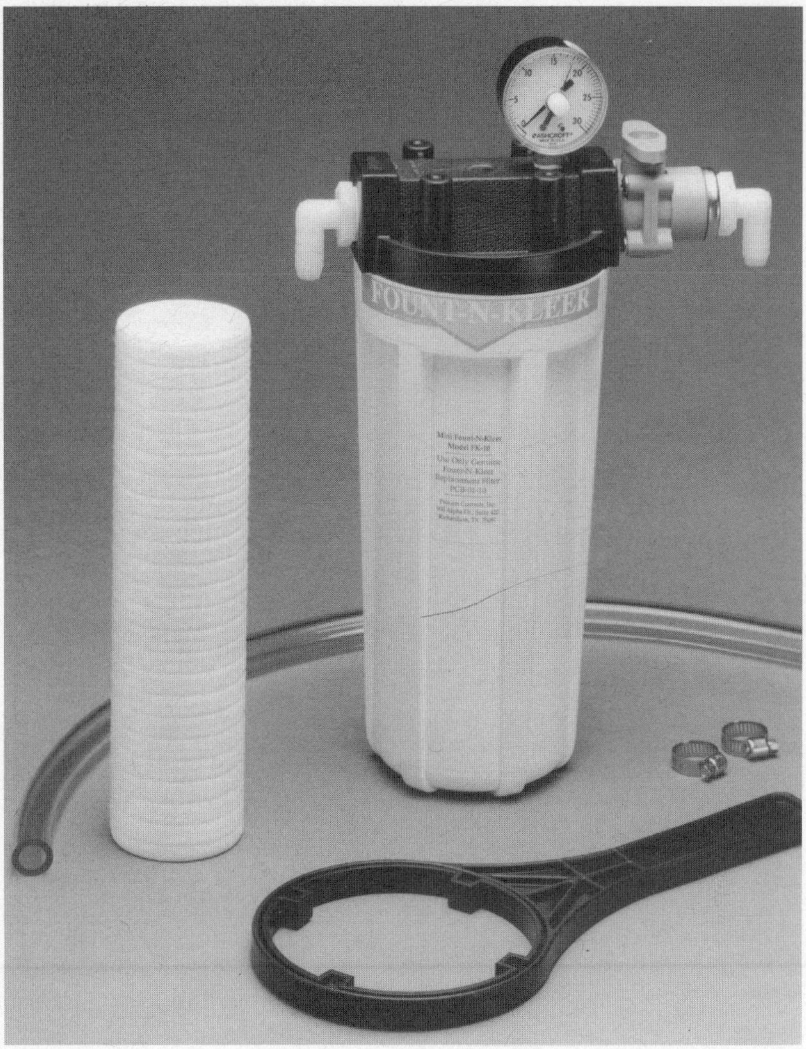

Fount-N-Kleer, a fountain solution filtration system *Courtesy Procam Controls, Inc.*

consistency of raw water hardness is more important than the actual hardness. Manufacturers can prepare fountain concentrates to work with water of practically any hardness, but they can not accommodate water that varies in hardness.

As mentioned earlier, conductivity is a measure of the capacity of a material to conduct electricity. Pure water is a very poor conductor of electricity. As materials dissolve or go into a solution, they form ions and the water becomes conductive. The conductivity of water increases directly with increases in the amount of dissolved matter (ions). Low (partially) ionizable materials such as gum arabic and alcohol are poor electrical conductors and actually lower conductivity of dampening solutions.

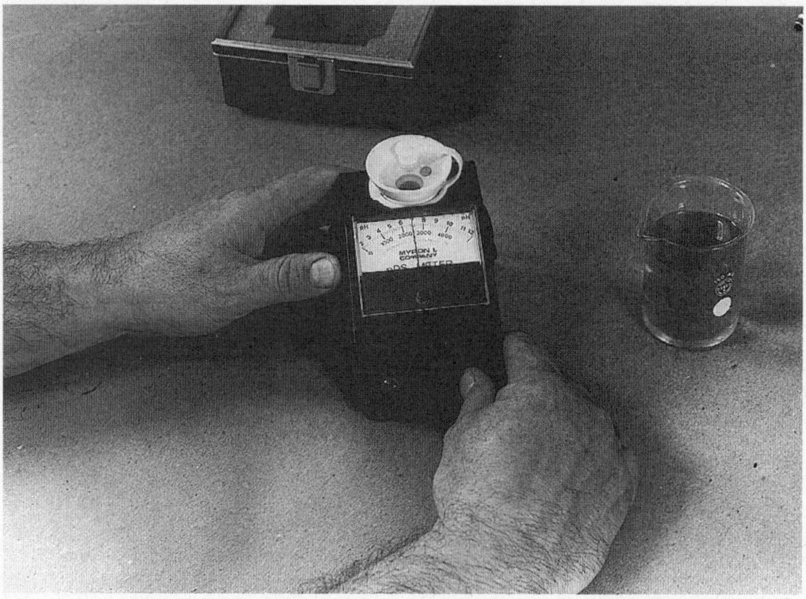

Myron L meter being used to measure the conductivity and pH of a sample of dampening solution

Pure water approaches a conductivity of 0 micromhos. Typical tap water might have a conductivity of 200 micromhos or more. As the amount of dissolved matter increases, the conductivity increases directly in a straight line. Thus conductivity is commonly used as a measure of water purity. Soft water has a conductivity of 0–225 micromhos, and hard water has a conductivity greater than 450 micromhos. The relationship between water hardness and conductivity varies somewhat, depending upon the specific minerals and compounds in the water.

If the water quality varies in conductivity and pH, the printer will not be able to control the dampening solution. If the conductivity of the incoming water varies less than ±50 micromhos, consistent dampening solution can be mixed. Day-to-day fluctuations of 200 micromhos indicate that some type of water treatment equipment may be needed to keep incoming water constant. Water treatments include reverse osmosis, deionization, filtration, or distillation.

If the conductivity of different amounts of fountain concentrates in water is known, it is easy to measure the strength of a solution by measuring its conductivity. The following procedure can be used to develop a graph that plots conductivity and pH against concentration.

1. Measure the conductivity and pH of the water normally used to make the dampening solution. Place water in a clean 1-gal. (3.8-l) bottle.

2. Add 1 oz. (29.6 ml) of fountain solution concentrate. Remeasure both conductivity and pH. Record these values.
3. Add another ounce (2 oz. total) of fountain solution concentrate and remeasure both conductivity and pH. Repeat this process until the amount of fountain solution concentrate added exceeds the manufacturer's recommendations.
4. Plot these values on a graph that has concentration (oz./gal. or ml/l) on the horizontal axis and conductivity and pH on the vertical axis.

Graph of concentration vs. pH and conductivity for a hypothetical combination of dampening solution concentrate and water

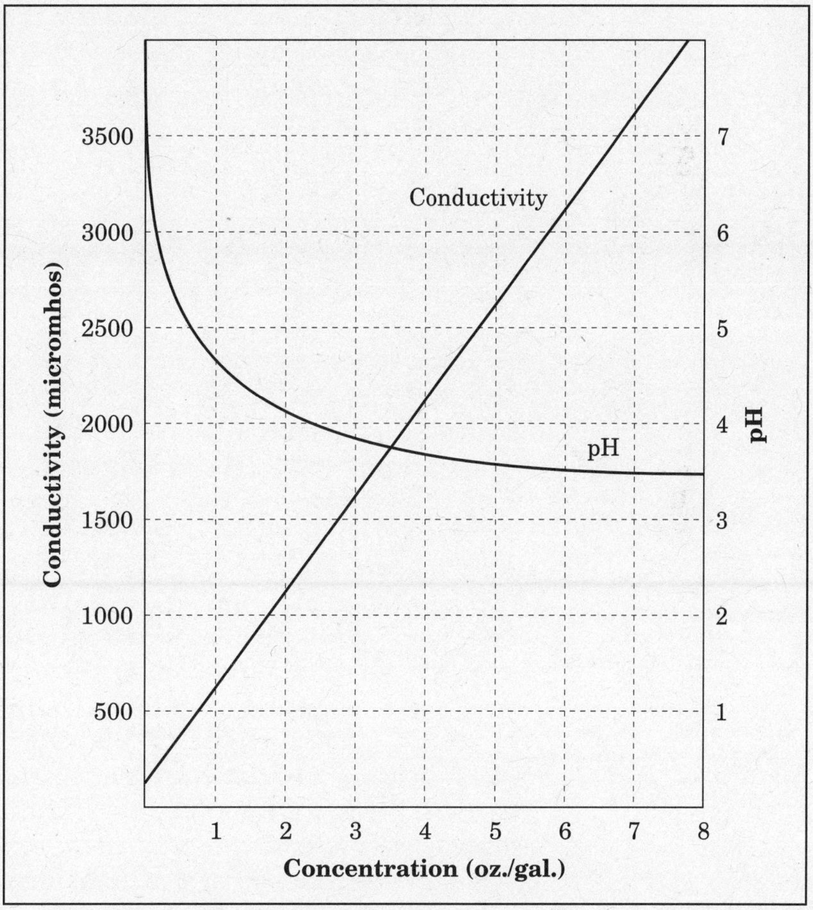

The most important factor in preparing dampening solution is to make sure that it is the proper concentration. Most acidic dampening solutions are buffered so that, as the amount of concentration increases, the pH drops initially but then levels off, while the solution's conductivity increases in a straight line. Thus conductivity is better than pH for determining the amount of concentrate in the dampening solution, but the dampening solution must still be in the proper pH range recommended by the fountain concentrate manufacturer.

With neutral dampening solutions and neutral water, the pH of the solution is constant, regardless of concentration. Therefore, conductivity must be used to measure the concentration of neutral or slightly alkaline dampening solutions.

Any unusual conductivity readings justify rechecking the conductivity of the water and the dampening solution concentrate. It is normal for the conductivity to increase during the pressrun because materials from the ink and paper contaminate the dampening solution. Therefore, conductivity measurements should be made before the dampening solution is used on press.

Dampening Systems

The dampening systems used for web offset lithography can be divided into two major categories: noncontacting and contacting. With a **noncontacting dampening system,** there is no physical contact between the supply of the dampening solution and the rollers that apply the dampening solution to the lithographic printing plate. The two noncontacting dampening systems used in web offset lithography are the *spray dampening system* and the *brush dampening system.*

With a **contacting dampening system,** there is some type of physical link between the supply of dampening solution and the rollers that apply the dampening solution to the printing plate. With one type of contacting dampening system, the contact is intermittent: a ductor roller alternately contacts the fountain pan roller and an oscillator roller, transferring dampening solution. This type of contact dampening system is usually referred to as a *conventional dampening system.* This system can also be called an *intermittent-contact, intermittent-flow,* or *ductor dampening system.* A second broad grouping of contacting dampening systems is the *continuous-contact,* or *continuous-flow, dampening system.* As its name implies, this system supplies a constant flow of dampening solution.

Conventional Dampening Systems

In general design, conventional dampening systems resemble inking systems. A supply of dampening solution is held in a fountain pan. A brass, chrome-plated, or ceramic fountain roller rotates in the pan. On some presses, this roller is covered with a cloth or paper sleeve to increase its water-holding

The conventional dampening system

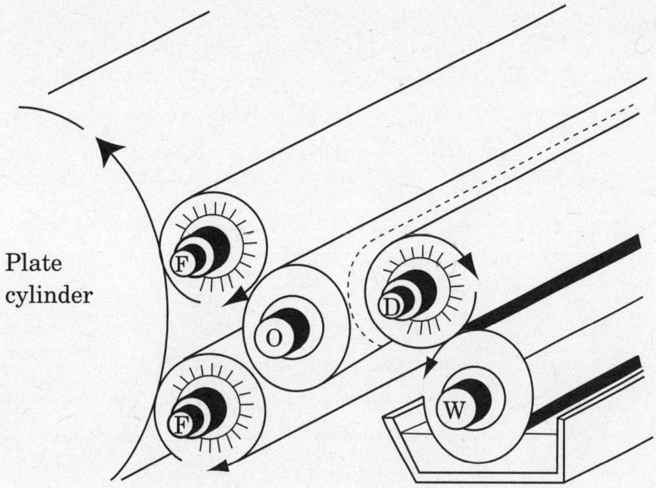

O—Oscillator roller (chrome)
F—Form roller (molleton-covered)
W—Water pan roller
D—Ductor roller (molleton-covered)

capacity. It is usually driven by its own motor, separate from the main press drive, or by a variable-speed drive off the press.

A ductor roller transfers dampening solution from the fountain pan roller to the surface of a metal oscillator. As in the inking system, the dampening ductor swings back and forth between the fountain pan roller and the oscillator. Some slippage has to be built into the dampening system. The fountain roller cannot run at press speed without spraying solution all over the press area, but other dampening rollers run at press speed. The ductor speeds up and slows down during its cycle to compensate for this speed difference. The ductor is made of a plasticized-rubber compound and is always covered to increase its water storage capacity.

An oscillator is the next roller in the dampening system. It is driven from the press drive and, like the oscillators in the inking system, oscillates from side to side. There is no setting adjustment on this roller, which is permanently fixed to the dampener unit frame. The dampening oscillator is usually aluminum, chrome-plated steel, or ceramic-covered.

The dampener form rollers directly wet the plate. Most presses have one dampening form roller, although some have two. Dampeners are nondriven, rubber rollers, usually covered with cloth or paper sleeves.

The conventional dampening system is an intermittent-feed system. Water does not continuously flow from the fountain pan to the plate. The amount of water in the dampening system is lowest just before the ductor contacts the oscillator. Then, water surges through the system when the ductor contacts the oscillator. These surges are more difficult to control than ink surges, because the flow of dampening solution to the plate is more direct. Because the problem is inherent in the design, the press operator must learn how to control it.

Absorbent cloth and paper dampener covers help to provide more uniform dampening by increasing the storage capacity of the rollers. Increased storage capacity in the dampening system acts like a sponge, absorbing excess water and giving it up when the supply becomes low. This produces a dampening flow to the plate that varies less and, therefore, delivers less total water. The advantages of increased storage are better control and minimum water delivered to the plate. The problem with large-capacity dampening systems is their slow response to changes. To increase the amount of water, the speed of the fountain roller is increased. On the other hand, to cut back on the level of dampening, it is necessary to turn the dampener supply off and let the press reduce the amount of dampening solution in the system. In both cases, skill is required by the press operator to change the setting without producing waste. In order to increase this storage capacity, a press operator sometimes puts a double cover on the roller, with the undercover made of cotton or flannel.

The most widely used material for covering dampening form rollers is cloth, usually a fabric called molleton, woven as a sleeve, slipped over the roller and tied at the roller ends. Molleton has a relatively long nap and is good for storing

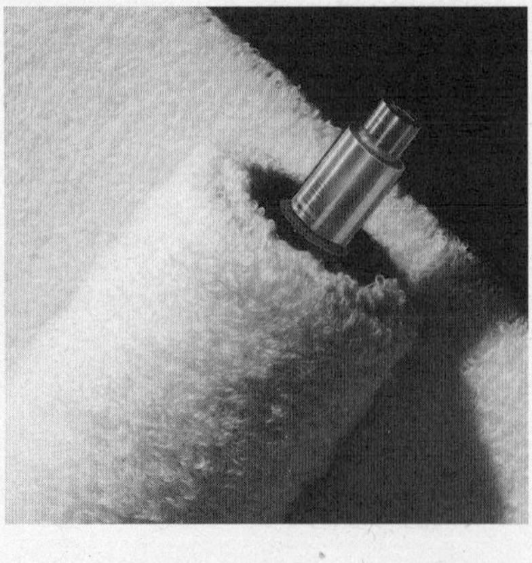

A prefabricated cloth cover *(left)* and a Jomac Super-Damp® dampener cover *(right)* *Courtesy Jomac, Inc.*

water; however, it releases lint when new and easily becomes greasy. In addition, depending on how much dirt or grease it picks up, its thickness can vary, changing the effective radius of the roller. This change in radius changes the roller setting, which in turn can break up the uniform film of water unless the press operator resets the dampener rollers.

Because of the inadequacies of cloth covers, paper covers were developed. The paper used is a special vegetable parchment, available originally as strips for winding around the roller and currently as tubular sleeves. When they get dirty, they are easier to clean or replace than cloth. Paper covers also absorb less grease. A major drawback to using paper covers is that they have limited water-storage capacity.

Setting the pressure between the various dampening rollers is critical. With too little pressure, the rollers drive inefficiently. Too much pressure wrings water from the

Two dampener roller covers: parchment paper strip *(left)* and paper dampening sleeve *(right)*

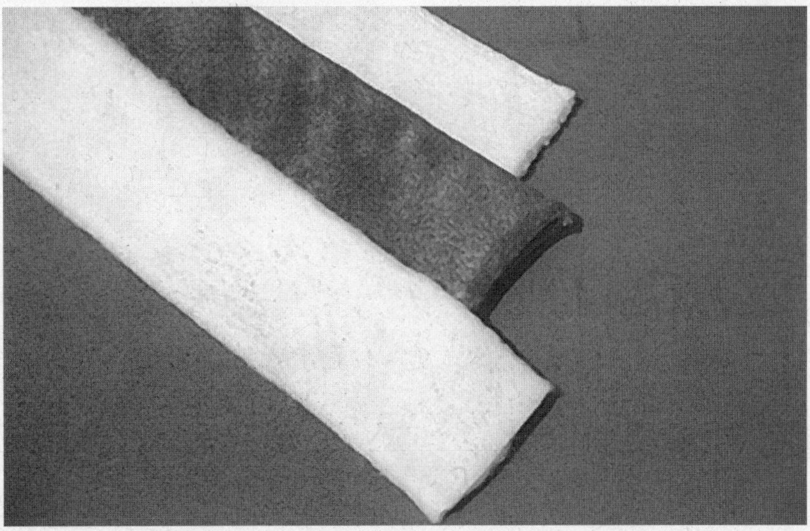

A variety of dampening covers *(from left to right):* Web-Mol®, Greensleeves, and "A"-Tex®
Courtesy Jomac, Inc.

rollers, and insufficient dampening solution reaches the plate. The basic setting procedure is the same as that for the inking rollers. Three plastic strips are used, or for more accurate results, the metal tongue of a roller-setting gauge may be inserted in place of the middle plastic strip.

As in the inking system, the reference point used in setting the rollers is the oscillator, which must parallel the fountain roller and the plate cylinder. This should be checked periodically as part of long-term maintenance. If the oscillator is not parallel, the press operator should not attempt to reset it. Such settings are extremely critical and should be made by a press mechanic.

In most cases, dampening form-to-plate pressure should be less than that between the dampener and the oscillator. Too tight a setting can *squeegee* water from the plate and also increase plate wear. Set just enough pressure so that adequate water transfers smoothly to the plate.

To set the ductor, the printing unit is inched until the ductor is at maximum pressure against the oscillator. A plastic strip is inserted at three points between the two rollers and tested for drag. The printing unit is then inched until the ductor touches the fountain pan roller. Again, the strips are used in three positions along the ductor to ensure correct setting and alignment.

All dampening systems meter, or measure, the water into the press. A conventional system accomplishes this in several ways. The fountain roller is driven, though not by the press drive. It has its own motor, which can be adjusted for faster or slower rotation. Fountain roller rotation may be controlled through a ratchet similar to that found on the inking system fountain roller. The second adjustment in the dampening system controls the duration that the ductor dwells against the fountain roller.

When the fountain roller rotates at high speed and the ductor dwells against it for a comparatively long time, water is spread over the entire surface of the ductor. On the other hand, when the pan roller turns slowly, and the ductor dwells for a short time, only a narrow band of water is deposited on the ductor. These are extreme settings. **Note:** Water should flow to the plate as continuously and uniformly as possible.

A third means of adjusting water feed is possible. This involves the setting of special tabs, squeegees, or rollers called water stops against the surface of the pan roller. This

One design of a water stop for regulating water flow

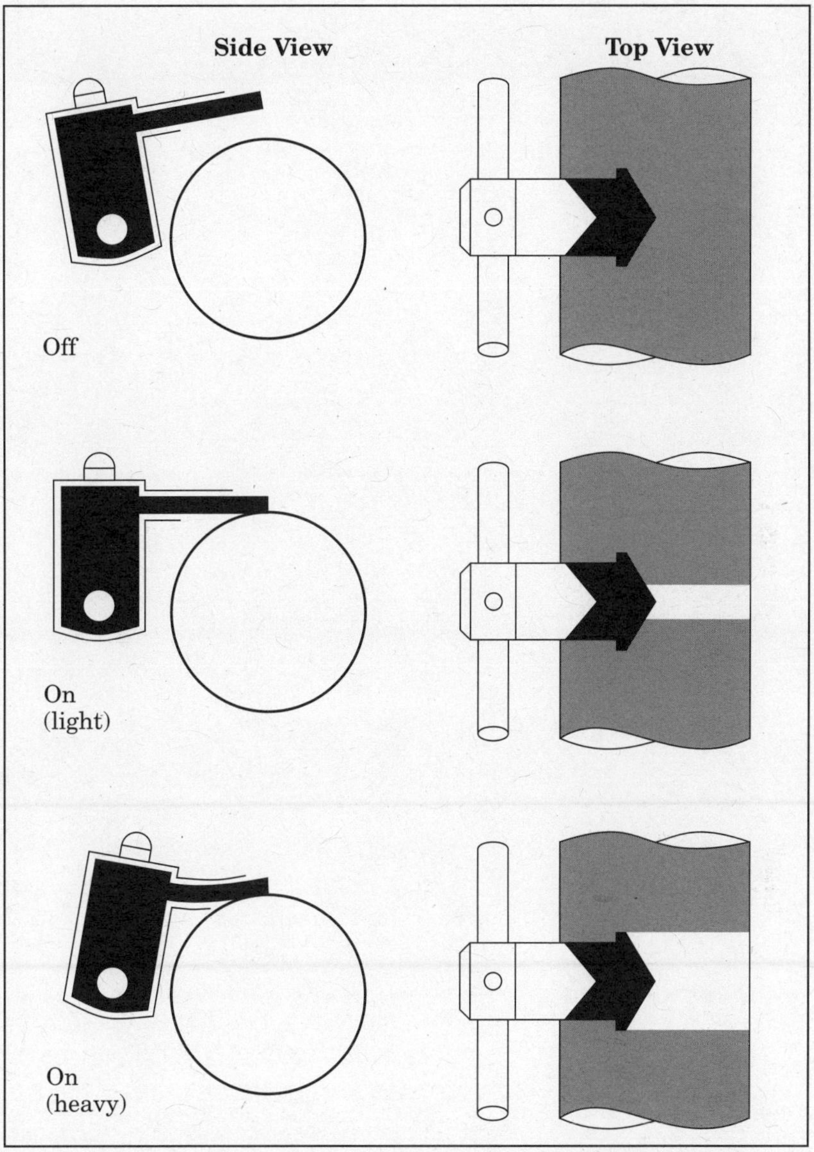

modulates the flow of water across the press and equates with closing the setting on the blade in the ink fountain.

Water stops are especially useful when running narrow webs. Dampening solution builds up on the roller ends if water stops are not used to hold it back.

Another variation of the intermittent-feed system is the flap ductor. Its fountain roller has a removable covering of canvas flaps, and the oscillator is mounted close enough to the flap roller to touch the ends of the flaps. Usually, one molleton-covered form roller wets the plate.

The Levey flap ductor dampening system

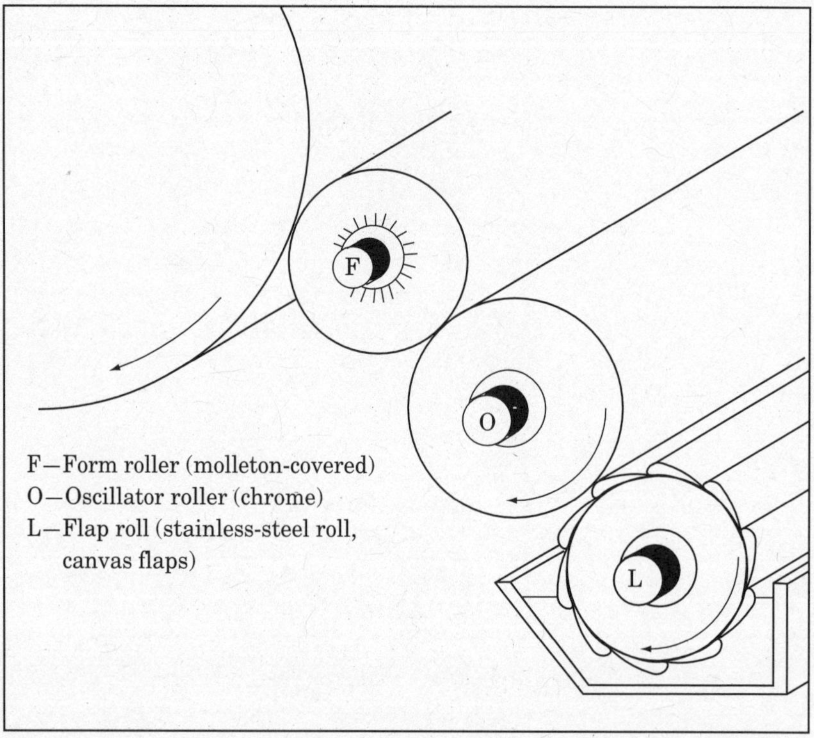

The principle of the system is simple. The flapper applies solution to the oscillator. Increasing the flap roller rotation transfers more solution to the oscillator. A major advantage is that the system eliminates ductor shock. The major disadvantage is that the system makes it difficult to modulate water feed across the press.

The big maintenance problem on the conventional dampening system is caused by the roller covers. They become greasy and ink-impregnated during running, fail to carry water adequately, and must then be changed. Paper sleeves are easiest to change. Cloth covers require the most work, but they seem to allow flexible roller settings because of their compressibility.

After removing a covered roller from the press, the press operator must not reverse the ends when reinserting the roller. If the press operator does, the roller rotates in the reverse direction, and the cover twists. A cloth roller becomes baggy and lints. To prevent this, some press operators paint a mark on one end of all covered rollers.

Cloth- or molleton-covered rollers need to be checked for roundness. Like an ink roller, if a dampening roller no longer conforms to the manufacturer's specifications, it should be reground or replaced. Low areas on the roller surface will not transfer dampening solution evenly.

The smooth metal surface of the oscillator can become greasy, breaking up the film of water on the oscillator. Such a roller should be thoroughly rinsed with an approved grease-cutting solvent. The solvent should then be washed away with water, and the roller gum-etched. A gum etch approved by the roller manufacturer should be rubbed down to a smooth film and allowed to dry. The roller should then be wet down to see if the water beads. If it beads, the cleaning operation should be repeated. If it doesn't, the roller is ready for operation.

Continuous-Flow Dampening Systems

Continuous-flow, or continuous-contact, systems supply a constant flow of dampening solution, thereby eliminating some of the problems associated with conventional systems. The two basic categories of continuous-flow dampening systems are plate-feed and inker-feed. In inker-feed systems, the dampening solution is fed indirectly through the inking system, while in plate-feed systems it is fed directly to the plate. Some continuous-flow dampening systems incorporate features of both plate-feed and inker-feed systems.

Continuous-flow systems eliminate some of the dampening control problems associated with conventional systems because the dampening solution is no longer supplied intermittently. A very important advantage of these systems is their rapid response to changes in fountain settings. This fast response is largely due to the absence of storage capacity in the system because the form rollers are not covered.

Inker-feed systems. An inker-feed, or integrated, system is quite different from conventional and plate-feed systems. One of its principal features is using the first inking form roller as a combination inking/dampening form roller. Another feature is the absence of a ductor roller.

An inker-feed dampening system often consists of two rollers that deliver dampening solution to an ink form roller. One is a chrome-plated steel roller, and the other is a soft roller that meters (controls) the thickness of the dampening solution film on the hard roller. The line of contact between the two rollers is called the **metering nip.** Depending on the particular press requirements, either roller could be the fountain roller. They are driven independently of the press, and their surface speed is not the same as that of the plate.

Dahlgren dampening system, an example of an inker-feed system

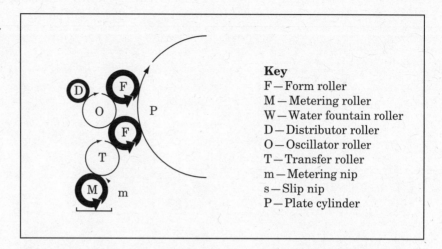

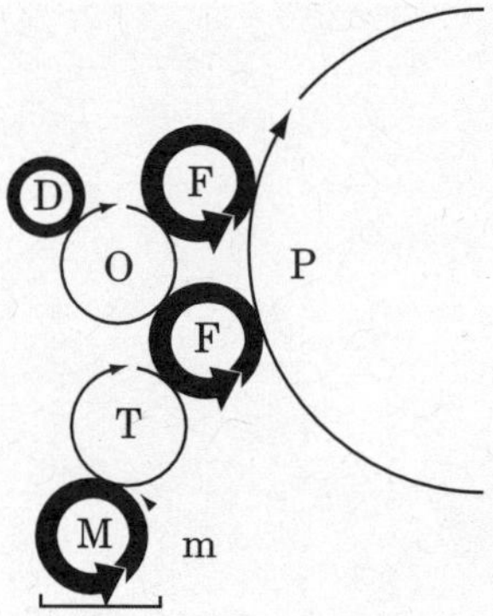

The hard roller rubs against the first ink form roller, which transfers the dampening solution directly to the plate. Dampening solution supply is controlled indirectly through speed control of the two rollers and the adjustable squeeze between them.

An important consideration of an inker-feed dampening system is that the dampening solution film must lay smoothly on top of the already inked form roller. The wetting properties of either isopropyl alcohol or a satisfactory substitute assist in the formation of an even film of dampening solution.

Setting the rollers on an inker-feed system is different from setting the rollers on a conventional system. The inking form roller is set heavier to the plate because it is considerably softer and larger than those in a conventional system. Follow the manufacturer's specifications for stripe widths.

Plate-feed systems. In addition to inker-feed dampening systems, there are several plate-feed continuous-flow systems. Unlike an inker-feed system, which uses the first ink form roller for dampening, these systems all have separate dampening form rollers. As with the inker-feed system, each has a metering nip formed between a soft metering roller and a hard chrome or ceramic roller. Because these two rollers are driven independently of the press, there is also a slip nip. Usually, the roller farthest from the plate can be skewed to modulate the water feed across the press. These systems have either a metering roller or a water pan roller. Most plate-feed continuous-flow systems also require the use of alcohol substitute in the dampening solution.

Four examples of continuous-flow plate-feed dampening systems

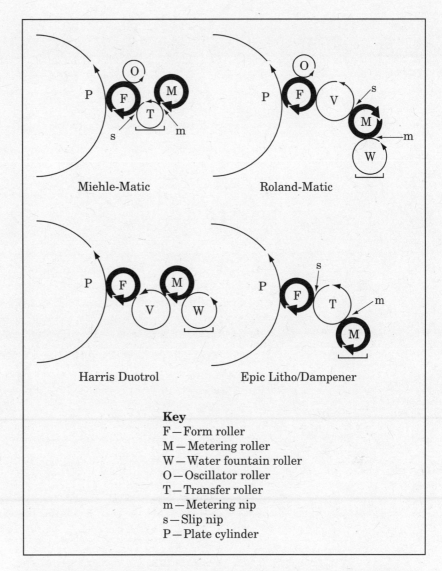

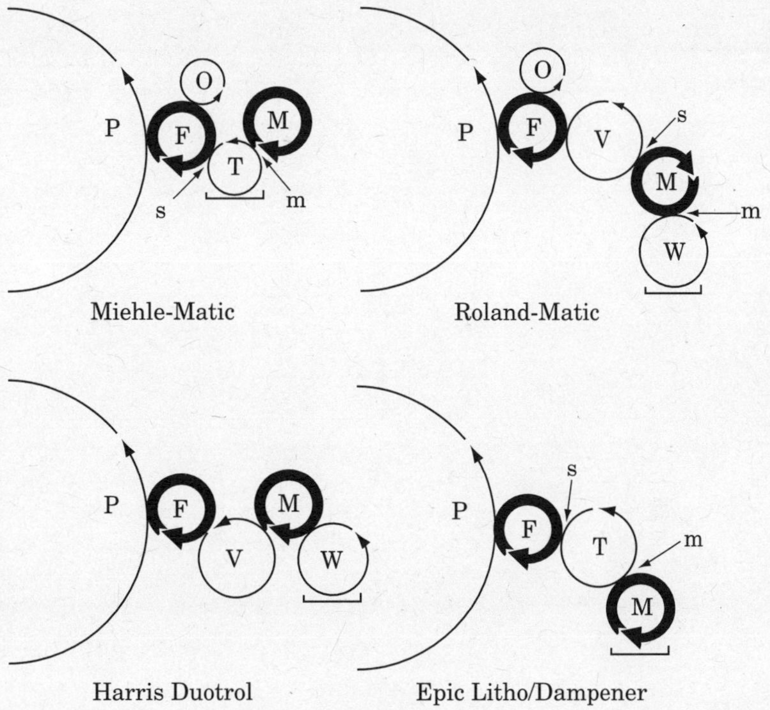

Key
F—Form roller
M—Metering roller
W—Water fountain roller
O—Oscillator roller
T—Transfer roller
m—Metering nip
s—Slip nip
P—Plate cylinder

Combination continuous-flow systems. A combination continuous-flow dampening system incorporates features of both inker-feed and plate-feed systems. In a combination system, an oscillating or vibrating bridge roller contacts both the dampener form roller and the first ink form roller.

The Epic Delta system consists of an oscillating bridge roller and a form roller that is driven at a slower surface speed than the plate. The differential speed results in a scrubbing action on the plate, giving the system a hickey-elimination feature. The bridge roller can be used either as a rider or as a connection between the dampening form roller and the inking system.

Another combination system has rollers that cannot be skewed to control dampening distribution. With this system, an air flow pattern (with water stops and an air bar) is used to achieve — as well as possible — an even distribution across and around the plate cylinder. At startup, the dampening form roller is contacting the plate ("on impression"), the ink form rollers are "off impression," and the bridge roller is in place, feeding dampening solution to the inking system. As a result of the bridge roller carrying dampening solution to the inking system, ink/water balance is quickly achieved.

Critical metering nip. All continuous-flow dampening systems have a metering nip (formed by a chrome transfer or pan roller and a resilient roller) that distributes the dampening solution into a thin, even film. The two rollers are geared to each other and run at almost the same surface speed. The thickness of the metered dampening film at the nip *exit* is dependent on the hardness of the resilient roller, the pressure exerted between rollers (determined by roller settings), and the viscosity of the dampening solution. An increase in the viscosity of the dampening solution results in a thicker metered film, and vice versa.

Reverse slip nip. With most continuous-flow systems, one of the rollers at the metering nip rotates clockwise and the other rotates counterclockwise. As a result, the surfaces of the two rollers are traveling in the same direction at the point of contact.

However, there are several dampening systems in which both rollers rotate in the same direction (both clockwise or counterclockwise). Consequently, at the point of contact, the two rollers are rotating in opposite directions, producing a **reverse slip nip.** The objective of this system is to reduce the interaction between dampening solution being fed to the plate and the solution returning from it.

A reverse slip nip produces a wiping action that is intended to prevent the flow of dampening solution through the nip. Theoretically, all of the metered dampening solution is carried to the printing plate, and all of the return solution is carried to the fountain pan.

Systems incorporating a reverse slip nip can operate with a relatively low alcohol concentration — 5–10%. In addition, response to changes in dampening feed rate is quickened due to the elimination of interaction between the metered film and the return solution. The elimination of interaction also results in a linear relationship between the speed of the metering rollers and the feed rate.

Noncontacting Dampening Systems

Brush dampening system. One major dampening system design employs a brush system. A brush roller is mounted above the fountain pan roller. The bristles of the brush roller ride in contact with the variable-speed fountain pan roller. The brush roller rotates at a constant speed and is set at a constant pressure against the fountain pan roller. This pressure is great enough to flex the bristles. The bristles flick solution at the oscillator, which is not in contact with the brush. The amount of solution fed is varied by changing the speed of the fountain pan roller, and water flow can be modulated across the press by using water stops. This system uses a single form roller that is often run bareback (without a cover).

The Heidelberg Harris brush dampening system

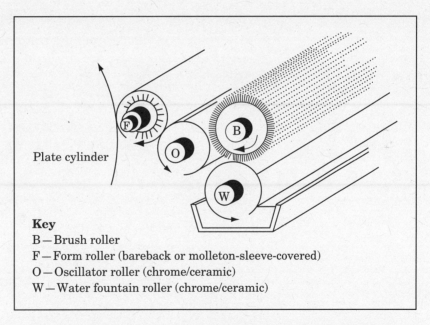

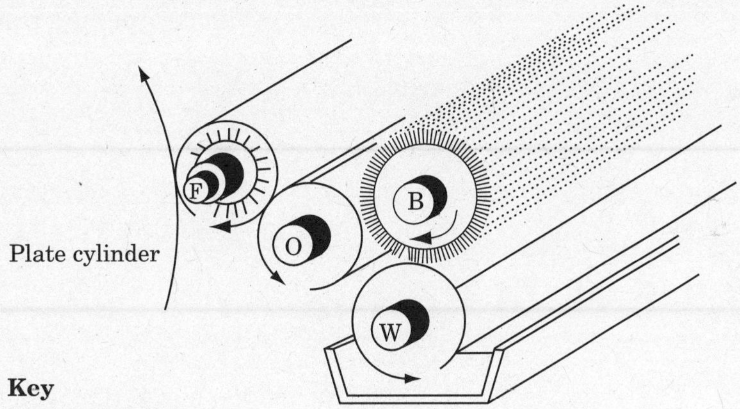

Key
B—Brush roller
F—Form roller (bareback or molleton-sleeve-covered)
O—Oscillator roller (chrome/ceramic)
W—Water fountain roller (chrome/ceramic)

A second brush system design incorporates a row of flicker fingers pressing against a brush roller mounted in the pan. The fingers flex the bristles and perform a metering function; the amount of flex determines the amount of water flicked. The amount of feed can be varied across the plate, because each finger is independently adjustable. The rotation of the brush roller can also be varied to transfer more or less water to the plate. Because of the relatively uneven

A brush dampener using flicker blades

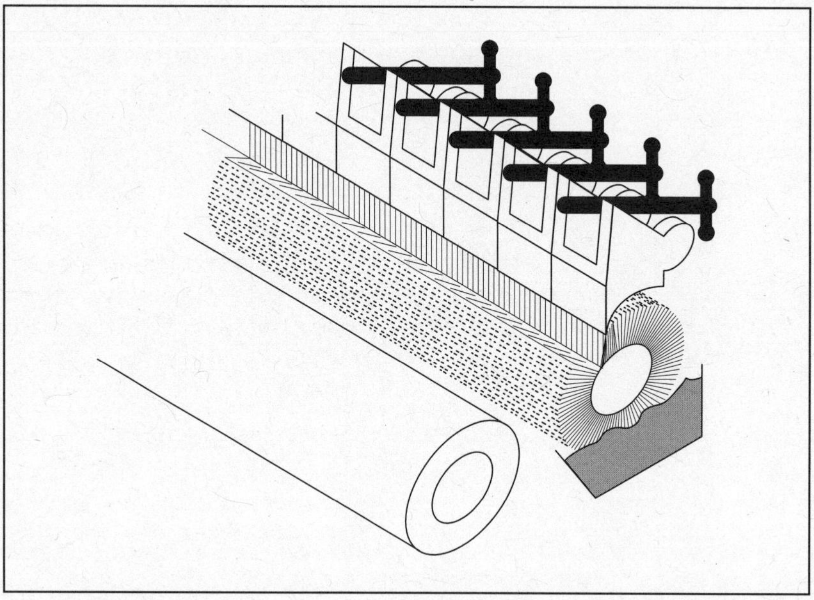

dispersion of water by the brush, these systems require a large amount of storage in the molleton covers to ensure uniform dampening.

The settings between oscillator roller and form roller and between form roller and plate on all brush systems are determined by the plastic strip method, which is discussed earlier in the chapter.

Goss brush dampening system, which uses flicker blades

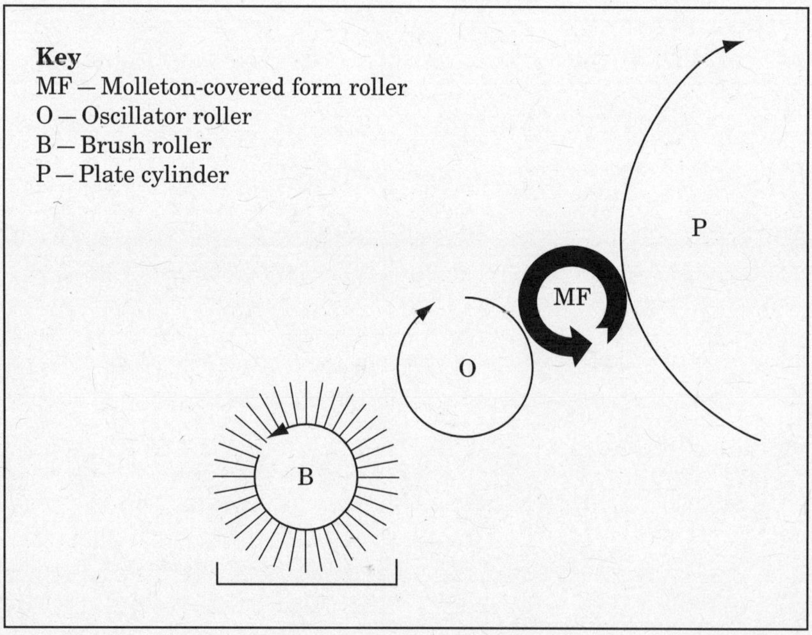

In operation, the brush roller should be set light initially, then advanced to its proper settings. Heavy settings can cause undue wear, which can break down the brush roller. When this happens, the press operator begins to find bristles on the plate, and those still on the roller lose their flexibility.

Some press operators change the conventional dampening system by running bareback dampeners. Brush systems are often run this way, because the entire system responds more rapidly to changes in fountain settings. Isopropyl alcohol or an alcohol substitute is sometimes added to the dampening solution to help bareback dampeners run efficiently. Isopropyl alcohol or an alcohol substitute acts as a wetting agent and reduces the surface tension of water, in effect making it *wetter*. This helps the uncovered rubber roller in picking up solution and wetting the plate. **Note:** The use of isopropyl alcohol in the dampening solution is subject to local, state, and federal regulations.

Spray-bar dampening systems. Several dampening systems spray fine mists of solution directly onto the rollers of

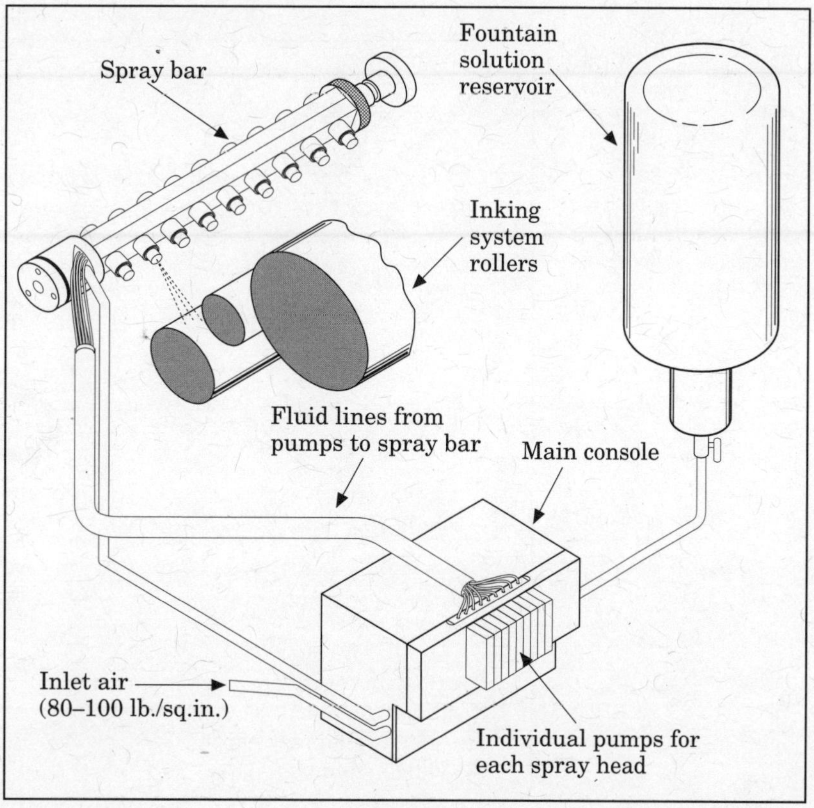

Smith dampening system
Courtesy Smith R.P.M. Company

The pumps in the main console convert the fluid stream into short pulses that come out of the spray bar as a fine mist. The spray bar itself is mounted directly over the inking system rollers.

their respective inking systems. The spray comes from a row of nozzles mounted on a bar across the press. Each nozzle can be independently metered. As indicated in the drawing, there is no recirculation of dampening solution. This is a distinct advantage in that fresh dampening solution constantly dampens the plate. The reduced exposure to atmospheric and press conditions virtually eliminates any changes in the dampening solution. This eliminates one of the big drawbacks encountered with continuous-contact dampening systems that recirculate the solution.

The biggest problem with running these system is the possible contamination of the individual pumps and spray nozzles by minerals that are present in most water supplies. Treating water so that it will not clog either the pumps or the spray nozzles helps to solve this problem.

The following illustration shows two different configurations for the Smith dampening system. In both cases, the spray bar is located so that it sprays down into an in-running nip. Depending upon the physical location of the rollers and the inking system, this may or may not require the addition of extra rollers as indicated in the diagram.

Two configurations of the Smith dampening system

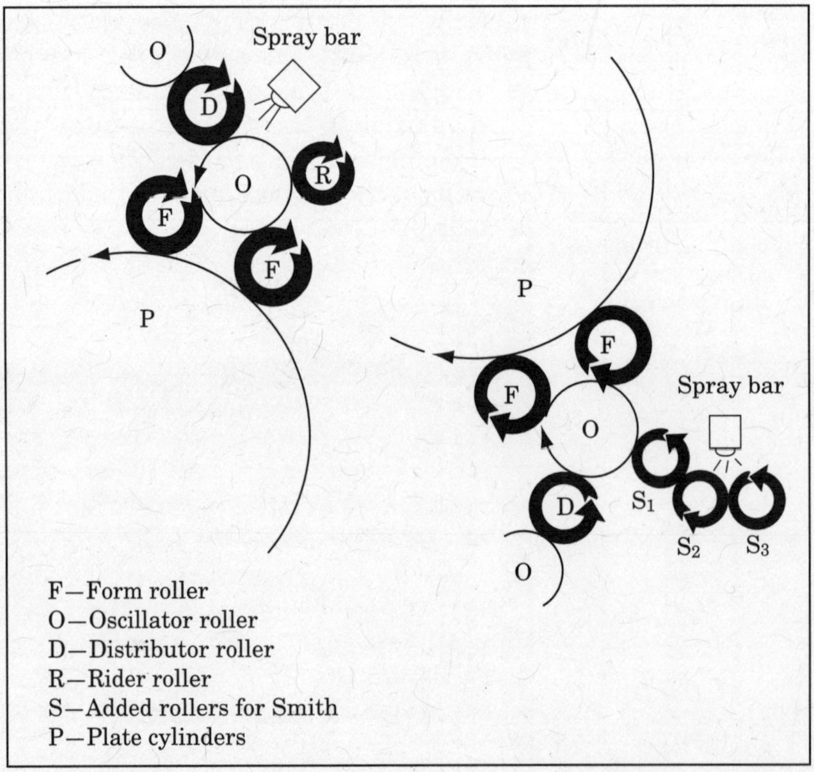

6 The Infeed

The infeed includes all equipment — from the roll stand to the first printing unit — that controls the speed, tension, and lateral position of the web. A properly setup roll and accurate infeed settings contribute to efficient operation along the entire length of the press.

A roll stand and a series of rollers lead the web into the first unit. The roll stand holds the roll or rolls and is usually arranged in line with the printing units. Where space limitations prevent an in-line arrangement, side infeeds can be used. In such a setup, the roll stand is mounted off to one side, and the web is turned into the press. Many newspaper and some commercial presses are fed from a level below that of the printing units. This keeps roll handling out of the pressroom.

In addition to the roll stand, most infeeds are equipped with metering rollers that control the rate at which paper flows into the printing units. The speed of the unwinding roll is controlled by a dancer, or floating roller, that is free to move up and down or forward and backward as the press runs. This dancer roller connects to a brake on the roll stand and prevents the roll from unwinding more than the required amount of paper.

A second dancer roller may be located between the infeed metering rollers and the first printing unit for additional tension control. This dancer roller activates the variable-speed drive of the metering rollers. Since the first dancer roller already controls the web, the second dancer roller compensates for a shorter range of tension variation.

An *inertially compensated* dancer roller is a device that operates at a constant effective weight during acceleration and deceleration. The roller is equipped with a flywheel at each end, which maintains the effective weight during a variable rate of movement by the dancer.

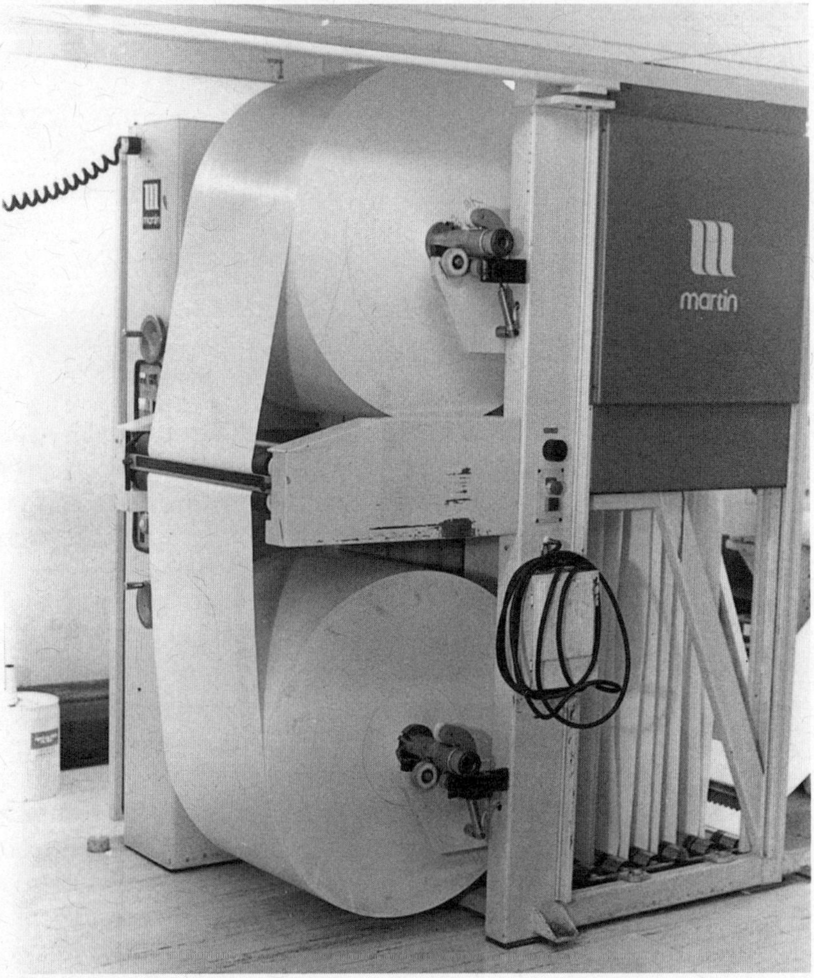

Zero-speed splicer and festoon
Courtesy Martin Automatic, Inc.

In addition to these elements, many infeeds carry other optional equipment. Almost all large presses have splicers that change to a new web without stopping the press. Also, most infeeds incorporate controls that laterally position the web before it enters the first printing unit.

There are single-roll stands and multiple-roll stands. A double stand, for example, can feed two webs at once. To further increase the flexibility of the press, an auxiliary stand is often added to the infeed. This stand holds additional rolls (usually two), increasing the number of webs that can be run simultaneously on the press.

The paper roll usually turns on a shaft inserted through its core. The shaft is expanded — either mechanically or through the use of an air bladder — to hold the roll in exact lateral position.

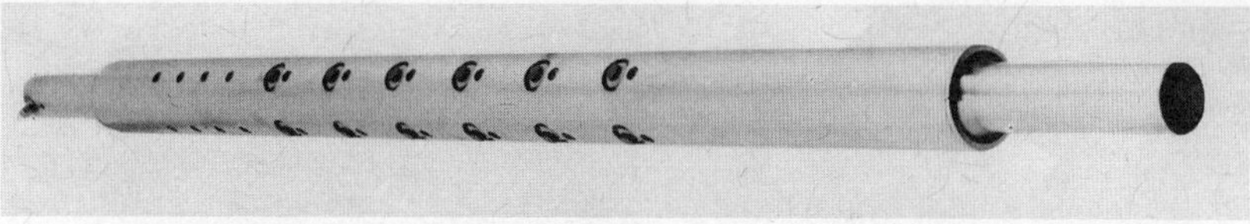

An expandable shaft, which holds the roll in exact lateral position
Courtesy Double E Co., Inc.

Paper feed is established by a dancer roller and roll brake working together. For the dancer to function, the paper feed rate off the roll must be controlled by a braking mechanism that acts on the unwinding roll of paper. Roll stands employ electromechanical, hydraulic, pneumatic, or magnetic brakes.

The roll brake is automatically actuated by the position of a dancer roller mounted between the roll stand and the press. The dancer roller is mounted in the infeed frame so that it rides in a loop of the web. When the dancer is at its normal position, moderate braking is applied to the roll shaft. When the roll feeds paper too fast, the web loop increases in size and the dancer moves with it. This motion signals an increase in braking, which slows the roll. The result is that the web loop shortens and the dancer returns to its normal position. If the roll feeds paper too slowly, the web forces the dancer out of its normal position, this time in the opposite direction. In this case, the dancer signals a decrease in braking and the roll speed increases. The result is that the web loop lengthens and the dancer returns to its normal position. The total amount of movement allowed in the dancer varies from one infeed to the next and depends on the means used to link the dancer with the brake. With a mechanical linkage, the dancer may move as much as 6–8 in. (150–200 mm).

Ultimately, the force that draws the paper off the roll comes from the paper web. Thus, the simplest possible infeed would contain only a roll stand and a dancer roller and would feed paper directly into the first printing unit. Actually, the infeed must perform still another important function. The web must be taut and flat as it enters the first printing unit. With a conventional infeed, three (sometimes two) rollers located between the dancer and the press perform this tensioning, or metering, function. Two of the infeed metering rollers are steel, driven rollers and the third is a rubber, nondriven roller. All three are set with a squeeze between them to control the web.

A speed control device varies metering roller speed, keeping it relative to press speed. This control should operate

The Conventional Dancer Roller

The dancer roller in the infeed section of the web press has two primary functions: to regulate the rate at which paper unwinds from the roll and to establish and maintain web tension. The conventional dancer roller is capable of doing a satisfactory job of controlling the unwind rate of the paper but is not capable of establishing and maintaining a constant tension.

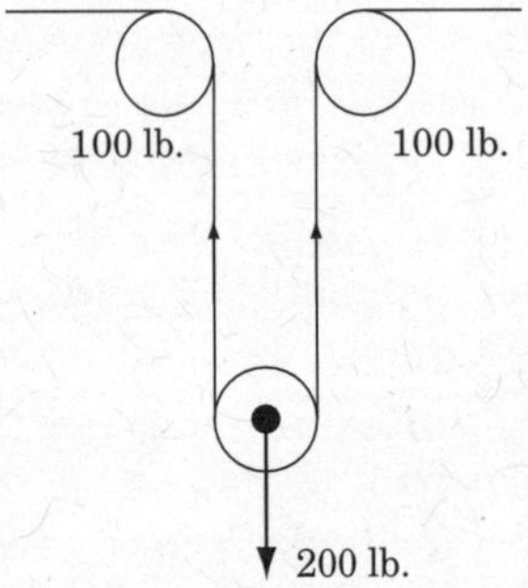

In looking at the drawing above, it can be seen that a roller weighing 200 lb. hanging in a loop of paper is going to impart to the web 100 lb. of tension. That is, half of the weight of the roller is supported by the other side of the paper loop in which it is hanging. Looking at the drawing below, it becomes evident that tension remains the same as long as the roller weighs 200 lb. whether it is in the high, normal, or low position. Carried further, this then means that the amount of brake applied to the shaft of the unwinding rolls does not establish or control tension because tension is a function of the effective weight of the dancer roller.

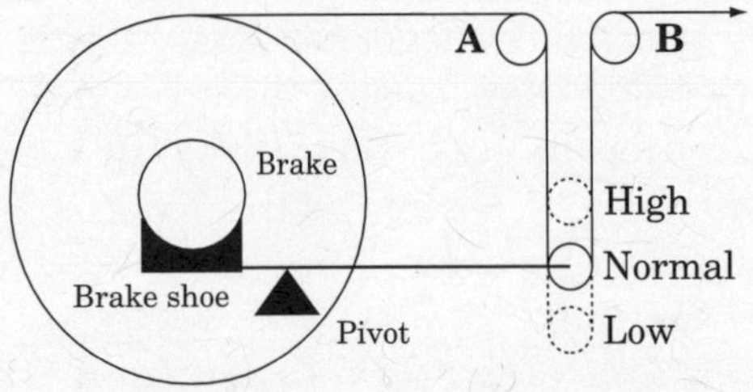

The function of the brake is to control the rate at which paper unwinds at whatever tension is established by the weight of the dancer roller. In the diagram, it can be seen that if the same amount of paper passes point A (coming off the roll) as passes point B (going into the press) the position of the dancer roller will remain at normal and no correction or change is made in the brake setting. If, however, less paper passes A than passes B, the loop in which the dancer roller is hanging will shorten and the dancer roller will move toward the high position. The dancer roller is connected to the brake in such a manner that movement toward the high position will relax the amount of brake being applied to the unwind roll. This, in turn, will allow the roll to unwind more rapidly at the established tension and will return the dancer roller to the normal position. Should more paper be passing point A than is passing point B, the loop will lengthen and the dancer roller will move toward the low position. This movement will apply more brake to the roll and will slow the rate at which the roll is unwinding and restore the dancer roller to the normal position.

It should be remembered that tension variations create problems with register, doubling, and slurring. A system such as is illustrated here does nothing to dampen out tension variations that originate in the web prior to it. For example, any tension variations at point A (which can be caused by an uneven roll, the action of the brake, etc.) will be passed through the loop and to point B and into the press. In a system like the one illustrated, not only the action of the brake but also movement of the dancer roller will create tension variations. Any acceleration or deceleration of the dancer roller, either up or down, will change its effective weight, and thus produces a change in tension. Unless a constant infeed is situated between this point and the press, these tension changes will produce printing problems.

over a short range. One such speed control, the P.I.V. drive, is often linked with a planetary gear box to narrow the variable speed range to within 2% of press speed. Even this may be an unusually high range. Tolerances for some presses in the speed of the infeed metering rollers is as little as ±0.3% of press speed — or even less.

A variable-speed drive that varies speed through two pulleys and a metal link belt

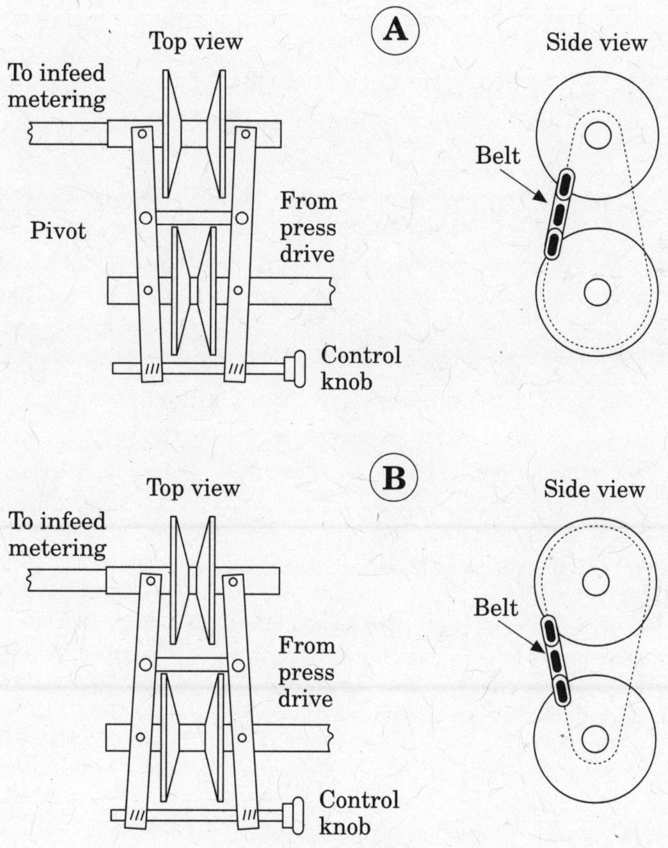

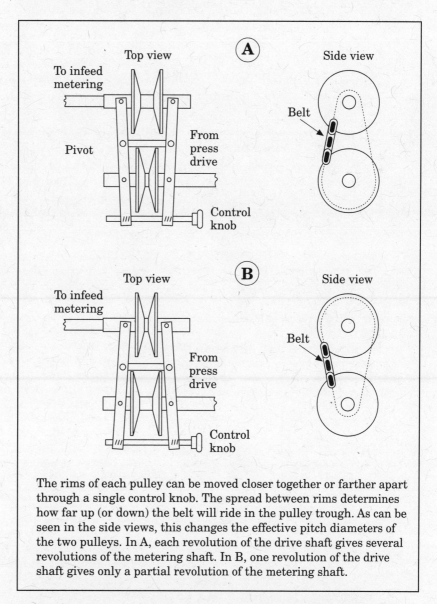

The rims of each pulley can be moved closer together or farther apart through a single control knob. The spread between rims determines how far up (or down) the belt will ride in the pulley trough. As can be seen in the side views, this changes the effective pitch diameters of the two pulleys. In A, each revolution of the drive shaft gives several revolutions of the metering shaft. In B, one revolution of the drive shaft gives only a partial revolution of the metering shaft.

The infeed metering rollers establish tension in the web; however, they do not adequately control it. Tension in a given paper under a given drawing rate can change with the unwinding of the roll: a change in the structure of the paper changes the paper's reaction to an applied force. (See the sidebar "Modulus of Elasticity" in Chapter 11.) The drawing rate established by the infeed metering rollers is constant. Thus, if the physical structure of the paper changes, the draw applied by the infeed metering rollers does not change with it, and tension is forced to change. These tension variations can lead to register problems in the printing units.

Because varying tension adversely affects register and print quality, a constant tension infeed is a crucial part of the web press. Inconsistent tension causes unit-to-unit misregister, doubling, and slurring.

Splicers

Continuous roll-feeding devices (automatic splicers) are standard on almost all web presses. The savings in time and waste reduction can be substantial. Automatic splicers are classified according to the running speed of the rolls when they are attached — *flying* and *zero speed.* A flying splicer or paster splices rolls while the paper is running at operating speed (on the fly). The zero-speed splicer makes the splice while the paper is stationary.

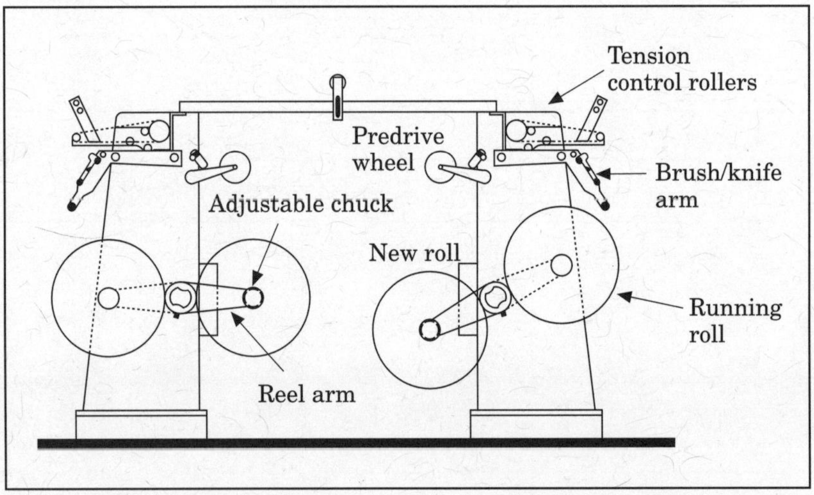

Typical two-arm flying pasters mounted in tandem, with rolls in running position

With this paster, drive wheels accelerate the new roll up to press speed.

Sensing devices monitor the status and position of the expiring roll. Some pasters monitor the roll with one or two butt switches. A butt switch is a spring-loaded metal finger pointing toward the roll core. It rides against the side of the roll with its tip set some predetermined distance from the roll core. As the roll diameter decreases to approximately 8 in. (200 mm), the first butt switch signals the paster cycle.

A flying paster on a Goss Urbanite press running five webs *Courtesy Jardis Industries, Inc.*

At this time, the paster rotates from the running position (which is also the loading position) to the splicing position. As this happens, the splicing arm and accelerating belts are also moving into position. The new roll is accelerated to press speed.

The actual splice is initiated by a signal from the second butt switch when about ¼ in. (6 mm) remains on the expiring roll. Anything left on the expired roll after splicing is core waste, which should always be held to a minimum.

During the splicing sequence, the splicer tracks the position of the roll nose — i.e., the lead edge of the splice bearing the adhesive. Some splicers employ a reflector tab on the side of the roll below the roll nose. When the second butt switch kicks over, a photoelectric eye is activated. The first time the tab passes the activated eye, a signal is sent to execute the splice. Other splicers accomplish the same thing with two metal fingers riding over a metallic tab. In this case, once the fingers are activated and make contact with the tab, a circuit is closed.

Both sensing systems perform the same function. They precisely locate the roll nose before signaling the pressure roller to drop, pressing the expiring web to the face of the new roll. Exact timing of the drop of the pressure roller relative to the position of the roll nose ensures that the *entire* adhesive area rolls down under pressure. Any other method

Splicing Sequence on a Flying Paster

With this typical three-arm flying paster, the slots on the roll core are inserted over keys on the paster arm. The butt switches ride against the side of the roll and kick over as the roll surface approaches the core.

The signal from the first butt switch occurs when the roll diameter is down to 8 in. (203.2 mm), as shown in figure 1.

This signal causes (2) the three-arm assembly to rotate into splice position, the acceleration belts to drop on the roll, and the splicing arm to press against the surface of the running web.

In figure 3, the second butt switch kicks over when the roll is 4 in. (101.6 mm) in diameter, activating the photocell. Note that the tab is located on the roll end just behind the splice area.

Once the photocell is activated the next time the reflector tab passes the cell, the pressure rollers press the expiring web against the face of the splice roll (4). The roll is allowed to rotate some fixed distance — in this case, 270° — and then the knife severs the expiring roll (5). In the last phase (6), the acceleration belts and splice arm rise and the roll rotates into running position.

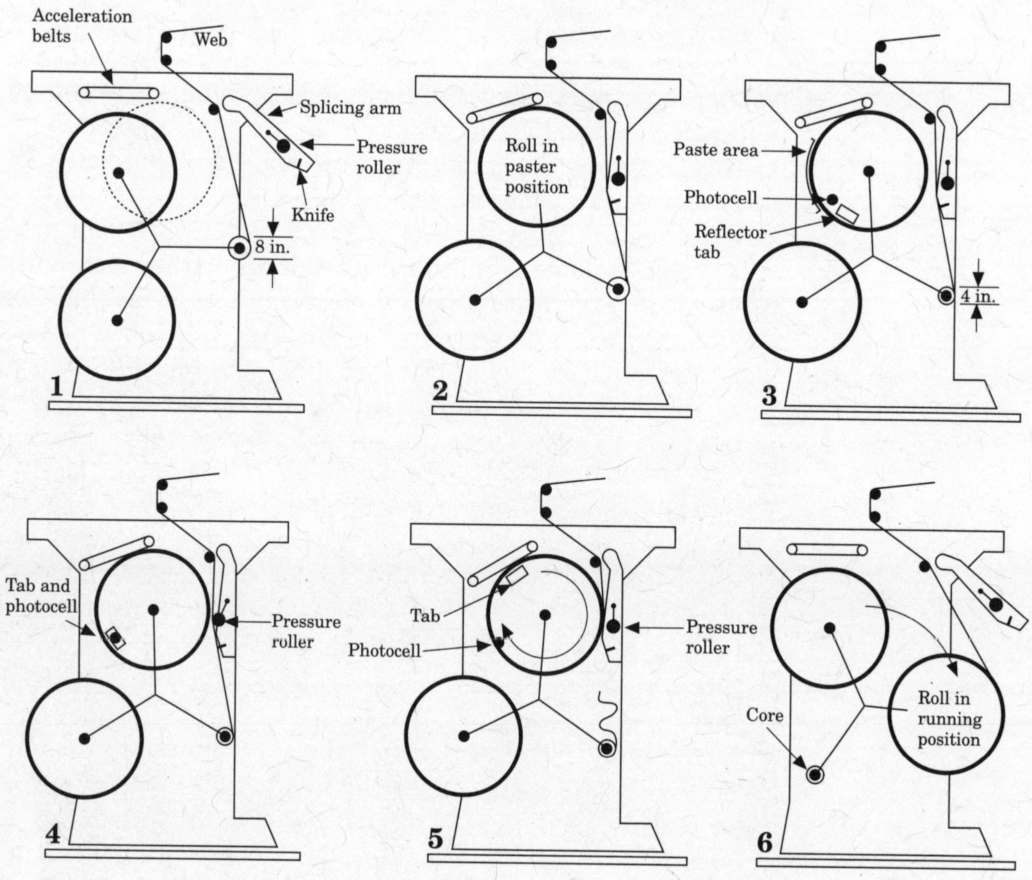

would involve the risk of a loose, sticky lead edge wrapping up in the press. A second reason that the roll nose must be located is that the action of the severing knife is timed from the drop of the pressure roller. This ensures sufficient tail on the expiring web to completely cover the adhesive area on the new web, which prevents the splice from wrapping up in the press rollers.

A high-speed automatic splicer executes a splice within several minutes — from the time of the signal that the roll is approaching the core until the completion of the splice. The actual splice — from the second butt switch signal until the splice is completed — occurs in a fraction of a second.

On all high-speed flying splicers, the splice roll must be in a preestablished position when the splicing begins. To make this possible, the rolls are mounted at the ends of arms, which rotate the rolls. A two-arm splicer can hold two rolls at once and a three-arm splicer can hold three. With either, the newly spliced roll moves into the running position shortly after the splice. This action rotates the expired core into the load position where it can be removed and a new roll can be mounted in its place and prepared for the next splice. To operate at high speed, a flying splicer has to be both rugged and precisely engineered.

Zero-speed splicers operate on a completely different principle. At the moment the rolls are spliced, neither is moving. The press continues to print at operating speed, feeding from

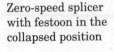

Zero-speed splicer with festoon in the collapsed position

Splicing Sequence on a Zero-Speed Splicer

Courtesy Butler Automatic, Inc.

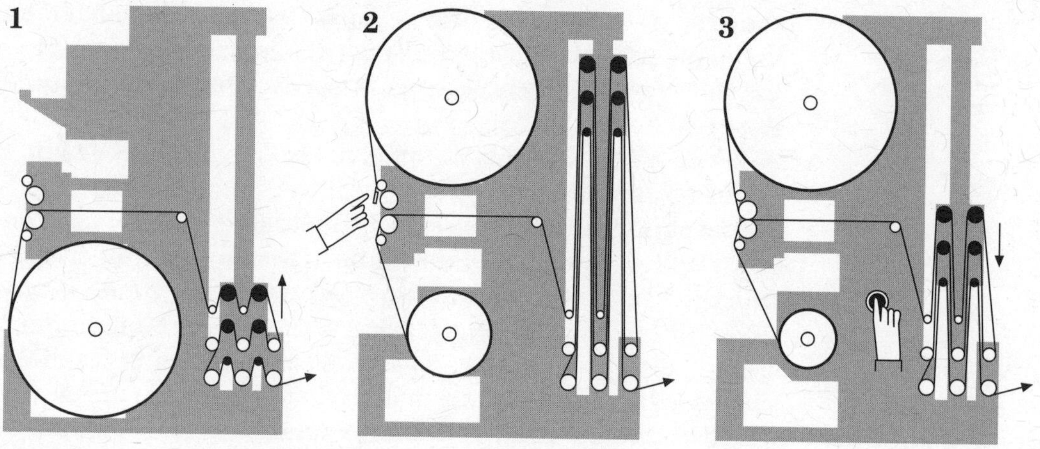

(1) The roll is feeding into the press, and the festoon has begun rising. (2) The festoon has expanded to store a full 80 ft. (26 m) of paper; a new roll has been mounted, and its lead edge prepared for the splice. (3) The expired roll has been stopped, and paper feeds into the running press from the collapsing festoon. The lead edge of the splice roll has been placed close to the surface of the expiring roll.

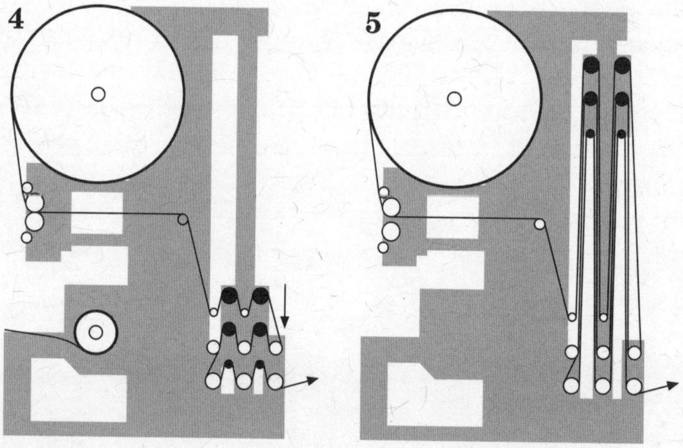

(4) The splice has been made, the expiring web severed, and the newly spliced roll accelerated up to press speed. The festoon starts rising and storing paper. (5) The festoon is fully expanded, and the roll stand is ready for the mounting of a new roll.

Detail view of actual splice

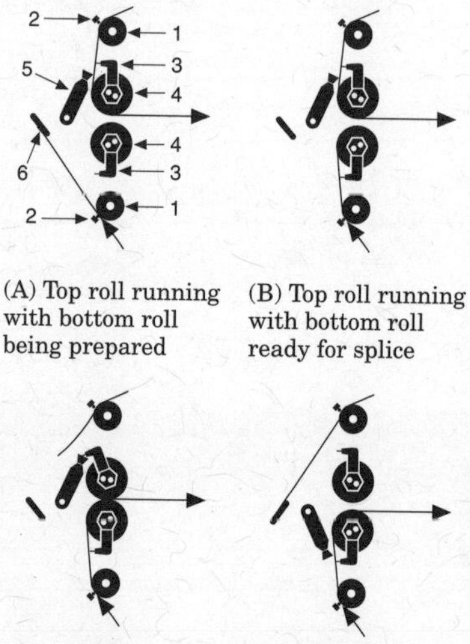

(A) Top roll running with bottom roll being prepared

(B) Top roll running with bottom roll ready for splice

(C) Moment of splice

(D) Bottom roll running with top roll being prepared

1 Idler rolls
2 Web cleaning brushes to hold severed web
3 Cutoff knives
4 Nip rolls
5 Cutoff brush
6 Vacuum blade

a reserve of paper. A collapsible *festoon* stores enough paper to supply the press during the actual splicing sequence. The movement of the festoon is controlled through a pneumatic piston. After the splice, the new roll is accelerated beyond press speed. This allows the festoon rollers to return to their original position and replenish their paper supply. Subsequently, the roll is slowed to press speed.

The time and cost savings are substantial on any properly operated automatic splicer. The automatic splicer permits continuous operation, thus saving signatures that would be spoiled while ink and water are being balanced after a press shutdown. Ideally, the only waste generated by an automatic splicer should be one signature — the one containing the splice.

Preparation

The first step in preparing the infeed is inspecting the roll before mounting it. This is the time to prevent press problems that arise from running a substandard roll.

The roll tender should look for any of several defects. The first and easiest to find is torn or damaged wrappings. The wrappings protect the roll from physical and moisture damage. Torn wrapping exposes the roll, which can significantly increase or decrease the amount of moisture in the outside layers of the roll. These moisture changes can affect web performance on press.

There should be no mill splices in the first 1–1½ in. (25–38 mm) of the outside of the roll. Paper manufacturers have greatly improved the quality of their product by reducing the number of splices per roll and by identifying each splice on the side of the roll. Defects appearing in a new roll should be recorded on the roll record form. This information should then be relayed to the manufacturer.

Next to damaged wrappings, probably the most common paper defect is out-of-round rolls. An out-of-round roll unwinds unevenly on the press and causes variations in tension. Rolls become out-of-round when dropped, picked up with excessive pressure by the roll clamp truck, or stored horizontally. Rolls should *always* be stored on end.

After removing the wrapper from the roll, brush the ends of the roll to remove dirt or slitter dust accumulated there. When positioning the roll on the shaft, align it exactly (from side to side in the press) with the roll that is feeding. This procedure ensures exact superimposition of the new and old webs when the splice is made. Care must be taken here because ink builds up on the printing unit blankets just beyond the edges of the running web. Sidelay controls maintain the side-to-side position of the web; therefore, the distance between the buildup of tacky ink on each edge of the blanket often exactly equals the web width. A misaligned splice results in paper running through this tacky area, which can break the web. If the web's edge catches on sticky blankets during the splice, the press operator should brush both edges of the splice roll with glycerine. This action will lessen the web's tendency to stick to the ink on the edge of the blanket and allow time for the sidelay controls to align the new web.

Dirt or dust can settle on the two-sided tape that is applied to the roll for splicing; therefore, the protective backing should be left on the exposed side until just before the rolls are spliced. Keep the adhesive away from the web edges. Adhesive can cause the web to wrap around an idler roller. For best results, consult the manufacturer's splicing instructions.

Preparing a splice

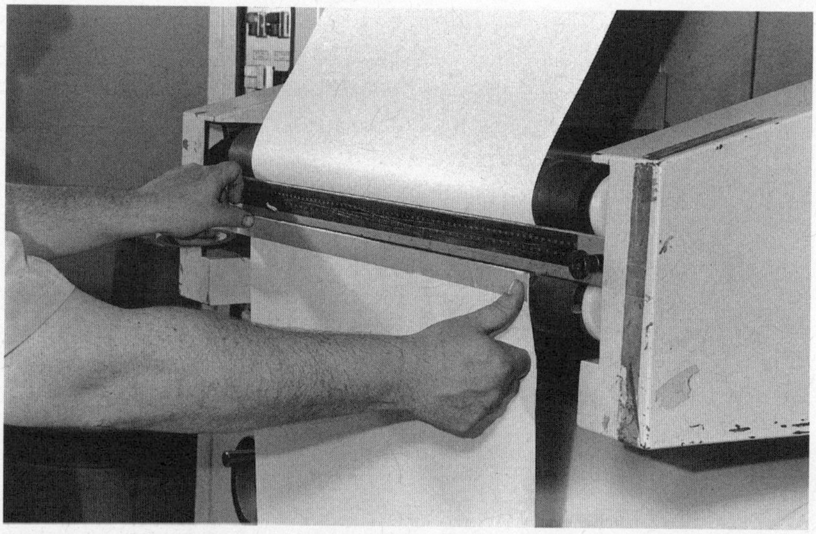

The arms of flying pasters should be numbered. In the event of a missed paste or a web break, the number of the feeding arm should be recorded. This system quickly identifies a malfunctioning arm if missed splices are attributable to it.

For splicers that require the lead edge of the new web to be cut to a certain shape, make a template to ensure accurate and consistent preparation of the splice edge.

Splice template

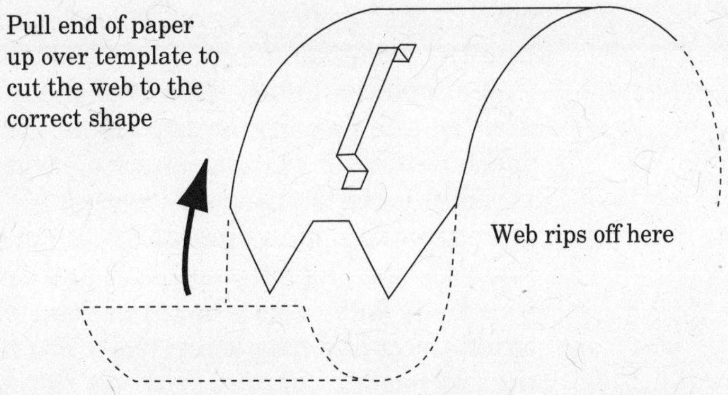
Pull end of paper up over template to cut the web to the correct shape
Web rips off here

Splice patterns are not interchangeable from one paster to another. Most paster manufacturers give specifications on preparing the roll for splicing. These should be followed exactly. A template constructed from sheet metal according to the paster manufacturer's specifications is recommended. A template will guarantee consistent, rapid preparation of splices.

Longer web leads maintain flatness and help to control the web during printing. Extra rollers in the infeed lengthen web leads.

Specific webbing arrangements depend on the number of webs being run and the particular printing unit to which each web is being led. For this purpose, press infeeds carry a number of nondriven, nonadjustable idler rollers. Paper should not traverse long unsupported spans, which easily wrinkle and reduce infeed tensions.

The infeed must hold the paper taut from the roll to the infeed tension control, and from the infeed tension control to the first printing unit. Theoretically, the dancer eliminates all tension variations emanating from the unwinding roll. Actually, the conventional dancer reduces, but does not eliminate, tension variations. As explained earlier, constant tension is maintained as long as the effective weight of the dancer remains unchanged. The dancer adjusts to changes in paper feed rate off the roll by moving in the web loop; however, the effective weight of the dancer changes during acceleration and deceleration. Thus, the dancer does not maintain consistent tension into the first printing unit.

The conventional infeed creates tension by running the metering rollers slower than the blanket cylinders. With a given paper, the tension established in this span directly relates to the speed difference between the printing unit and the metering rollers — assuming no slippage is occurring at either point, and assuming that the paper's reaction to stress has not changed.

The web commonly slips over the metering rollers. The draw on the web in this span is determined by the effective speed of the metering rollers. To prevent slippage, the web speed must equal the surface speed of the metering rollers. To control slip, many infeed metering systems carry two rollers — one steel driven roller and one rubber idler. The web is led between and wrapped around nearly the entire circumference of the steel roller. The high amount of wrap on the steel roller not only provides the considerable traction needed for control but also makes it impossible to measure the exact speed of the web through the metering rollers. The rubber roller has greater compressibility than the steel in the nip; therefore, the surface speed differs between the two rollers. Hence, paper speed through a conventional infeed is unpredictable because the paper runs at the surface speed of the rubber roller, not the surface speed of the driven steel rollers. More importantly, no conventional infeed metering system controls tension variations arising from the paper.

7 Dryer and Chill Rolls

Dryers

Heatset inks currently dominate the commercial web offset field. Web offset forms printing and newspaper work, on the other hand, chiefly rely on quickset and absorptive inks that do not require drying and chilling capacity built into the press. The need for a dryer and chill rolls depends on the ink used and how it dries.

Quickset inks (including web offset newspaper inks) dry chiefly by penetration. Pigments and resins are dispersed in a thin hydrocarbon solvent. After impression, the solvent penetrates the paper, leaving pigment and resins on the paper surface. This drying process, especially typical of newspaper inks, leaves the print with a dull, flat finish, which limits the application of quickset ink in commercial printing. Other quickset inks oxidize after the solvent-absorption phase. The resins cross-link to form a dry ink film. Although the gloss of these inks better suits commercial printing, their use is restricted by the need for highly absorbent papers. This makes them incompatible with many coated stocks commonly run in commercial web offset.

Heatset inks dry with a high gloss and, in principle, are compatible with all stocks. The drier is as complex as that found in any ink. Drying equipment is required on the press to evaporate volatile solvent. Chill rolls cool the heat-softened binding resins. The solvent reduces the ink's viscosity, leaving solid pigment particles embedded in semisoft resins. Final solidification or setting occurs with the cooling of the binding resins. Final drying occurs off the press and consists of an oxidation process several hours to several days long.

The solvent evaporates quickly and violently; air temperature in the dryer may reach 500°F (260°C). The average time the web spends in the dryer is only about 0.7 sec., but it exits with a surface temperature of up to 300°F (149°C). Less than

Setting of quickset ink

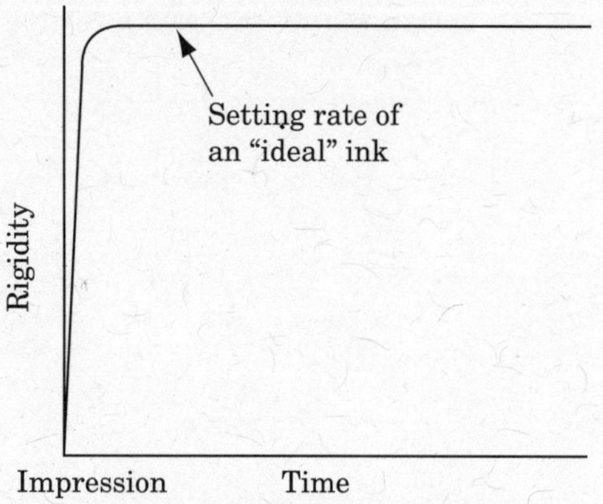

Ink setting can be thought of as a process in which the ink film rigidifies into a solid state. An ideal ink-setting curve, such as the one shown above, would have the ink rigidify into a solid phase immediately after the impression.

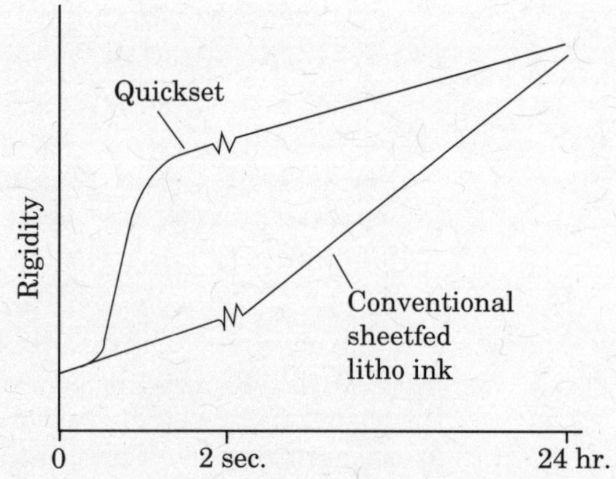

Quickset inks show a characteristic two-stage curve. As the solvent is absorbed by the paper, rigidity rapidly increases. How fast the ink sets in this phase strongly depends on the absorptivity of the paper. Rigidity increases during the oxidation-polymerization stage, but the increase is much slower. Note that the film thickness of a first- or second-down quickset film can strongly affect the setting rates of later-down films. Thick films can act as sealants and slow the setting of later-down colors.

a second later the chill rolls cool the web to about 75°F (24°C). The ink must respond to this processing. Ink leaving the chill rolls only half set produces wasted signatures due to marking in the folder, which leads to a press shutdown and folder cleanup.

All blanket-to-blanket presses employ floating dryers, because the web has ink on both sides. Floating dryers are classed according to the method used to heat the web. The oldest is the **open flame** or **direct-impingement dryer.**

Setting of heatset ink

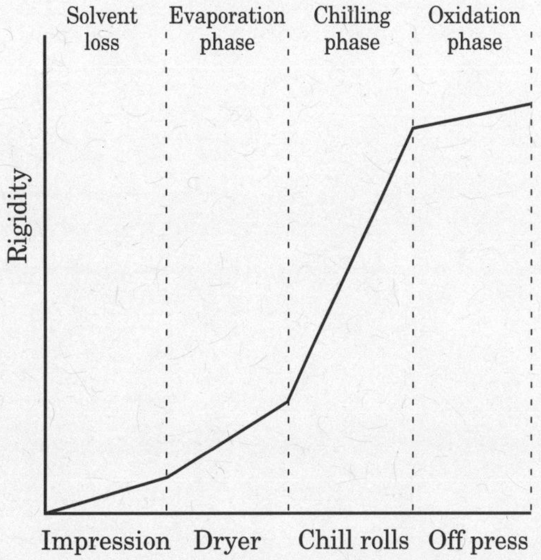

After impression, some of the solvent in heatset inks is absorbed by the paper, resulting in a decrease ink the ink's fluidity. This effect is more pronounced with some stocks than others. Thixotropic setting—the formation of weak molecular bonds in the ink—tends to occur. This setting process aids ink stability through successive nips in multicolor printing. (Highly thixotropic inks are harder to handle on press, often requiring steady agitation to maintain fluidity in the fountain.) The evaporation and chilling phase contribute the most to the increase in ink-film rigidity. Today's solvents have boiling points from 470°F (243°C) to 630°F (350°C). The temperatures required to remove the necessary amount of solvent are also high enough to soften the resins and other materials used to bind the pigments to the paper, making chilling necessary. After cooling, the resins and embedded pigment particles form a tough, solid film. The oxidation phase proceeds slowly over a matter of hours and is accomplished by the combining of atmospheric oxygen with the ink film.

High-velocity hot-air dryers blow hot air at the web. Spaced between the nozzles are exhaust ducts that vent solvent-laden air and help to maintain air circulation in the dryer. The mixture of hot air and ink solvent vapor is then recirculated through the combustion chamber, which burns much of the solvent.

The removal of solvent-laden air from the web

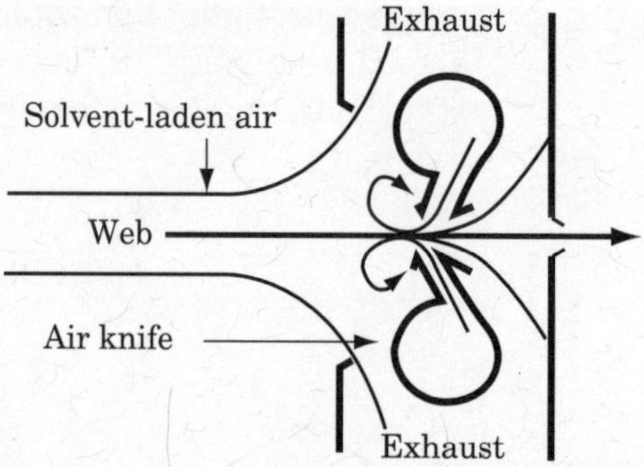

If the boundary layer reaches the chill roll saturated with solvent, the solvents may condense and collect on the chill roll surface. Solvent buildup at the chill rolls can resoften the ink and lead to marking on the chill rolls and smearing in the folder. Devices variously called scavengers, scrubbers, or air knives, disturb this layer and exhaust solvents before they leave the dryer.

Combination dryers use both the open-flame and medium-velocity hot-air techniques. The first half of the dryer usually contains the flame nozzles, and the second half the hot-air section.

The high-velocity hot-air dryer has one important advantage over the flame dryer. Next to the moving web is a thin layer of air that moves with the web, a boundary layer that is part of the moving web's aerodynamics. When solvents are evaporated, they accumulate in this boundary layer until it

Nozzles of a high-velocity hot-air dryer

is saturated. Once the air is saturated, more heat is needed to continue solvent evaporation. This lowers dryer efficiency. In a high-velocity hot-air dryer, therefore, turbulence is introduced into the boundary layer to prevent saturation.

Initial designs of high-velocity hot-air dryers had a problem with web control that resulted in longitudinal wrinkles caused by the long span of web in the dryer. These wrinkles are called corrugations. This problem has been solved by alternately spacing nozzles to put a controlled ripple in the web. A web deformed in this way does not corrugate, even at high speeds.

Putting a controlled ripple in the web
Courtesy Grace TEC Systems, Inc.

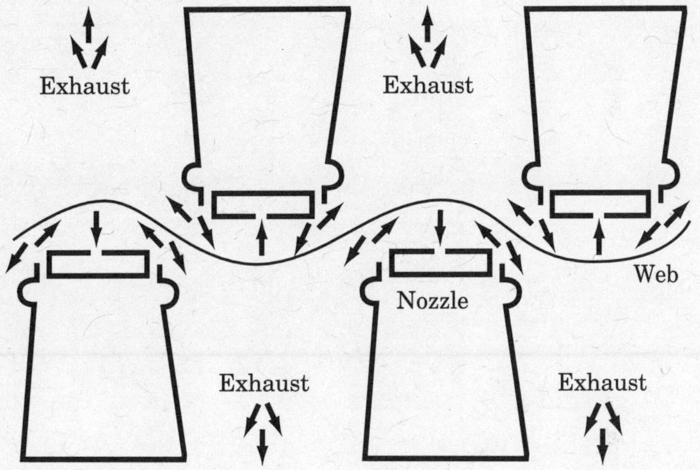

Early high-velocity hot-air dryers often caused the web to flutter in the dryer, due to the force of the air jets beating against the web. Later, it was found that by allowing a controlled ripple to form in the web, the web would show even greater stability in the dryer than if left undisturbed. The ripple is created through careful spacing of opposing blowers and exhausts in the dryer. This principle has since been incorporated into most present-day hot-air dryers.

Heatset web offset presses generally have made use of pollution control equipment, such as condensers or afterburners, to meet environmental regulations. An example of an air pollution control device that can operate in either the catalytic or thermal oxidizer mode is shown on the next page.

Chill Rolls

The chill roll section, the section of the press where heatset inks are cooled below their setting temperature, is an assembly of driven steel drums positioned after the dryer. The chill

The CONVERTIBLE SR-9000 catalytic/thermal oxidizer, an air pollution control device that can operate in either the catalytic or thermal oxidizer mode
Courtesy Catalytic Products International

Chill roll tacking system, which uses electrostatic force to reduce the gap between the web and the chill roll
Courtesy Hurletron Incorporated

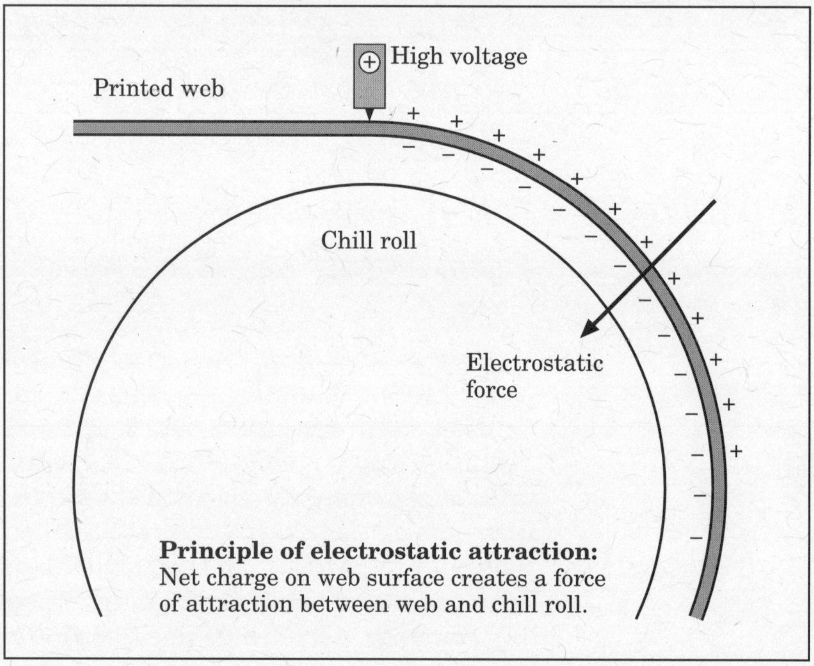
High voltage
Printed web
Chill roll
Electrostatic force
Principle of electrostatic attraction:
Net charge on web surface creates a force of attraction between web and chill roll.

The evolution of chill roll design

The earliest chill-roll design pumped water into one end of the shaft, filling the roller shell, and back out the other end of the shaft. Maximum circulation tended to occur around the center of the roller, while water close to the roller ends stagnated and gradually heated. This inefficiency (most pronounced on wider presses) gave poor cooling to the edges of the web.

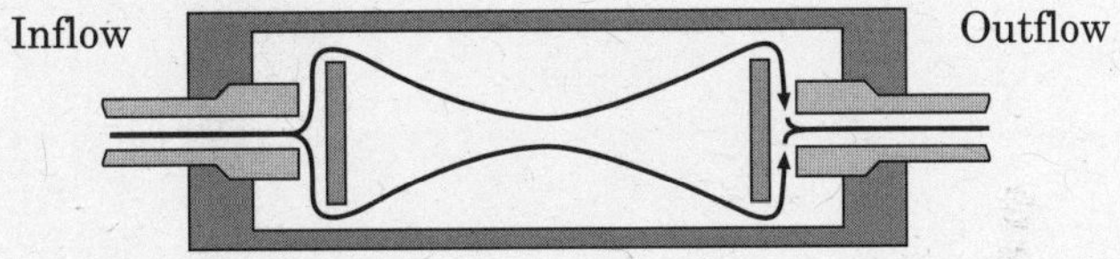

The installation of baffle plates increased the efficiency of the earlier design. The plates forced incoming and outgoing water toward the roller walls. But though the roller ends were efficiently cooled, the middle tended to be less so.

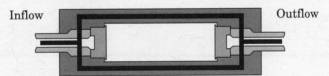

The jacketed roller shown here uses a thin "shell" of water to cool the roller. This design forces all the coolant close to the outer wall, greatly reducing the quantity of water needed. By using a small and better controlled volume of water, the cooling of the surface is more uniform across the roller width.

rolls are cooled by refrigerated water circulating through them. The number of chill rolls needed is controlled by the press speed. The faster the web press runs, the more chill rolls that are needed. For example, a web press operating at 3,000 ft./min. (15 m/sec) might require as many as nine chill rolls.

Most chill rolls are driven by the press drive through a variable-speed transmission (as are infeed metering rollers). The speed of the chill rolls is adjustable over a fairly wide range. With this variable-speed control, the chill rolls regulate web tension in the long span from the last printing unit through the dryer. Because there is no nip at the chill rolls (on many presses), there is often slip between the web and

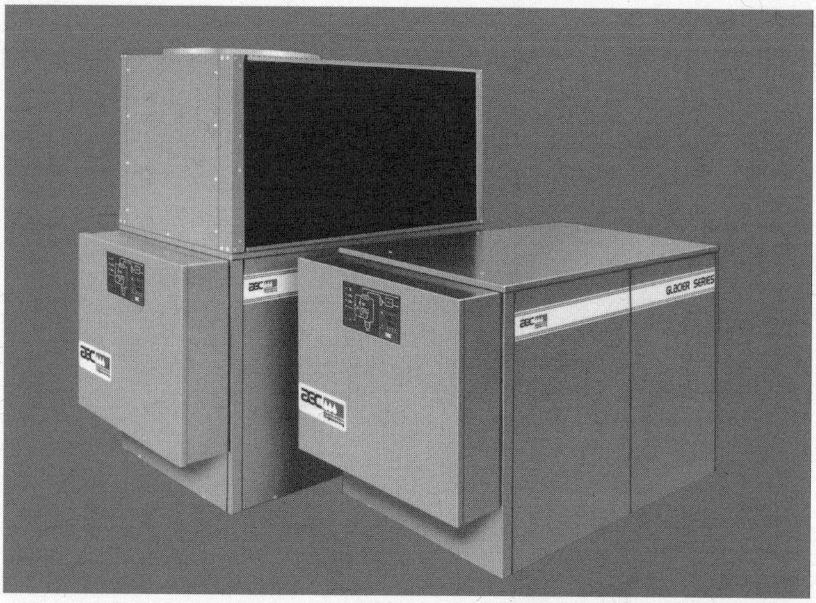

Glacier Series portable chiller, designed for flexibility in beside-the-press chill roll and ink temperature control systems
Courtesy AEC, Inc.

Chill stand
Courtesy Jardis Industries, Inc.

the rolls. Web slip over the chill rolls can exceed 1% of press speed. This slip is a major cause of marking on the chill rolls.

Water circulation in the chill rolls should be through a closed system. This minimizes mineral deposits inside the chill rolls, which can impair chilling efficiency. In addition, chill roll monitors should measure temperature and the flow rate of the water.

Operation

Ultimately, the press operator should control *web temperature* through the dryer and chill roll sections. Dryer and chill roll temperatures are only indicators of web temperature. This difference is very important. It is possible to change the effectiveness of the dryer by changing only press speed.

The dryer and chill rolls must coordinate as a single system. For example, increasing dryer heat to counteract smearing in the folder may aggravate the problem. A properly set dryer removes solvent from the ink; however, if the chill rolls were not cold enough, resins remain warm and soft. Furthermore, if the boundary layer leaves the dryer in a solvent-saturated state, the chill rolls condense the vapors onto the web. As the solvent works back into the ink, the web begins marking and tracking.

Set the dryer temperature according to the paper, the inks, the press speed, and the length of the dryer. A change of 20 lb. in basis weight of paper can require a significant change in dryer temperature or running speed from one job to the next. Heavier paper requires more heat to effectively dry the ink.

Other paper factors place an upper limit on temperature. Paper burns at 451°F (223°C), but scorches at temperatures considerably lower. More importantly, the dryer removes significant quantities of water from the web, reducing its moisture content. One result is that paper shrinks appreciably in the dryer. On most presses, this creates a continuous potential for problems in tension and cutoff variation. Eventually, dryer heat can drive out enough moisture to make the paper brittle.

Coated stocks may require slightly higher dryer temperatures because of lower solvent absorption. On the other hand, a heavily coated stock may blister if heated excessively. Paper blisters when a sudden blast of dryer heat vaporizes internal moisture faster than it can escape. It usually occurs when the paper is tightly sealed by heavy coating and printed with solids on the top and bottom of the web.

Ink characteristics dictate specific dryer temperature. Two inks with two different solvent boiling points can appear to be the same, but dry at significantly different temperatures. Some resins yield solvents less readily than others. Slow solvent release requires higher dryer temperature. The appearance of the ink will not indicate this.

The duration that the paper spends in the dryer must coincide with press speed and dryer length. Higher press

An optical pyrometer, which is used to monitor web temperature

speed reduces the time for the heat to release the solvent. With a short dryer, press speed must be slowed to adequately dry the web. Dryers often hold running speeds considerably below the rated speed of the press.

The dryer should be set to the *minimum* temperature required to burn off the ink solvent. When the paper is chilled, folded, and delivered, it should not mark, smear, or set off. Minimum heat lessens the chance of blistering, reduces moisture loss, and, in many cases, improves printed ink gloss. Maintain minimum heat by judiciously matching press speed to dryer temperature, and vice versa. Increasing press speed while maintaining dryer heat lowers web temperatures.

To determine minimum dryer temperature, set press speed at the desired rate and the dryer at a *safe* temperature — neither too high nor too low. Check web temperature after the last chill roll; make sure that it is at room temperature or below. If the temperature is too high, several remedies are possible: reduce dryer temperature; reduce dryer temperature *and* press speed; or reduce chill roll temperature. Do the latter either by lowering the temperature of the circulating water or by increasing the rate of circulation.

Never raise the dryer temperature without first making sure that the web is being adequately chilled. When press speed or dryer temperature is increased thereafter, always make sure that the web temperature after chilling is no higher than room temperature.

Chill Roll Plumbing

The accompanying illustration shows several different methods for plumbing three- and four-roll chill systems. At the top of the illustration are drawings that show the physical layout of the chill rolls. It should be noted that the roller markings A, B, and C (and for the four-roll system, D) do not represent

Chill roll plumbing

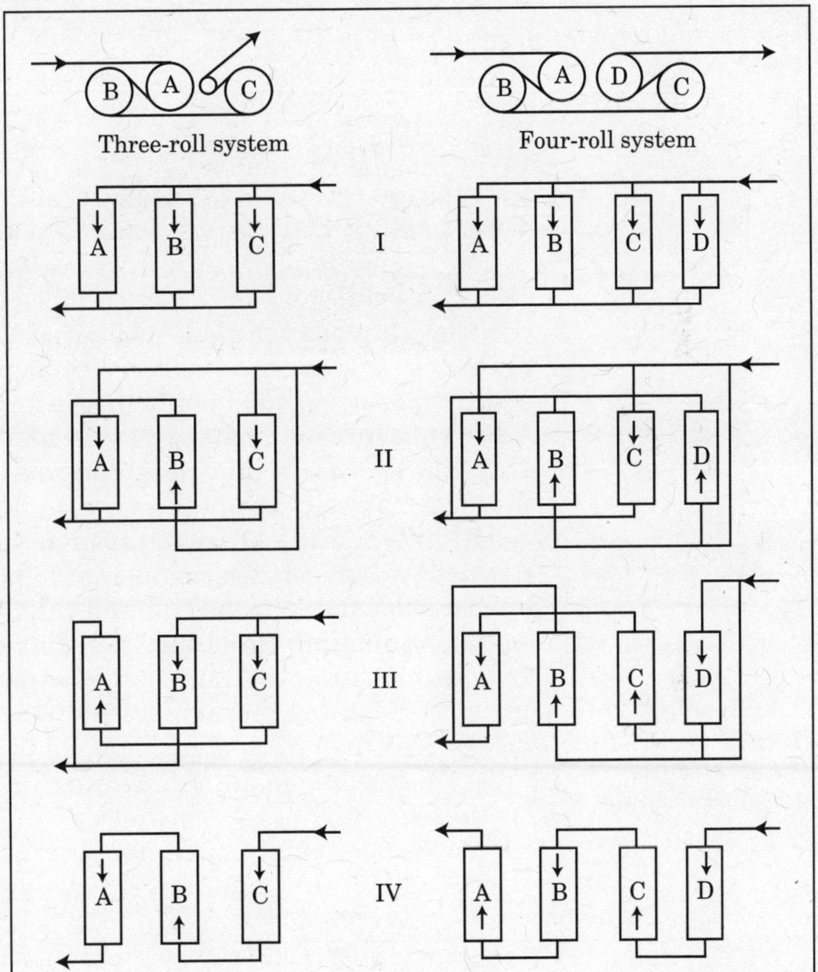

the physical location of the rollers but rather the sequence in which the web out of the dryer runs over the various rollers. For clarity, in the four systems marked I, II, III, and IV, the rollers are shown from left to right in the order in which the web contacts them.

Table A shows the flow rate in gallons per minute or liters per minute through each chill roll for the various systems illustrated. These rates assume a total water supply of 25 gal./min. (95 l/min.). In the case of diagram IV, it is further assumed that it is possible to pump the entire water supply through all of the chill rolls hooked in series.

Table A:
Flow rate per chill roll in gallons (liters) per minute with a 25-gpm (95-lpm) supply

Diagram	Three-Roll System		Four-Roll System	
I	8.3 gpm	31.4 lpm	6.2 gpm	23.5 lpm
II	8.3	31.4	6.2	23.5
III	12.5	47	12.5	47
IV	25	95	25	95

For the purpose of the calculations it is assumed that the paper coming out of the dryer is at a temperature of 270°F (132°C), paper temperature off of the last chill roll is 75°F (24°C), the chill rolls in the three-roll system are large enough to provide the same amount of surface contact with the web as that for the four-roll system, and the temperature of the water being supplied to the chill system is 55°F (13°C).

For both three- and four-roll systems (Table B), plumbing diagrams III and IV provide slightly better cooling because of the increased velocity of the water running through the individual chill rolls. The four-roll system illustrated by diagram III works nearly as well as diagram IV, although the flow rate of water through the chill roll is only 12½ gal./min. (47 l/min.) for diagram III as opposed to 25 gal./min. (95 l/min.) for diagram IV.

Table B:
Average web temperature after chilling

Diagram	Three-Roll System		Four-Roll System	
I	76.5°F	24.7°C	76.6°F	24.8°C
II	76.5	24.7	76.6	24.8
III	75.6	24.2	75.3	24.1
IV	75.0	23.9	75.0	23.9

Table C shows the side-to-side web temperature variations in the web after chilling. The temperature variations for diagram I are significantly larger than those for diagrams II, III, and IV. The problem with diagram I for either a three- or four-roll system is that because of the plumbing method all of the chill rolls are cold on the same side of the press and relatively warm on the opposite side of the press. With diagrams II, III, and IV, the cold water input is alternated from side to side as the web goes across the chill rolls. If it is necessary to lower the web temperature to 75°F (24°C) in order to avoid marking in the folder, the 8°F (4°C) side-to-side temperature differential produced by plumbing as indicated in diagram I will mean that the cold side of the web must be chilled to 67°F (19°C) in order for the warm side to be down to 75°F (24°C). This extra cooling requirement limits press production speeds.

Table C:
Side-to-side temperature variation after chilling

Diagram	**Three-Roll System**		**Four-Roll System**	
I	8.1°F	4.5°C	8.0°F	4.4°C
II	2.7	1.5	0.1	0.1
III	2.0	1.1	0.0	0.0
IV	0.9	0.5	0.0	0.0

As indicated in all four diagrams, the chill rolls are plumbed from the last to the first. Chill roll temperatures should decrease successively from the first roll that the web touches to the last. This arrangement prevents *thermal shock* — surface-only setting. Furthermore, the first roll should reduce the web temperature by 40–50%; the remaining rolls should lower the web to room temperature. If the temperature is more than 15°F (8°C) lower than room temperature, condensation could accumulate on the chill rolls. Also, on a set of chill rolls that are 40-in. (1016-mm) wide, it should be possible to limit side-to-side temperature variation to less than 8°F (4°C). The use of a portable infrared (IR) pyrometer helps to control and monitor the correct temperature needs.

8 Folders

Most web offset presses are equipped to deliver a folded product or signature. Folders are selected depending primarily on the nature of the finished work to be produced. Page size and format, number of pages, and grain direction requirements in the finished product are primary considerations. Production speed and the degree of flexibility needed for varying the number of pages in the signatures are also important.

Folding Principles

An understanding of folding principles is important in choosing the right folder to perform the job required. Keep in mind that the grain of the paper always runs in the direction of web travel. Former folds and chopper folds are made parallel to the grain; jaw folds are always made across the web at right angles to the grain.

A *former fold* results when the web is pulled over the nose of a triangular metal former board. This folds the web in half—in the direction of web travel. Many folders are arranged to first make a former fold in the web, followed by additional folds. In some specialized folders, only a former fold is made, followed by a knife cutoff and delivery of the finished products.

In a *jaw fold,* the paper web flows around a cylinder and is tucked into the jaws of a second cylinder by the tucker blade from the first cylinder. A knife in the same set of cylinders cuts the web into individual signatures. If a second jaw fold is made after the first, a *double-parallel* folded signature is the result.

A *chopper fold,* or *quarter fold,* when employed, is the final folding operation. After jaw folding, the signature is conveyed in a horizontal plane with the folded edge forward. It passes under a blade that feeds the signature between two rotary folding rollers. The resulting backbone or spine fold is parallel to the paper grain. Chopper folding speeds are normally somewhat limited in comparison to other folds because the folding method does not maintain a positive grip on the signature. For this reason, high-production chopper folders employ a more sophisticated method of dividing the stream of signatures leaving the jaw fold section. Using one or more pairs of choppers, they output more signatures per hour. Multiple chopper folders deliver signatures in two or four streams.

Folder Designs

Combination Folder

The combination folder is so named because it combines former, jaw, and chopper folding in one machine. Its popularity is attributed to its versatile folding capability. Primarily designed for web widths in the popular 34–40 in. (864–1,016 mm) range, a combination folder delivers *tabloid* signatures (eight pages per web), *double digest* signatures (thirty-two pages per web, or sixteen pages — two-up), and *magazine-size* signatures (sixteen pages per web). Changeover of the machine for each of these different product sizes varies with the design of the folder, but in most cases is relatively simple.

Assume that the press has a 22-in. (559-mm) plate cylinder circumference (and therefore a 22-in. cutoff) and the running web is 34 in. (864 mm) wide. The former fold would in effect be creating a four-page, 17×22-in. (432×559-mm) signature. This is the size of the signature at cutoff.

The cut signature passes to the first jaw fold, where the first parallel fold is made. The jaw fold halves the 22-in. (559-mm) length of the signature. The product after a single jaw fold is an eight-page, 17×11-in. (432×279-mm) signature, called a tabloid.

From this point, several options are available. The tabloid-sized product can be sent directly to the delivery with no further folding. Alternatively, the signature may receive a second parallel fold. This involves another jaw fold, where the eight-page tabloid is folded into a sixteen-page, 17×5½-in. (432×140-mm) signature. This product is sent to the bindery, where it is cut halfway along the 17-in. (432-mm) side, producing two sixteen-page, 8½×5½-in. (216×140-mm) signatures, called a digest fold, two-up. Most often, the product coming out of the folder delivery is two-up and then cut into two 8½×5½-in. (216×140-mm) digest signatures.

The third alternative is to pass the signature through a chopper fold instead of the second parallel fold. The chopper folds at right angles to the jaw fold and parallel to the former fold. It takes the eight-page, 17×11-in. (432×279-mm) signature and folds it into an 8½×11-in. (216×279-mm), sixteen-page signature. This signature is called the quarter, or magazine, fold.

A magazine format — 8½×11-in. (216×279-mm) or 8¼×11-in. (210×279-mm) trim size — is delivered by sequential folds: a former fold, a single parallel (jaw) fold, and a chopper fold. The untrimmed page height of the signature as delivered is one-half the folder cutoff length and its page width is one-quarter the initial width of the web. Paper grain in the finished signature runs parallel to the backbone.

The double-digest (or double-parallel, two-up) signature is produced by first folding over the former and then following with two parallel folds. This format is suitable for printing books, pamphlets, and leaflet signatures in two-up form. The two halves are separated at the appropriate point in the bindery. Paper grain in the finished signature runs at right angles to the backbone.

In addition to the regular tabloid format, signatures of oblong proportion can be produced on the combination folder by laying out the press plates on a two-up basis. For example, two signatures with trim size of 8½-in. (216-mm) backbone by 11-in. (279-mm) page width could be trimmed out of a signature delivered in tabloid form and later cut apart in the bindery.

In its capacity for making a variety of different products, the combination folder broadens the versatility of the press. This folder delivers one stream of signatures at a time — all identical in size, format, and paging. There are more specialized folders available that deliver one size of signature with variability in the number of pages.

Ribbon Folder

Many of the folders used exclusively in publication work are equipped with angle bars on top instead of former boards. The web or webs are first slit into several ribbons of a width required by the desired product size. Each ribbon is turned over an angle bar and guided into position so that all ribbons align with each other ahead of the jaw-folding section. The metal turning bars are perforated for low-pressure air — like most formers — so that smearing of the printed image is avoided by floating each ribbon on a cushion of air wherever it wraps around a bar. The ribbons of paper are collated (assembled) in the desired combinations and brought down

LISA shear-cut slitting wheel with housing
Courtesy Converter Accessory Corp.

to the cutoff knives and folding jaws in either one or two streams. In this manner, the press simultaneously delivers either one or two sets of signatures of the same size. If two streams are delivered, they can have either equal or different numbers of pages according to the way the ribbons are webbed through the folder.

Ribbon folders are often made with a collect/noncollect feature so that two successive signatures can be collected after cutoff, then jaw-folded together. By this means, two sixteen-page signatures are collected, folded, and delivered instead of the four eight-page signatures that result from

Former/ribbon deck
Courtesy Jardis Industries, Inc.

Hurletron Model 777 ribbon tacking system, which reduces dog-ears in delivered signatures by inducing a controlled electrical charge into the ribbons
Courtesy Hurletron Incorporated

This electrical force removes the cushion of air between the ribbons and in effect tacks the ribbons together as they progress through the folder.

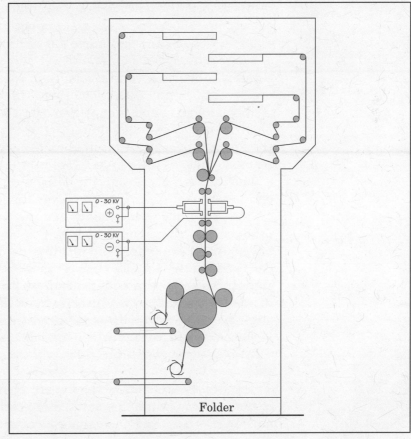

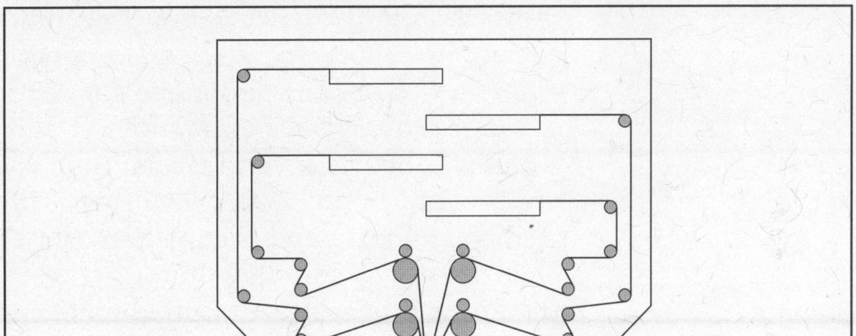

running on a noncollect basis. Such folders are usually designed to produce two sets from one conveyor when collecting, or four sets from two conveyors when not collecting. The collect feature requires a folder cutoff length that equals one-half the cylinder circumference of the printing units. The total page output from the folder depends on the page input — as determined by the number of printed webs and the pages per web. Some folders allow one stream to run collect while the other stream runs noncollect.

Double-Former Folder

The double-former folder is found principally in publication and commercial printing plants. It is primarily intended for the high-speed production of a single size of folded product. The backbone fold, made by running the paper webs over a former, is the only fold it produces. Although limited to one basic size, it delivers up to four streams of signatures simultaneously and in a wide variety of page combinations. These signatures have open heads.

The machine has two formers and four deliveries. The centerlines of the formers are perpendicular to the press centerline. The formers are slanted with noses pointed downward. A web slitting and angle bar section first slits the one or more printed webs into narrower ribbons of specified equal width. The several ribbons run over turning bars and are brought in line with each other — much in the manner of a ribbon folder — and then pulled over the formers. The ribbons are cut off into individual signatures immediately below the formers by a set of cutoff and delivery cylinders, which transfer them to the delivery conveyors.

The number of pages in the delivered signatures depends on how the ribbons are webbed over the formers. If all of the ribbons are pulled over one former, two mating deliveries produce signatures containing half the total number of input pages. As an example, two webs totaling thirty-two pages are delivered as two sixteen-page signatures. Four eight-page signatures are delivered if the half-width ribbons are equally divided between the two formers. Sometimes, additional angle bars are used to interleave multicolor and monotone ribbons. This feature provides further flexibility in the placement of color pages within the signatures.

Cutoff

The folder corresponds to the repeat length or circumference of the printing units. The cutoff and printing circumference of the press are fixed and cannot be changed. Although the

A double-former folder
Courtesy Heidelberg Harris, Inc.

Cutoff sections are alternately delivered to the left and right. This prevents any one station from being overwhelmed with press output. The web-slitting and angle bar section preceding the former is not shown.

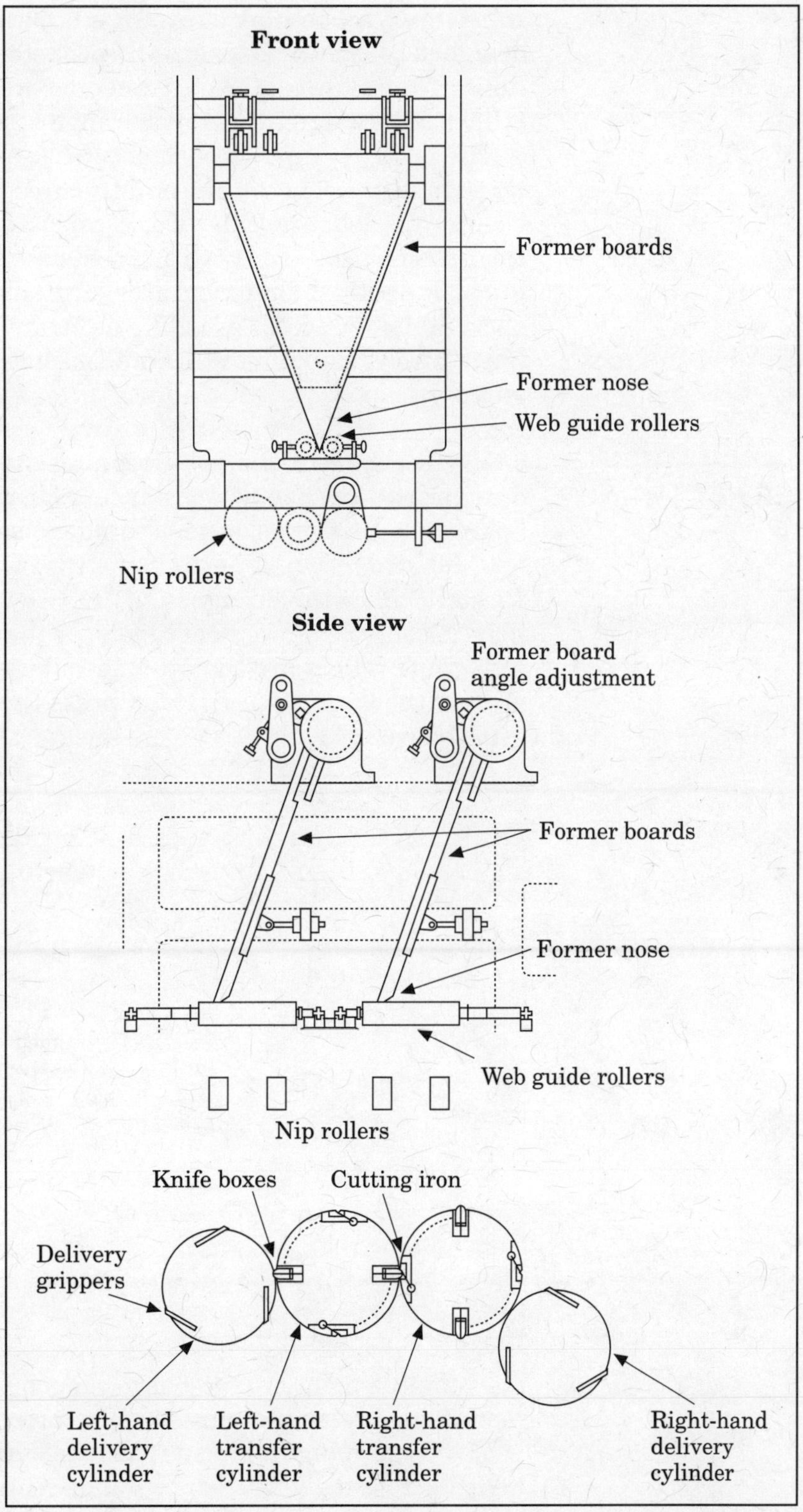

web width can be varied, the signature sizes producible by a web offset folder are essentially predetermined within small limits. Therefore, all jobs planned for web equipment must fall within a relatively narrow range of page dimensions.

The utility of a press is sometimes broadened by providing more than one folder design in the press line and perhaps a sheeter for delivering flat work. Such additions to capital investment increase operating costs and must be justifiable under individual circumstances. The same holds true for optional folder accessories like electronic web cutoff monitoring controls, signature stackers, on-press gluing devices, and stitchers.

Mechanics of Folding

On former folders, the web first runs over a former board. The former board is triangular in shape, with the apex of the triangle — the former nose — pointing downward. More than one web can be run (one on top of the other) over the former. Directly below the former nose are two web guide rollers that help to control the web passage over the former. Below the web guide rollers are the nipping rollers that, in addition to pulling the web into the folder, press the lengthwise crease into the web.

The former board and related elements

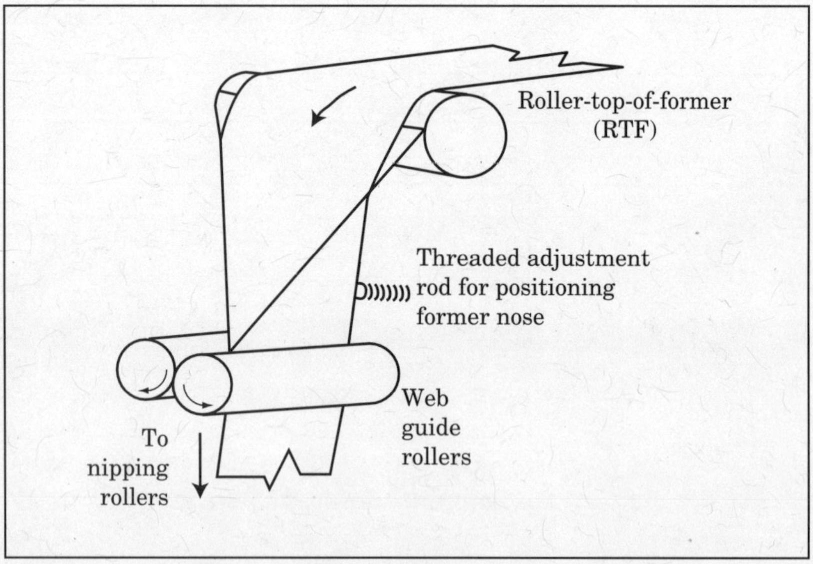

From this point on, the basic components of the folder are mounted on rotating cylinders. The press cutoff is located just below the nipping rollers, so that the cutoff section can be folded across its width. The cutoff is made by a blade on one cylinder that cuts through the web into a slot lying across the width of a second cylinder. Before the web is cut, sharp pins spring up out of the face of the second cylinder and punch through the lead edge of the web just behind the cutoff. These pins pull the lead edge of the web around the cylinder and release just as the jaw fold is made. *Pinless* former folders are designed to operate with 16- and 32-page presses. The draw roller, slitter, turner bar, and ribbon register assemblies operate independently from the main folder; therefore, the folder accommodates from one to three webs. Smooth operation is enhanced by an antijam device. The basic cutoff length is the same as the plate cylinder circumference.

Setting of the impaling pins
Courtesy Heidelberg Harris, Inc.

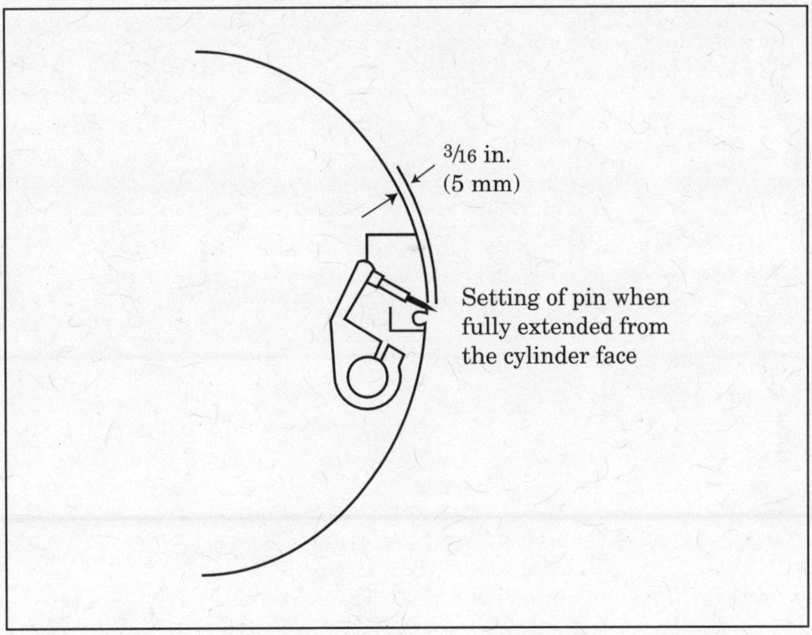

The jaw fold is made across the width of the signature at right angles to the former fold. A tucker blade fixed on the surface of one cylinder swings into a jaw on an opposing cylinder. The paper is between the blade and the jaw. The jaw is mechanically timed to close just as the tucker blade swings out of it. The leading edge of the jaw closes on the paper and creases it.

The chopper folder folds parallel to the former fold. It is often the most difficult part of the folder to operate correctly. Moving tapes carry the paper up to a headstop. An instant after the signature reaches the headstop, the chopper blade descends, forcing the paper between two folding rollers that

How the Jaw Fold Is Made

The movable jaw on this folder is attached to a cam-operated shaft. The jaw opens and closes in the manner indicated by the arrow.

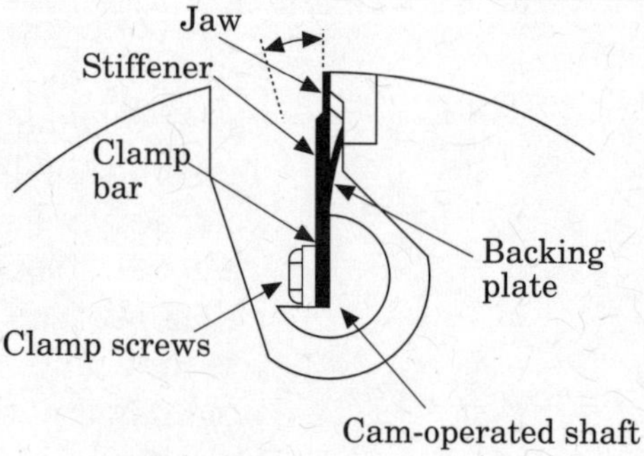

The web is cut off at point A. Note that two cutoffs are being made for each revolution of the folding cylinders. Pins pierce the lead edge of the web (B), maintaining control of the signature. The tucker blade (C) creates a slight protrusion in the web surface.

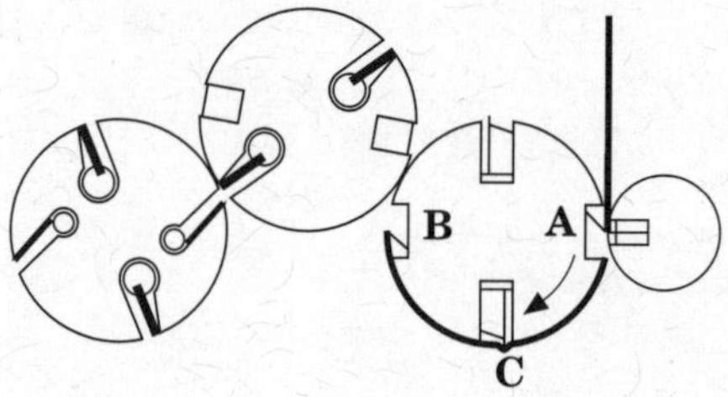

As the cylinder revolves, the jaw on the opposing cylinder closes on the ridge of the signature created by the tucker blade (D). When completely closed, the jaw pinches the fold into the signature. The pins have retracted, releasing the signature from the first cylinder.

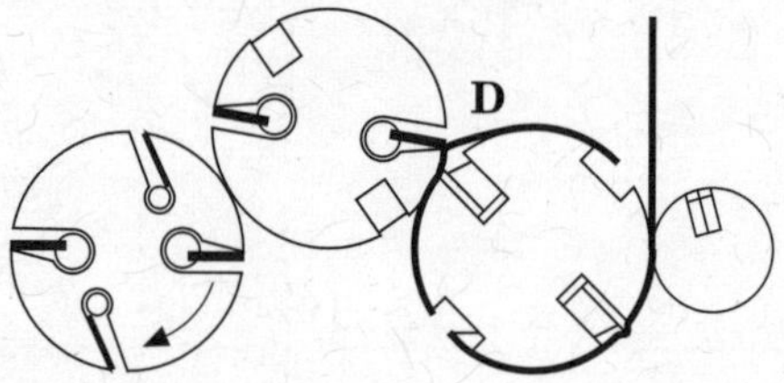

As the cylinders continue turning, the cutoff pins retract, allowing the jaw to pull the signatures from the face of the first cylinder (E). The signature is then carried to point F where the grippers on the third cylinder take control of the signature. The signature is carried around the third cylinder and, on release, dropped onto the delivery tapes at G.

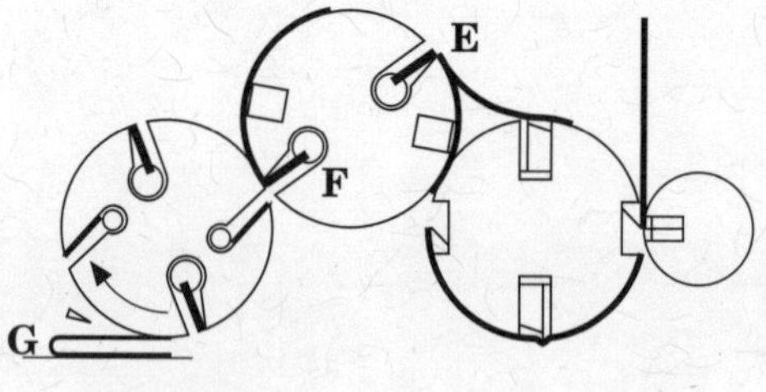

In double-parallel folding, a second set of tucker blades are activated on the second cylinder (H). These will insert the signature into jaws on the third cylinder (J)

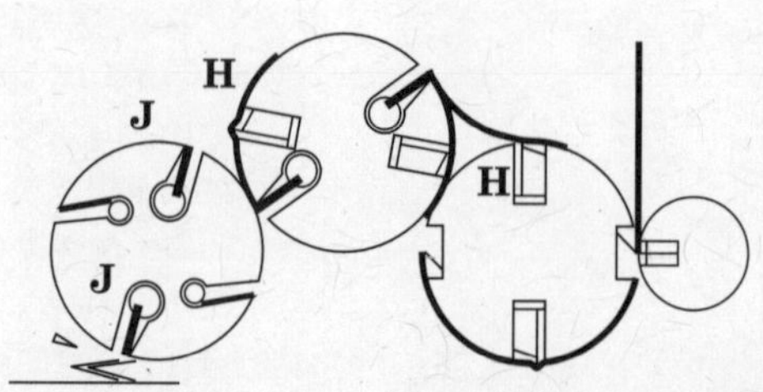

Courtesy Rockwell Graphic Systems, Rockwell International

Chopper fold mechanism

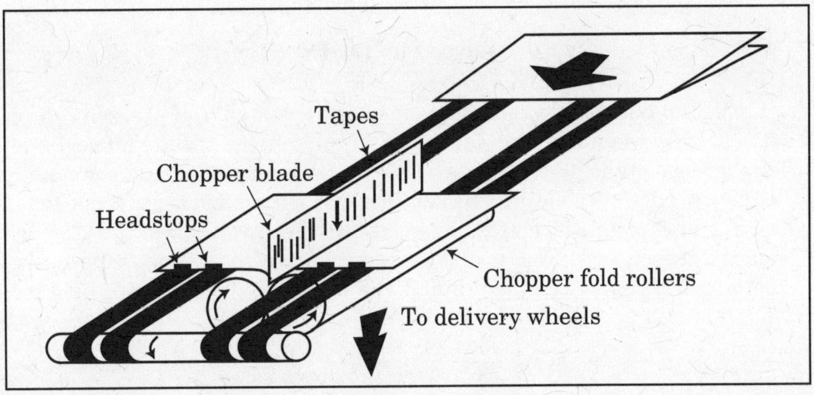

crease the paper while drawing the signature through. The signature then drops into star (delivery) wheels, which drop it on delivery belts.

In addition to these components, some folders carry collect cylinders. Assume that a job has been stripped to run with one part of the job on the top half of the plate and the other part on the bottom half. The press cutoff is set to make two cutoffs per revolution of the plate cylinder. The top half of the plate cylinder image is cut off and passed to the collect cylinder, where it is held by the first set of pins. As the lower half of the plate cylinder image is cut off, the second set of collect pins come into position. These pins already hold a top-half cutoff. They accept a bottom-half cutoff, and the two are held together. The cylinder turns, and the third set of pins comes up and takes the new top-half cutoff. Meanwhile, the second set of pins carrying both a top-half and a bottom-half cutoff are releasing them into the jaw fold. A new bottom cutoff is made as the first set of pins comes around, which is still carrying the first top-half cutoff. These accept a bottom-half cutoff and carry both to the jaw folder.

In this particular case, the collect cylinder is carrying three sets of pins. Each set of pins is timed to accept a section every time it approaches the cutoff and to release *every other* time it approaches the jaw fold cylinders.

The above elements were discussed separately for the sake of clarity, and it may seem that the folder is crammed full of rotating cylinders. In reality, all these elements are carried on no more than four or five cylinders, each cylinder carrying out several operations. For example, the first cylinder often carries the tucker blade for the first jaw fold, as well as the pins and the female cutting iron for cutoff. The next cylinder carries the folding jaws for the first jaw fold and the tucker

How Collect Cylinders Operate

(1) The top half of the plate cylinder image is cut off and passes to the collect cylinder, where it is held by the first set of pins. (The circumference of the knife cylinder is one-half the circumference of the plate cylinder, the circumference of the collect cylinder is three time the circumference of the knife cylinder, and the circumference of the jaw cylinder is equal to the circumference of the plate cylinder.) (2) As the lower half of the plate cylinder image is cut off, the second set of collect pins come up; they already hold a top-half cutoff. They accept a bottom-half cutoff, and the top-half and bottom-half cutoffs are held together.

1

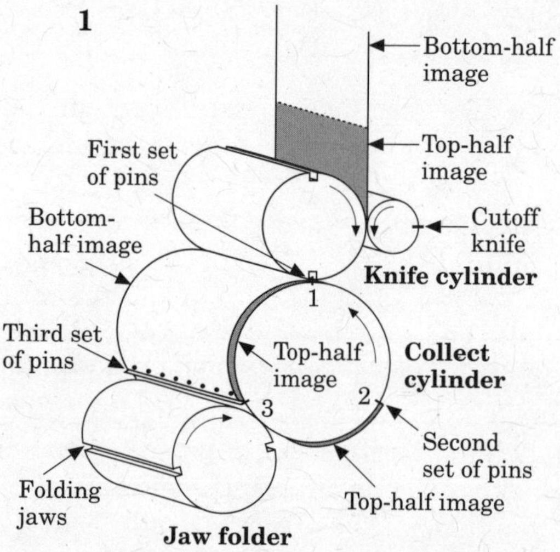

2

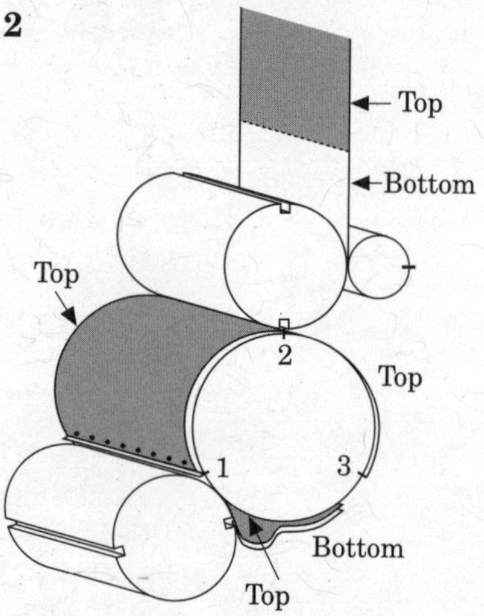

(3) The cylinder turns and the third set of pins comes up and takes the new top-half cutoff. While this is happening, the second set of pins carrying both a top-half and bottom-half cutoff are releasing them into the jaw fold. (4) A new bottom-half cutoff is made as the first set of pins come around, which is still carrying the first top-half cutoff. These accept a bottom-half cutoff and carry both to the jaw folder.

3

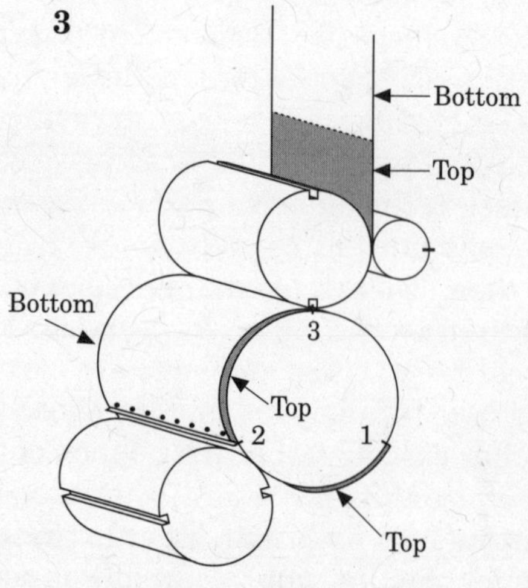

4

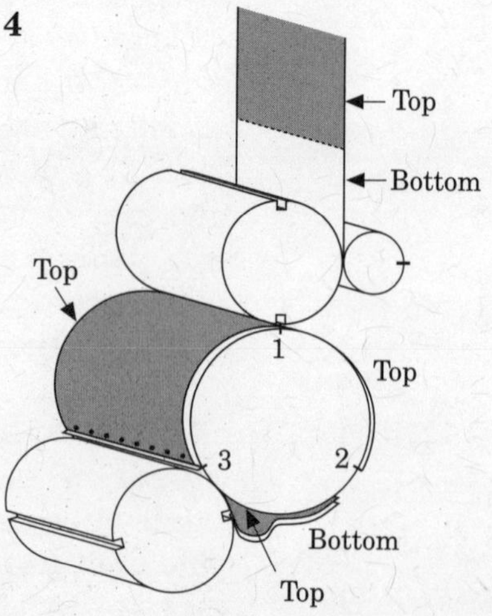

The arrangement of the major components of a typical combination folder
Courtesy Heidelberg Harris, Inc.

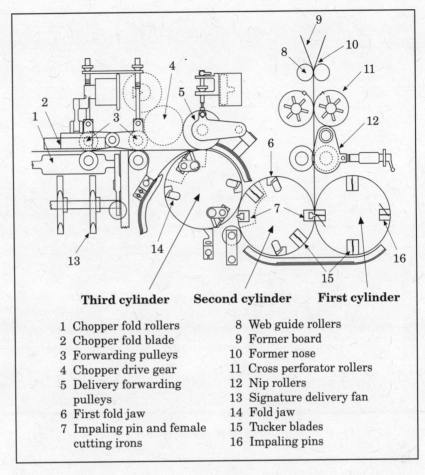

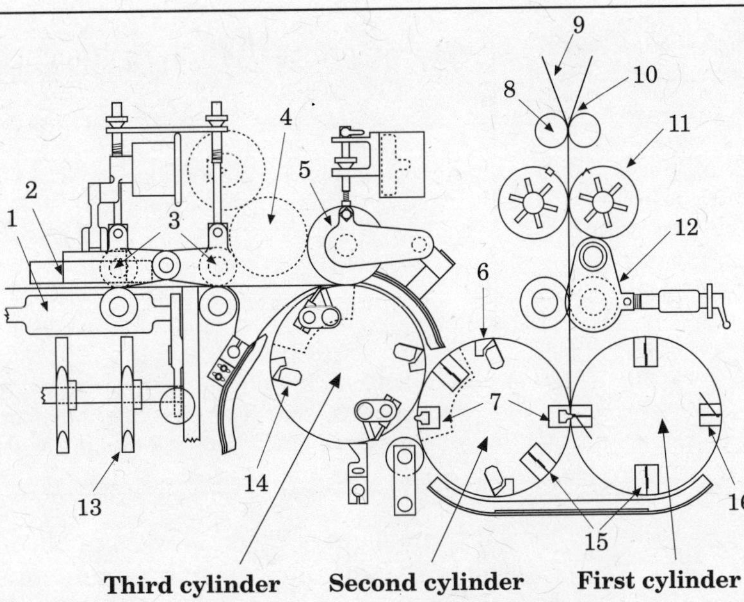

1 Chopper fold rollers	8 Web guide rollers
2 Chopper fold blade	9 Former board
3 Forwarding pulleys	10 Former nose
4 Chopper drive gear	11 Cross perforator rollers
5 Delivery forwarding pulleys	12 Nip rollers
6 First fold jaw	13 Signature delivery fan
7 Impaling pin and female cutting irons	14 Fold jaw
	15 Tucker blades
	16 Impaling pins

blade for the second jaw fold. Collect cylinders are an exception to this. They perform the single function of collecting printed sections in proper sequence.

Angle bars lie across the path of the web at a 45° angle. When the web is wrapped around the bar, it changes direction by 90°. Angle bars are sometimes used to interleave ribbons. Instead of being run down a former board, the web is slit along its length into two or more ribbons by one or more slitters. Ribbons then pass over an arrangement of rollers and angle bars that gather them, superimposed over each other. The web then proceeds to subsequent folding operations.

Adjustments, Operation, and Folder Maintenance

Though few settings have to be made on a folder, those that are required have to be precise. The operating speed of the folder precludes visual evaluation of its performance. Sometimes, a setting that works well when the folder is turned over slowly may not work the same when the folder is running

Lap
Courtesy Heidelberg Harris, Inc.

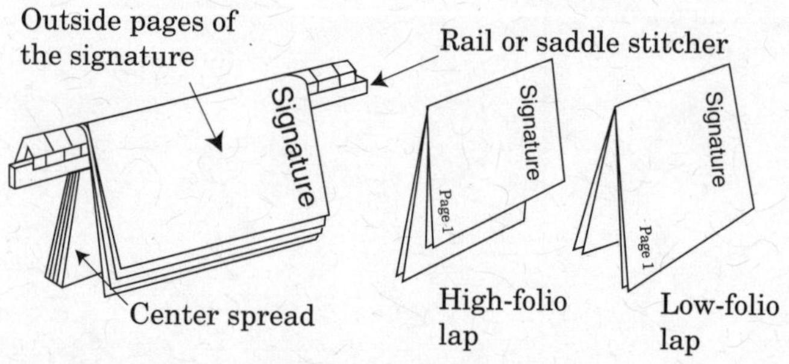

Parallel folds are sometimes made off-center to put a lap on the finished signature. This simplifies the opening of the signature to the center spread during saddle-stitching or sewing operations.

at high speed. Precise working habits and accurate and complete records of settings from previous jobs are invaluable aids to efficiently set and operate the folder.

One device that aids visual inspection is called a stroboscope or strobe light. This device emits light in extremely short pulses. When synchronized to a repetitive operation, the action seems to stop under the light. Any element in the operation — a folding jaw, for example — can be examined under the strobe light and its operation checked while the press is running.

The setting of the former board angle is critical within close tolerance. If set too far forward, the nose smudges or tears the web. If set too far back, uniform tension is lost and the web wrinkles along the fold. **Note:** Once the former nose is correctly set, it should not be necessary to change its position.

The web guide rollers below the former nose can be set at both ends, close or far apart from each other. The position of the former may create differences in the distances traveled by various parts of the web. The web center may run tight over the former nose while the web edges are running slack, or vice versa. By adjusting the guide rollers, the press operator can equalize these distances. The final effect is that all parts of the web enter the nipping rollers under uniform tautness.

The nipping rollers immediately below the web guide rollers can also be set closer to or farther away from one another. The nipping rollers run faster than press speed. Thus, there is slippage at this point, which makes pressure settings critical. Setting these rollers properly is difficult.

The critical factor is the caliper and grade of paper. Cutoff systems that employ no-slip nips and have the nip rollers running at the correct paper speed adapt to changes in either the caliper or the surface of the paper.

The pins that grip the lead edge of the section after cutoff and the jaw fold tucker blades are adjustable on some folders. If they are, their normal setting should be according to the manufacturer's instructions. This is especially true of the pins. If they do not spring out far enough, the lead edge will not be gripped sufficiently. If set too high, they may not release in time.

Tucker blades can be set on some folders to allow for different thicknesses of paper. On other folders, the tucker blades reciprocate; that is, they retract into the cylinder and come out again as the cylinders turn.

During the various folding operations, several devices including brushes, springs, and rollers control the signature. A tight setting on these elements restricts smooth paper passage; a loose setting defeats their purpose. The settings of these components should be uniform, so that no unbalanced forces are applied to the signature as it passes from point to point in the folder.

Folder settings are primarily determined according to basis weight. A 100-lb. coated stock usually passes through a tabloid fold without much difficulty. Some folder manufacturers suggest 70-lb. coated stock as the minimum weight for the chopper, even though this fold is made in the direction of the paper grain. A double-parallel fold (second jaw fold) often cracks stocks with a basis weight in excess of 70 lb. Sixty-pound coated stock should be the maximum when running two webs superimposed. Determine the folder's capability through experience if specific guidelines are not previously provided by the folder manufacturer.

Paper grain is an important factor in folding because the fibers in a web lie predominantly lengthwise, in the direction of web travel. Because of the grain direction of the paper, cleaner folds can be made along the length of the web than across its width. Former folds and chopper folds are made along the web length, while jaw folds are made across its width.

When multiple webs are being run over the former, several special considerations apply. When a full- and half-width web are run over the same former board, the narrower web should always be on the bottom. This gives better control of the half-web. Whenever more than one web is run, the top web or webs should be made successively looser. Too much tension on the top webs wrinkles the bottom web.

Proper maintenance contributes to efficient long-term folder operation. The maintenance schedule should include regular, thorough lubrication of all points suggested by the manufacturer.

Expect some wear and tear on moving parts in the folder. The cutoff knives become dull, producing ragged cutoffs. The easiest way to determine their condition is to inspect the last job run. Knives should be mounted according to the manufacturer's instructions. The last nips prior to cutting are very important to maintain the correct diameter. Any lose in diameter will contribute to web tension problems.

9 In-Line Finishing

In-line finishing equipment is attached to a printing press (usually a web offset press) to establish an in-line manufacturing system. A typical in-line finishing package on a commercial web press includes a remoistenable glue applicator, a perforator, plow folders, and a variable cutoff unit. There is considerable flexibility in in-line system configurations, which may be set up in U, L, or T shapes, or in a straight line depending on spatial limitations. This chapter examines the major characteristics of each broad class of in-line finishing equipment.

Gluers

There are several in-line gluing options available, which have increased product variety and helped to enhance advertisement and promotional capabilities.

Paster Wheels

Some folders paste signatures together before delivery. Paster wheels apply paste or glue to the paper. They are driven by the paper and lay down a line of paste. Hypodermic needles are also used for pasting. Usually, a 0.03-in. (0.76-mm) head is employed, but the heads can be changed to lay down more or less paste as the job may require. By the use of intermittent feeds, skip-pasting is possible.

Remoistenable Pattern Gluers

Remoistenable pattern gluers apply a pattern of glue, scratch-off material, or fragrance across the web. A band of remoistenable glue is usually applied prior to the dryer so that it can be dried. When subsequently remoistened by the end user, this band of glue seals a return envelope. A pattern gluer may also be used after the chill rolls as a wet gluer.

There are several options in using remoistenable pattern gluers. The use of sticky-back ribbon surfaces gives maximum flexibility for patterns around and across the web.

Extruder applicators apply bands of glue only in the web direction. Pattern gluers provide a variety of options for product enhancement.

A precision-ground rubber feed roller meters the glue against a transfer roller. On-the-run independent adjustment of the feed roller helps to provide uniform coverage across the web. A variable-speed electric motor turns the feed roller independently to prevent drying while the press is idle. A transfer roller transfers glue film from the pan roller to printing pads on the plate cylinder.

Remoistenable pattern gluer
Courtesy SPEC, Division of Sequa Corporation

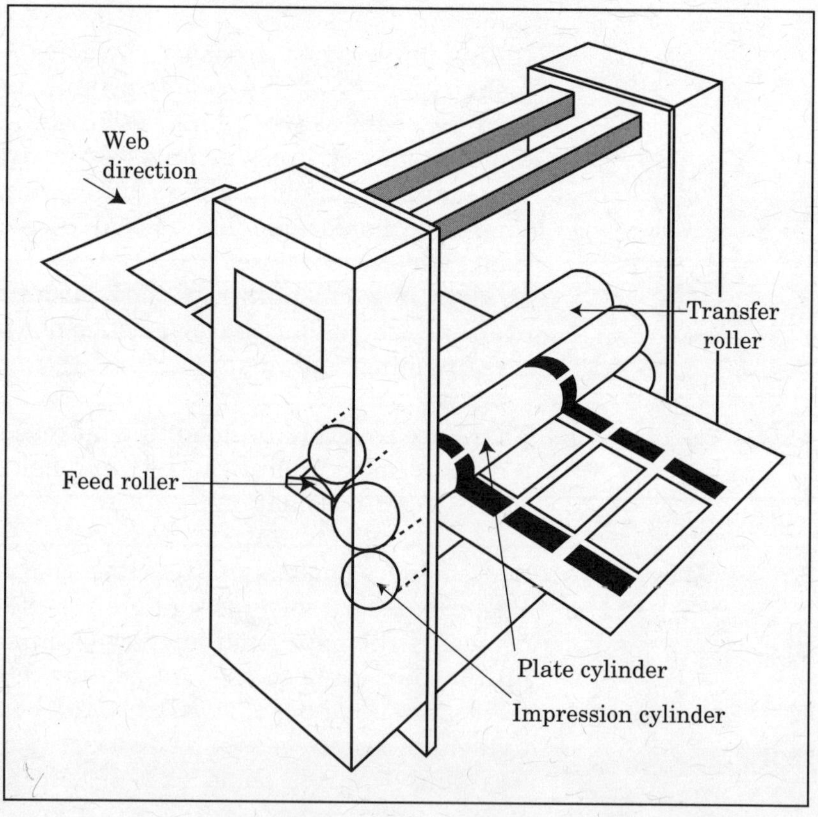

A glue pad cylinder is scored for locating pads and is undercut 0.125 in. (3.2 mm) for sticky-back rubber pads or 0.14 in. (3.6 mm) for standard rubber plates. The glue pad cylinder can be adjusted laterally or through 360° for circumferential register. An impression cylinder of full press size supports the web while glue is applied, with on-the-run adjustments for printing pressure. Where segmented gluing is needed, various widths of glue pans and transfer rollers are available. The glue pad cylinder and the impression

Pattern glue unit
Courtesy Vits-Blava Technologies Corp.

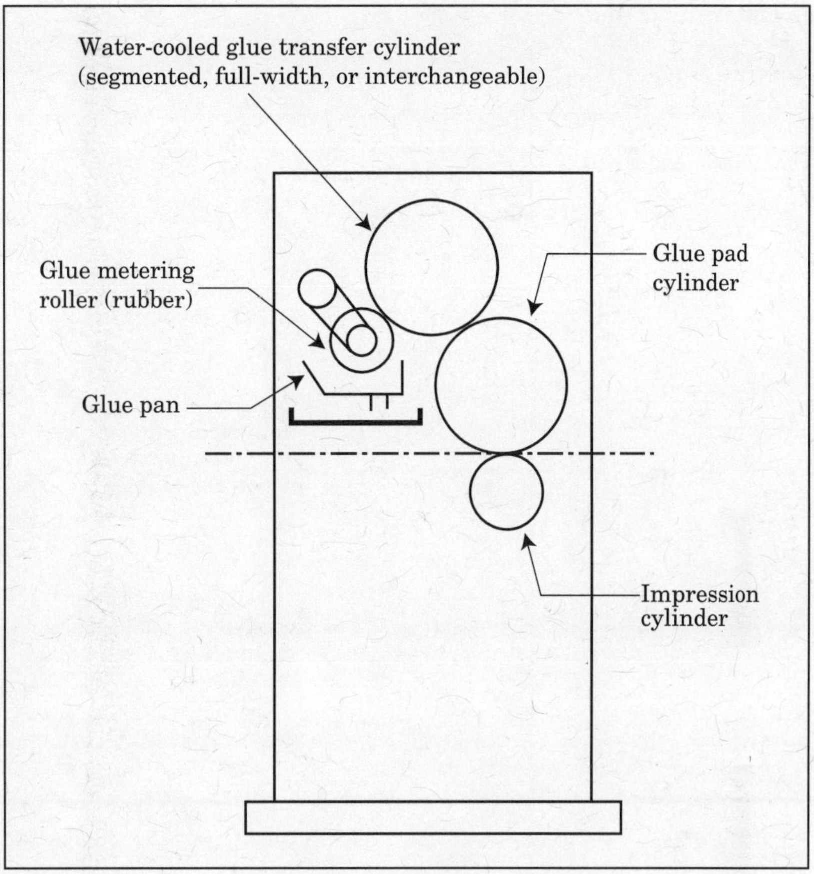

cylinder are mounted in eccentric housings with manual or automatic operation from the press controls circuit.

Remoistenable pattern gluers are used in the production of direct-mail pieces, return-mail envelopes, free-standing brochures, magazine insert cards, and newspaper inserts.

Segmented Gluers

The glue pans and transfer rollers of remoistenable pattern gluers may be segmented. The segmented gluer efficiently applies remoistenable glue, because it reduces waste from evaporation and cuts down makeready time. Segmented gluing capability allows specific patterns of glue, ruboff or wash-off inks, and/or fragrances to be applied to the printed product. On the standard 38-in. (965-mm) sixteen-page web offset press, up to six different segments are possible, which allow the product designer/commercial printer an extensive range of combinations of fragrances, glues, and removable materials. Segmented gluers feature the same design as remoistenable pattern gluers, with the addition of segmenting capability.

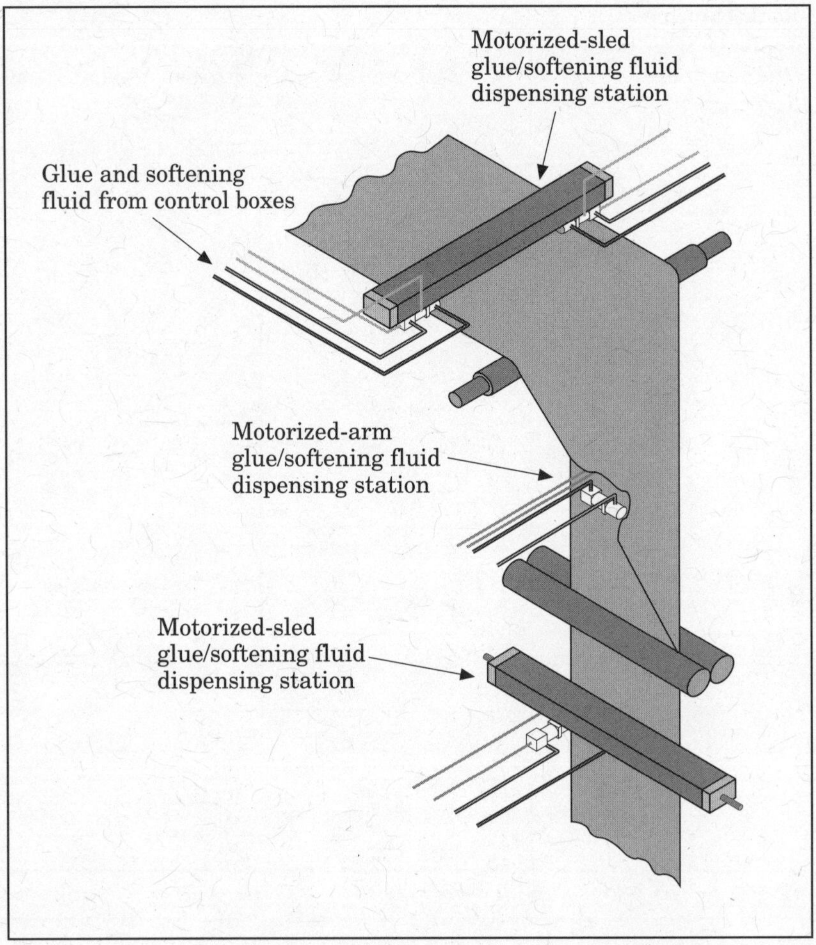

RoBond system, which provides controlled fine-line gluing with web softening
Courtesy Valco Cincinnati, Inc.

Envelope Pattern Gluers

These gluers seal the edges of envelopes; they can also seal the flap to produce a complete mailing piece. The envelope pattern gluer is normally mounted after the perforator. In addition, combination gluer/perforator or gluer/plow folder units are available. The pattern gluer is eminently suitable for complicated glue patterns for which an extruded stream in the web direction will not fulfill the job requirements.

Spot Gluers

Spot gluers apply glue spots in a pattern across the web or in a continuous line around the cylinder. They are designed to operate at high speed. Spot gluers are used in the production of magazine inserts and gatefolded products used in magazines, catalogs, brochures, and other publications.

Backbone Gluers

The backbone gluer is designed to automatically produce spine-glued books and other variations directly from the

Backbone gluer
Courtesy SPEC, Division of Sequa Corporation

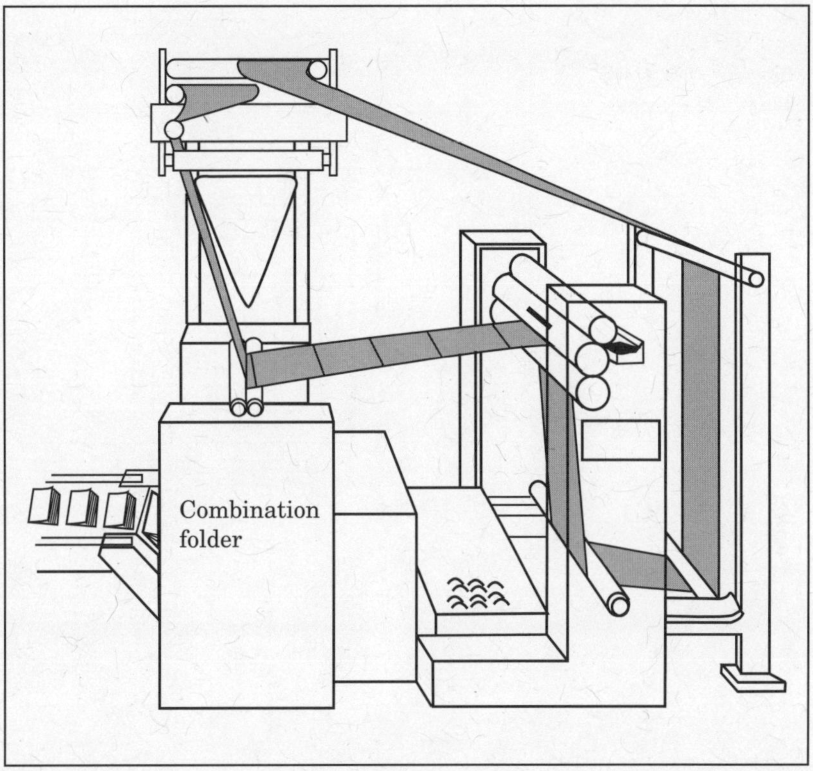

combination folder of an eight-page, grain-short press. This requires the use of a standard gluer and the combination folder.

Auxiliary Folders

Auxiliary folding devices are intended to increase the variety of products that come off the in-line print manufacturing system by enhancing the capability of the existing folder.

Prefolders

A basic prefolder consists of angle-bar and plow-folding sections. The angle bar shifts the web laterally from the center line of the press, usually up to eight inches in either direction. It accommodates odd-numbered page layouts across the web and centers the repositioned web in the appropriate position for the former board after the plow fold is made.

The plow-folding section produces either one or two folds in the direction of web travel. Subsequently, the web enters the combination folder.

Plow Folders

Producing continuous folds in the web direction, the plow folder is an adaptation of a device that is used in the production of kraft-paper bags. For in-line finishing applications,

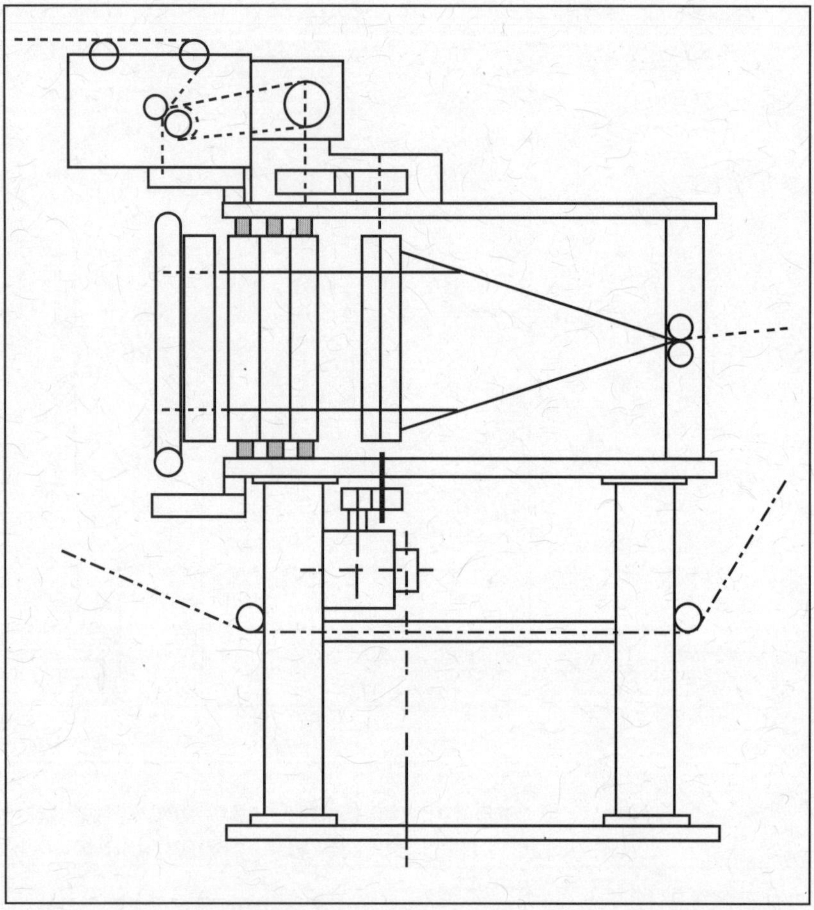

Double-former prefolder
Courtesy Vits-Blava Technologies Corp.

a plow tower consists of up to four plow heads and a driven paper-pulling nip to fold flaps onto gates in the direction of web travel. Since the plow head is movable and reversible, it offers greater flexibility than a former in location and number of folds.

Fold sizes vary from as little as 1 in. (25.4 mm) to as wide as half the web. Installing a number of plow stations in-line permits multiple folds to be made to the web or ribbons. Up to six plow stations have been incorporated into finishing lines to execute multiple and sequential folds.

Insert Folders

Insert folders convert 8½×11-in. (216×280-mm) signatures into either a delta fold (approximately 3½×8½ in. — 92×216 mm) or a half-fold (5½×8½ in. — 140×216 mm) either for inserting into an envelope or for labeling.

A typical insert folder receives a stream of overlapping signatures that have been plow-folded and converted to the

8½×11-in. (216×280-mm) format. A bump turn aligns the signatures closed-end-first before making the required folds. Subsequently, the folded products are delivered to a sheeter; the printed material is ready to be inserted or labeled.

Pattern Perforating Units and Numbering Units

Located after the chill rolls, perforating units use sticky-back perforating strips mounted on aluminum plates in a plate cylinder, perforating the web against a blanket or backup cylinder. Slitter wheels and numbering units are frequently added to the perforator for coupon products. Pattern perforating is usually carried out after the chill rolls, since this is where the web path is common to all folders, sheeters, and finishing lines. Theoretically, a pattern perforator can also be installed before the first perforating unit; however, piling may occur on subsequent blankets due to paper surface disturbance.

Numbering can be carried out by indexing heads with raised type or by ink-jet printing. In addition to perforating, the unit can improve the accuracy of folding by scoring the stock.

Using a vertical web path allows easy access for maintenance and conserves space. In a complex in-line finishing system with several pieces of folding, cutting, perforating, and gluing equipment, space considerations may be of paramount importance.

Variable Rotary Cutters

Rotary cutters are an essential element in producing the final product off an in-line finishing system. They are used for producing bleed and/or nonbleed products in increments of the printing circumference. They deliver streams of folded products cut in increments of one, one-half, one-third, or one-fourth of the press repeat. The cutter can also remove trim between products.

Variable rotary cutters execute required-size and bleed cuts; however, paper waste control is an important consideration in this cutting operation. Some cutters are capable of producing a contoured or diecut style of cutoff in addition to a straight single-knife or double-knife straight-bleed cut.

A typical rotary cutter includes an infeed section that performs a minifold where needed; an adjustable idler roller to receive folded ribbons; a driven roll with nips; and a driven shear shifter module with male/female cutting heads. The cutting couple consists of a hardened anvil cylinder, a knife cylinder, full-web-width knife bars, and control bars. The variable-speed delivery section has a full-width continuous delivery belt.

Options include miniplow folders, driven nip rollers (for high-bulk products), and two-stream capability.

Sheeters

Sheeters deliver a wide range of fully trimmed sheets or folded products. They significantly reduce bindery costs through operating efficiency at speeds over 45,000 sheets/hr.

Sheeters have additional capabilities built into them. Gap-cutting is achieved by adjustable knife assemblies that cut a 0.125–2.00-in. (3.2–50.8-mm) gap across the web. A cutter head provides speedy and accurate makeready by using pinned knife holders that drop into place. Plow-folding stations increase product variety. Sheeters are capable of producing fully trimmed sheets, half sheets, four- and eight-page products, and multipage, gatefolded products.

An in-line sheeter
Courtesy Strachan Henshaw Machinery, Inc.

10 Auxiliary Equipment

Auxiliary equipment refers to devices mounted on the press that perform operational functions. Few of these devices are standard equipment, because their functions are either specialized or because the economics involved may limit their application to specific web offset operations. The equipment listed here can significantly improve print quality and increase productivity.

Remote Control Console

Most press manufacturers offer free-standing remote control consoles with their presses. A **remote control console** is a computerized device that enables the press operator to control numerous press functions without leaving the inspection

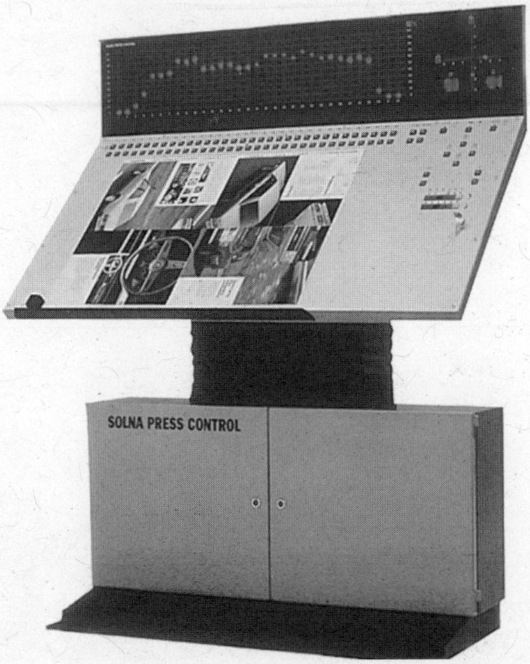

Remote control console for web offset press
Courtesy Solna Web USA, Inc.

Microcolor II system for adjusting ink key settings from a remote control console
Courtesy Graphics Microsystems, Inc.

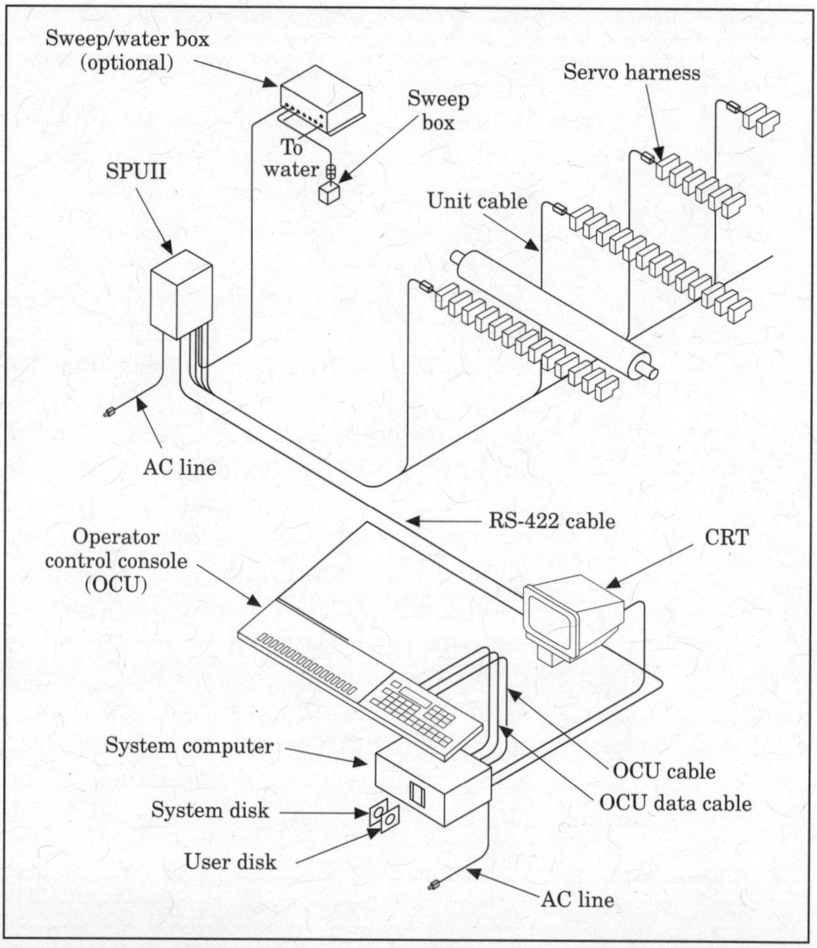

Microcolor II, a full-featured digital-computer ink control system
Courtesy Graphics Microsystems, Inc.

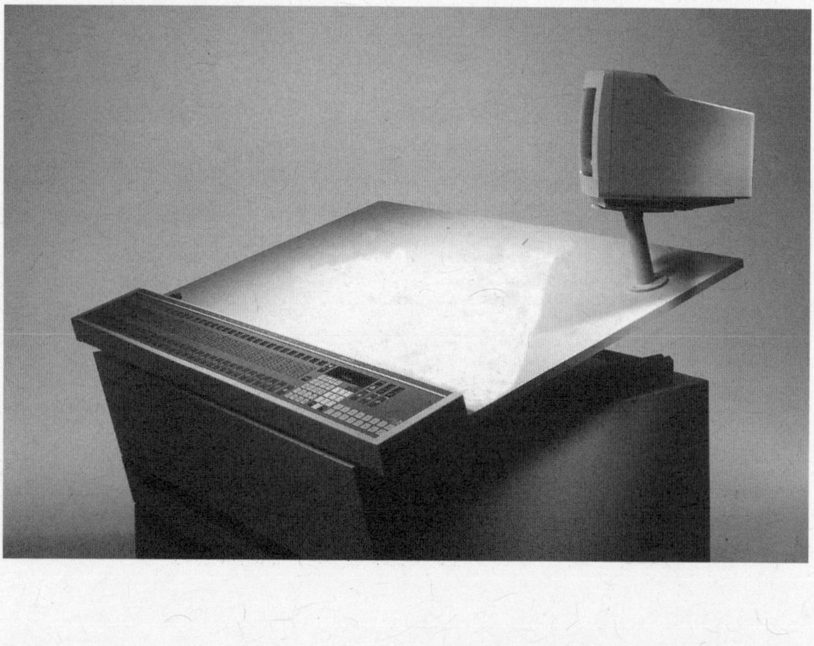

table. These functions include inking, dampening, and image register. Most remote control consoles allow the press operator to adjust the position of the plate cylinders.

The console usually includes a remote set of ink fountain keys, usually a tumble switch or push-button array numbered to press position. The press operator determines which fountain position is to be altered and depresses the appropriate button to increase or decrease ink feed. The drive system that adjusts fountain key position is either continuous or modulated. Usually, in case of electrical failure, the fountain keys on press can be manually adjusted. Some systems display the fountain blade profile through an array of light-emitting diodes (LEDs). The details can be recorded on floppy disk or other medium, allowing the press operator to preset the fountain the next time the job is run.

Plate Scanner

Another auxiliary device is the plate scanner, which can be interfaced to an inking control console or record plate readings on tape or some other medium. A **plate scanner** is a device that measures the image area percentages at selected

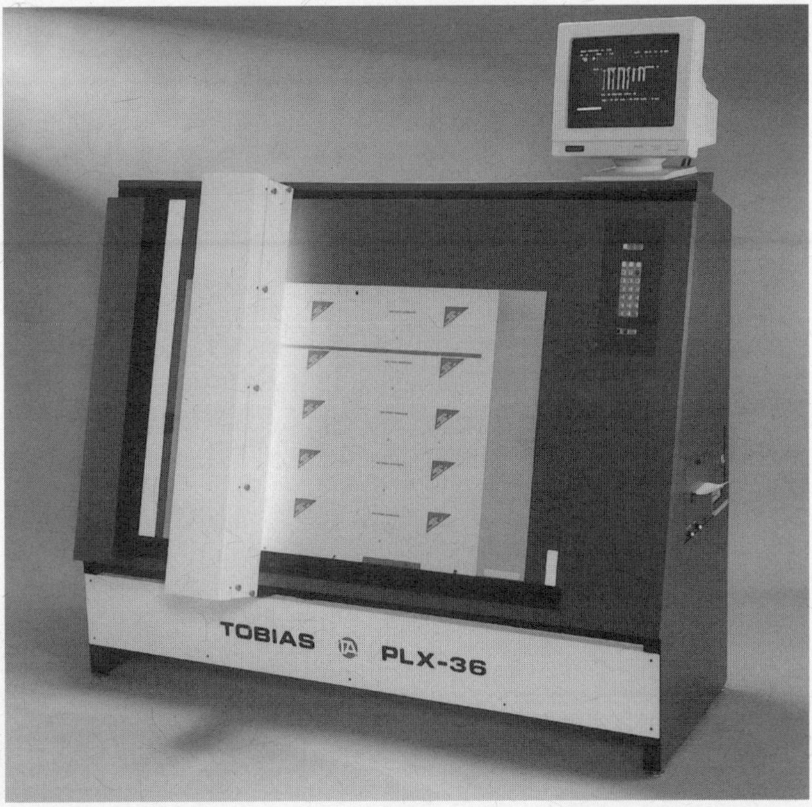

Tobias PLX-36 plate scanner
Courtesy Tobias Associates, Inc.

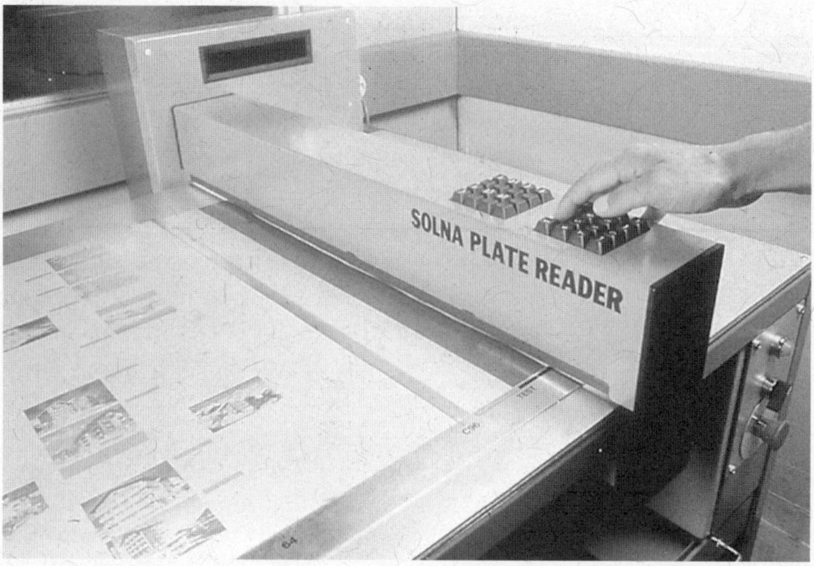

A plate scanner
Courtesy Solna Web USA, Inc.

increments across the printing plate prior to mounting the plate on press. The information is recorded, often on a magnetic storage medium, so that it can be used to preset the ink fountain. Many plate scanners produce a printout that graphically displays the ink density of each individually controlled ink zone.

Scanning Densitometer

A **scanning densitometer** is a computerized quality control table that measures and analyzes printed color bars using a densitometer. The results are compared with a prerecorded tolerance program, and a printout indicates the degree of

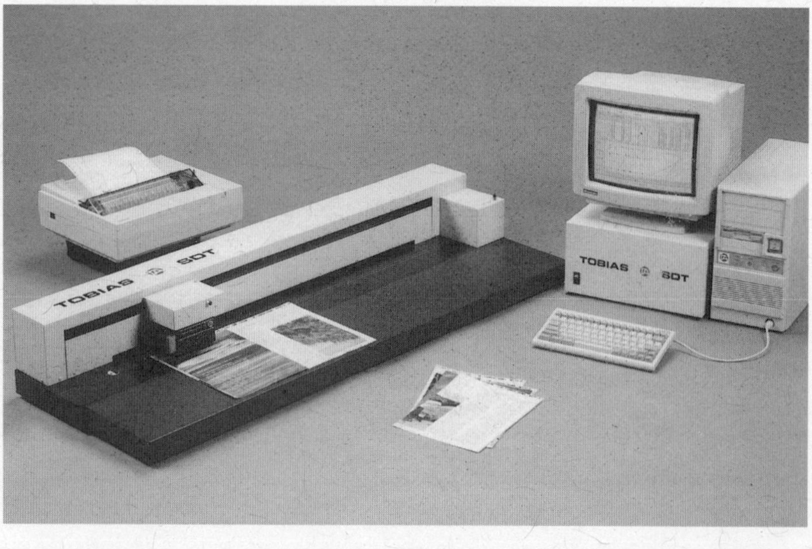

Tobias SDT scanning densitometer
Courtesy Tobias Associates, Inc.

variation. Ink fountain keys and fountain rollers can be adjusted using the information provided by the scanning densitometer. Some scanning densitometers also provide information on dot gain, print contrast, slurring, and doubling. Most systems provide a data printout.

Closed-Loop System

A closed-loop system is the combination of a remote control inking console, scanning densitometer, and computer to automatically control and adjust inking. Many systems monitor solid and halftone densities, dot gain, print contrast, and trapping.

ColorQuick, an on-press color measurement system that provides closed-loop color press control when used with the Microcolor II (or other) ink control systems *Courtesy Graphics Microsystems, Inc.*

Web Preconditioners

Web preconditioners or preheaters are located in the infeed, before the infeed metering rollers. Their principal job is to moisture-condition the web and burn off paper lint and slitter dust. Preconditioners may also help to reduce paper stretch and blistering problems.

Preconditioners consist of two sections extending across the web width, one above and the other below the web. The web is heated to 175–200°F (80–90°C). Because of these high temperatures, chill rolls are needed following the preconditioners to cool the web so that its temperature does not affect

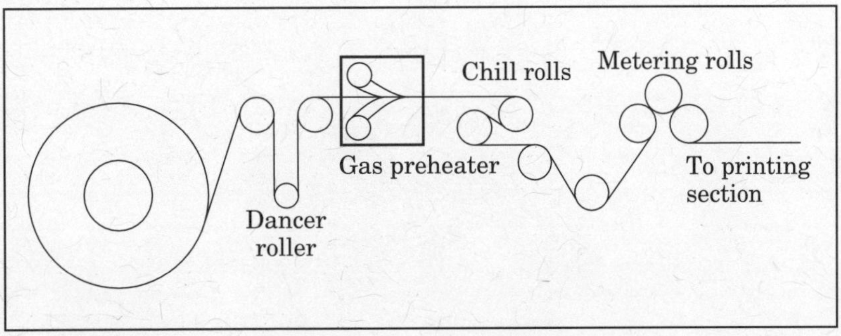

Web preconditioner, or preheater

the operation of the first printing unit. High-temperature preheating can combine with dryer heating to aggravate problems of paper cracking in the folder.

Sheet Cleaners

Sheet cleaners are frequently mounted on the press in front of or in place of preconditioners. These cleaners remove loose paper, lint, and dust from the surfaces and edges of the web before it reaches the first printing unit. A sheet cleaner usually consists of a brush that rides the web and a nozzle that vacuums the web clean. It is especially useful in an operation running high-lint paper like newsprint. Sheet cleaners, however, do not remove paper fibers that are partly bonded to the web surface. Unfortunately, forces at the printing nip can

Ultrasonic noncontact web cleaner *(top)* and narrow-slot high-velocity web cleaner *(bottom)*
Courtesy Web Systems, Inc.

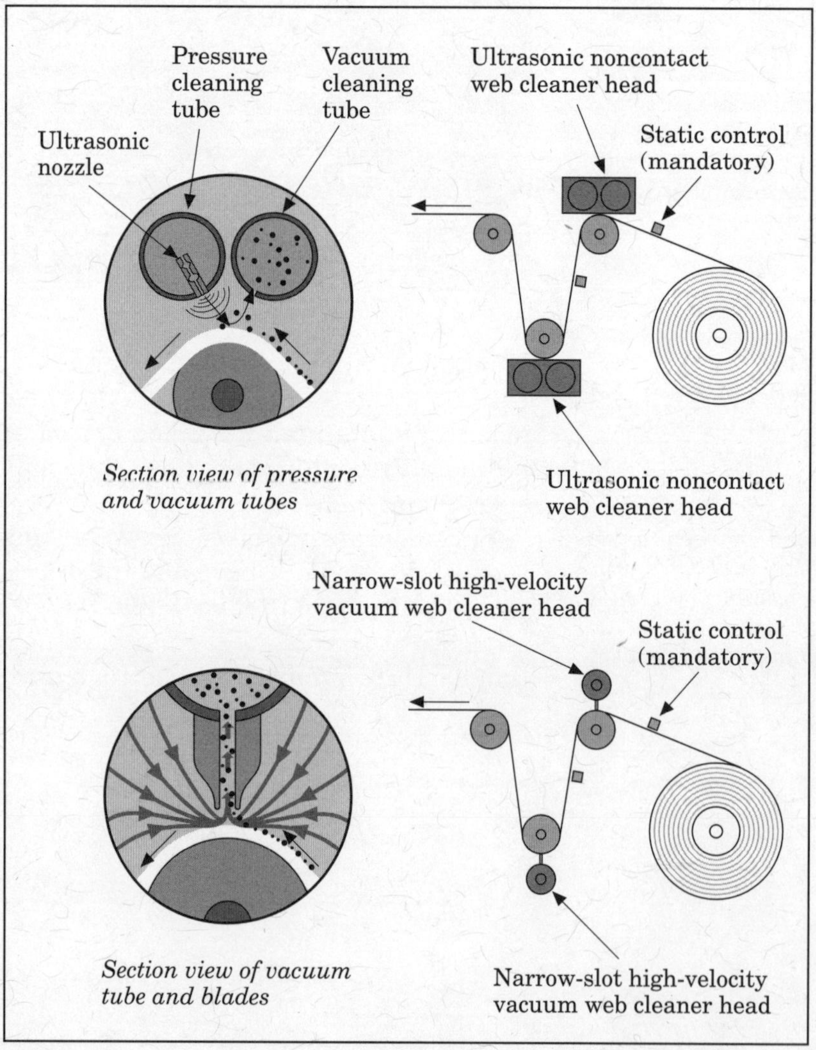

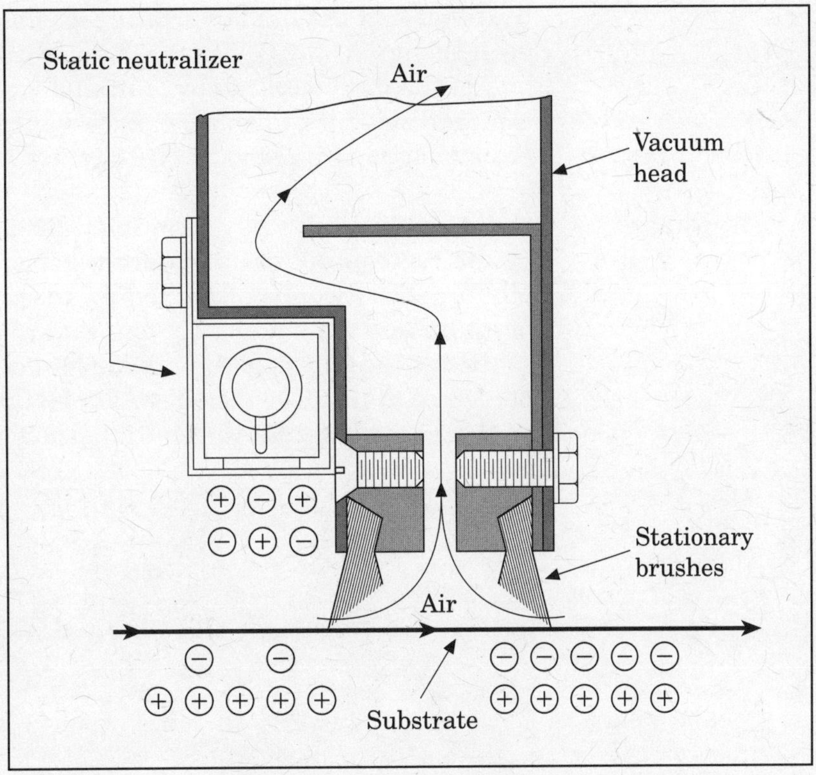

Herbert ION-O-VAC MK I sheet and web cleaning system, which combines high-intensity air ionization, stationary brush action, and high-velocity air flow to achieve surface cleaning
Courtesy Louis P. Batson Co.

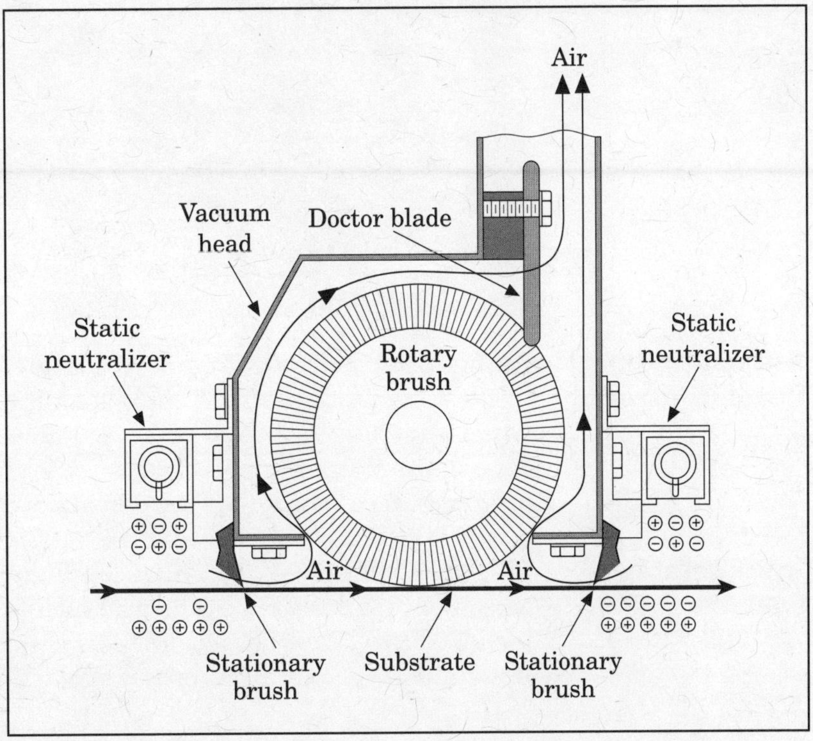

Herbert ION-O-VAC MK IV system for sheet and web cleaning, which combines high-intensity air ionization, high-speed rotary brushing action, and high-velocity air flow to achieve surface cleaning.
Courtesy Louis P. Batson Co.

pick these off the paper surface, creating lint in the press even though a sheet cleaner is in operation. Sheet cleaners and preheaters both remove lint and fuzz; however, sheet cleaners also pick up loose particles of coating from coated stock that can't be burned off.

Ink Agitators

Certain inks back away from the rotating fountain roller. Ink agitators keep ink in the fountain in constant motion, lowering its viscosity, allowing it to flow to the forward part of the fountain and transfer to the fountain roller. The agitator is a cone that extends into the ink mass close to the fountain blade and roller. The cone revolves as the agitator moves back and forth across the width of the fountain.

Conical ink agitator

Automatic Ink Level Controller

An ink level controller is a device that checks the level of the ink in the ink fountain. It signals an ink pump to pump ink when a certain level is reached. Ink level controllers eliminate manual ink replenishment and reduce the waste caused by color variations and print density inconsistencies.

Ink Pumping Systems

When the volume of printing is low, inks may be purchased in cans and manually fed to the press. High-volume web printers usually have large containers (e.g., drums) or reusable tanks from which the standard process colors of ink can be pumped to the press.

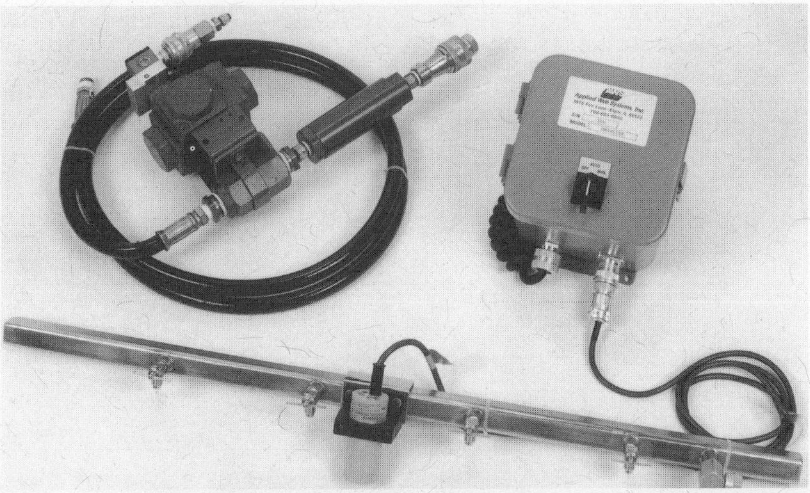

AWS Inkqualizer™ automatic ink level controller
Courtesy Applied Web Systems, Inc.

Pumps for heatset ink pumping system
Courtesy Flint Ink Corporation

With a typical ink pumping system for dispensing ink from drums, the pumps are normally air-operated ram-type pumps with piping going to the gear side of the press and then hoses

An installation of a four-color heatset ink pumping system *Courtesy Flint Ink Corporation*

Pumping system for color inks at the *Baltimore Sun* newspaper *Courtesy US Ink Corporation, a Sun Chemical Company*

to the different printing units. The piping for tank dispensing is the same except that the pumps used in this application are screw-type pumps.

In either case, flow meters can be placed in lines so that readings can be taken at the start of a job and again at the end of the job to determine how much ink was used. Piping can also be designed so that the ink sequence can be changed as dictated by job characteristics.

Water-Cooled Ink Oscillators

When the press is running, inking system temperatures reach as high as 165°F (74°C) or more, sufficient to set some heatset inks on the rollers. For this reason, water-cooled ink oscillators are commonly used on web offset presses. Chilled water circulating through the ink oscillators maintains roller temperatures at a level that will not set the ink. The system should be equipped to heat the inking system to the desired temperature on start-up and then to cool it to maintain that temperature during running.

Some water-cooled oscillators are single-ended, with water inflow and outflow at the same end of the roller. Others are double-ended, with the water inflow at one end and outflow at the other. Double-ended oscillators cool more uniformly across their width.

Water-cooled inking system

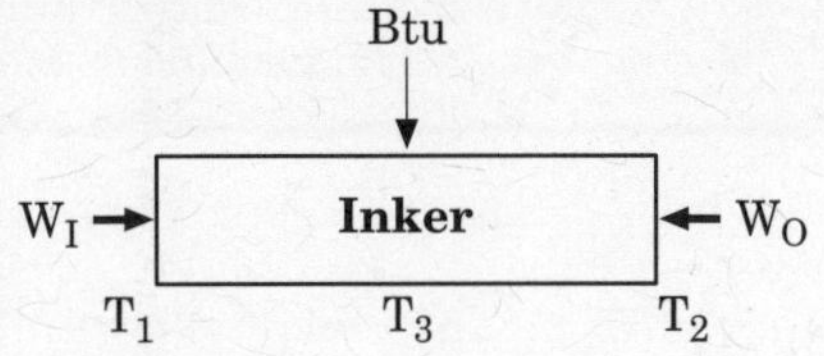

$$W_O = W_I + \frac{\text{Btu/min}}{k}$$

$$\text{Avg. Temp.} = \frac{W_I + W_O}{2}$$

	Btu/min	k	W_I	W_O	Avg. Temp.
Thermostat at T_1	100	5	65°F	85°F	75°F
	200	5	65	105	85
	300	5	65	125	95
Thermostat at T_2	100	5	85	105	95
	200	5	65	105	85
	300	5	45	105	75
Thermostat at T_3	100	5	75	95	85
	200	5	65	105	85
	300	5	55	115	85

Fountain Solution Recirculation Systems

Fountain solution recirculation systems pump solution into each fountain pan from one or more central tanks. These systems allow all fountains to be serviced from a single point, and they should filter the solution to remove solids that may impair print quality. Some systems have a refrigeration unit

Properly designed inking temperature control system

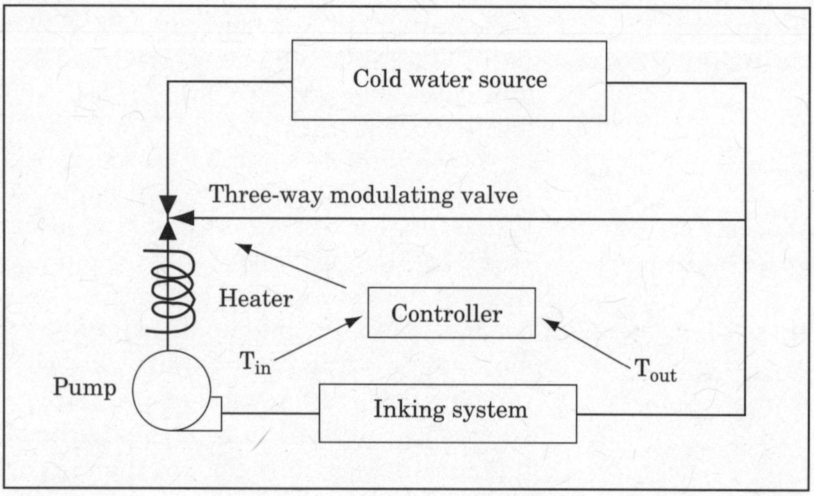

to keep the solution cool, in order to minimize changes. This is an especially valuable feature in dampening systems running alcohol, because alcohol evaporates at a lower rate when chilled. This reduces alcohol use and saves money.

Fountain solution recirculation system *(left)* with a unit to control alcohol content *Courtesy Baldwin Dampening Systems*

The hydrometric float measures the specific gravity of the solution and adds alcohol as needed. Solution constantly circulates through both systems.

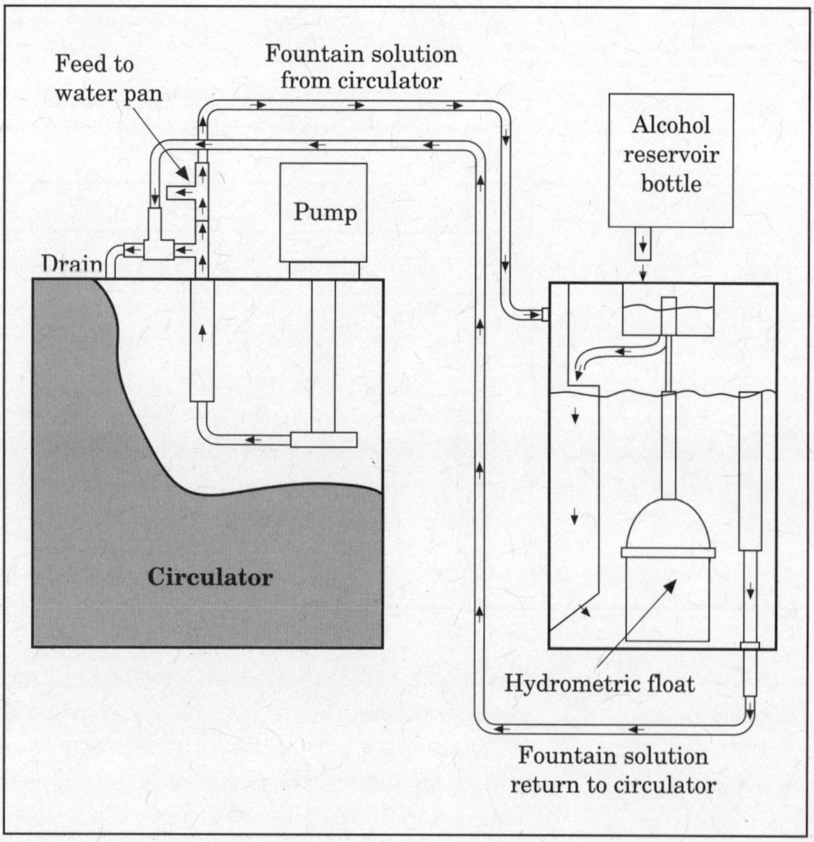

Fountain Solution Mixers

Automatic fountain solution mixing devices are often incorporated into recirculation systems. The units mix in small quantities, constantly adding fresh solution and maintaining greater uniformity.

Solution control devices are also especially useful if alcohol is being used. Controls are available that can maintain alcohol content to within ±1% by monitoring the specific gravity of the solution and adding alcohol as required.

Refrigerating Fountain Solutions

The concept of cooling fountain solution is by no means a new one. The advent of continuous dampening systems in the late 1960s significantly increased the demand for refrigerated lithographic dampening systems.

Uni-Flow™ fountain chemistry and temperature control system with AccuFeed™ fluid metering
Courtesy Applied Web Systems, Inc.

Continuous dampening systems require temperature control much more than conventional systems, because the continuous system includes a metering nip in which performance is proportional to the viscosity of the dampening fluid. Viscosity is highly sensitive to temperature. For this reason, variations in the temperature of the dampening solution produce variations in viscosity, which result in variations in metered film thickness.

The use of refrigeration offers a second benefit in that the temperature of the dampening system is held constant. This can prevent problems that could affect the quality of a job. If enough cooling capacity is available, the fountain solution can be run quite cold, as low as 40°F (4°C). With systems running alcohol, this can mean a reduction in alcohol consumption of as much as 50%. However, running cool benefits any dampening system, because chemical actions or changes occur more slowly at lower temperatures.

The effect of temperature on the viscosity of water

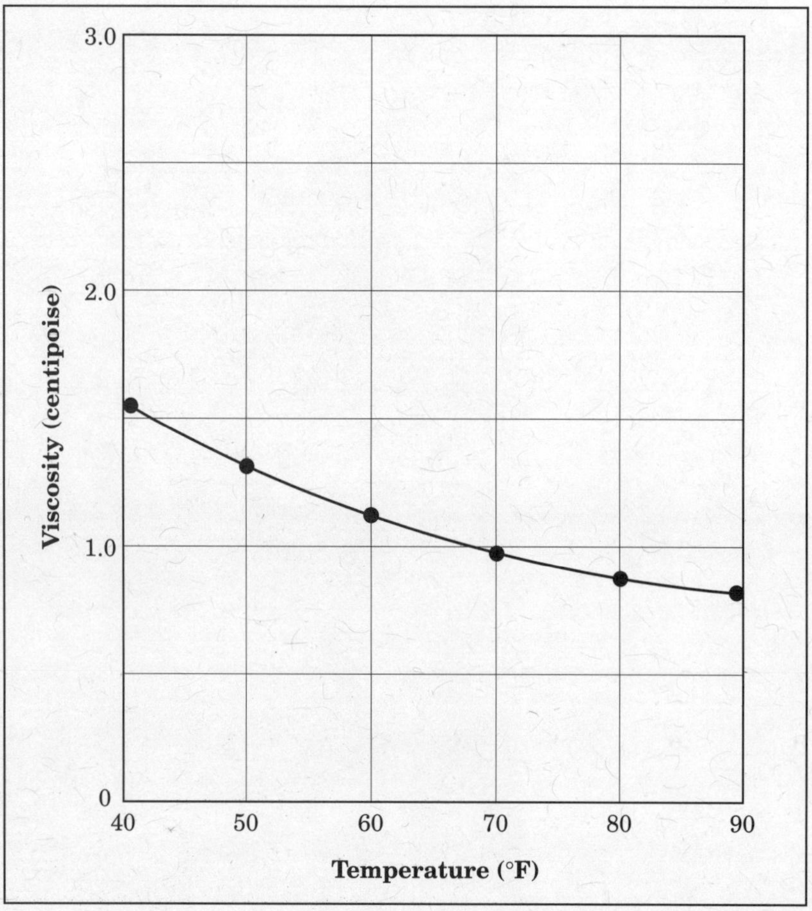

Automatic Blanket Washers

A blanket wash should follow all but the shortest of press stops. Automatic blanket washers perform these washes quickly and effectively. One type of washer consists of a row of nozzles, mounted over the blanket, from which solvent is sprayed onto the rubber surface. Solvent and loosened material are carried off by the web. Blanket washers do not effectively remove certain paper coating buildup; however, they can retard buildup if used during each paster cycle. (Note: The solvent used in automatic blanket washers must be compatible with the blankets and with the blanket washer itself.)

An inherent danger of some blanket washers is that solvent vapors tend to follow the web into the dryer. Flame

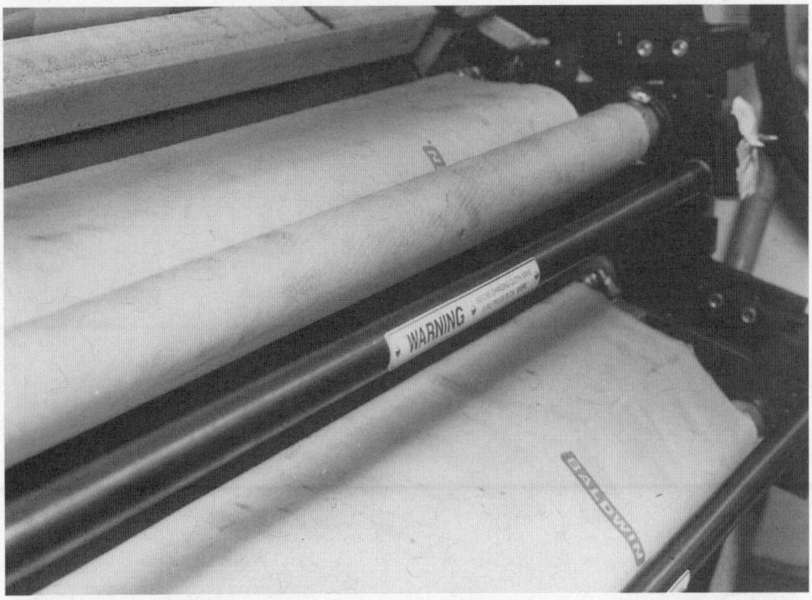

Automatic blanket washer installed on a web offset press
Courtesy Baldwin Graphic Products

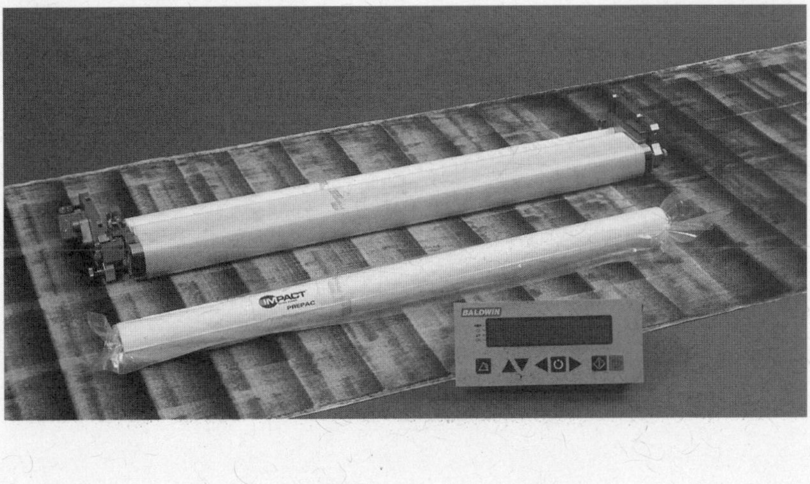

IMPACT™ automatic blanket cleaner and press cylinder cleaner
Courtesy Baldwin Graphic Products

dryers with line burners located near the entrance to the dryer burn off the solvent vapors. Solvent vapors can, however, accumulate in high-velocity hot-air dryers and possibly explode. Alternatively, solvent may be sprayed onto a separate web of material that rubs against the surface of the blanket. Blanket washing systems like this successfully remove piling on the blanket and provide the added advantage of reducing solvent deposits.

Side-lay Sensors

Web side-lay sensors detect minute lateral web movement and signal steering devices to adjust the paper's position. One automatic side-lay device is a U-shaped apparatus with the web moving through the space between the two arms. One arm houses a light source and the other a photoelectric sensor cell, or eye. As the web passes through, the light to the cell is partly blocked. The strength of the signal from the

A typical sensing device for automatic sidelay control

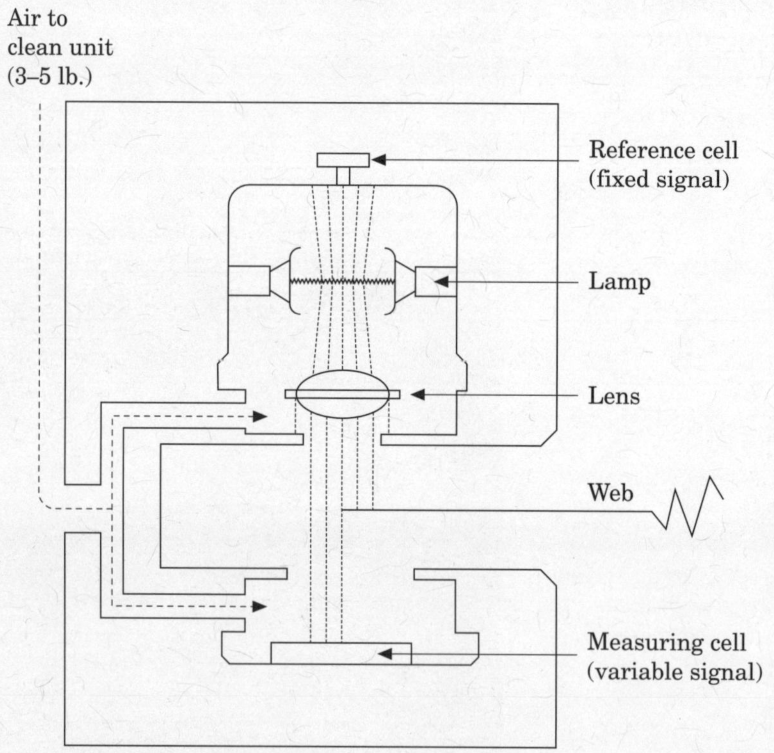

The position of the web is monitored by electronically comparing the fixed signal with the variable signal. The result is used to control a box tilt or other web steering device. The pressurized air keeps lens and measuring cell free of dust and airborne dirt.

photocell unit varies directly with the amount of light reaching the cell, which is in turn determined by the position of the web edge across the face of the cell. The strength of the signal determines the amount that the web steering device (box tilt, cocking roller, etc.) corrects the web's position.

Center-guiding positions the web center relative to the press and folder. It is accomplished by mounting side-lay sensors in pairs at each station on the press where guiding is necessary. Center-guiding complements folder operations. Edge-guiding, on the other hand, holds only one edge of the web fixed relative to the press and folder. The guiding device monitors the edge of the web that is used to register later operations. A web guide should be located in the infeed in order to center the printing on the web. A second web guide between the press and folder keeps the fold in the center of the web.

Web Break Detectors

Web break detectors are devices that mechanically, electronically, or pneumatically detect a break in a web of paper, subsequently stopping the press. The original design of web break detector consists of a mechanical roller or finger that rides against the moving web. In the absence of paper, the roller or finger changes position and activates a photoelectric

Electronic web break detector

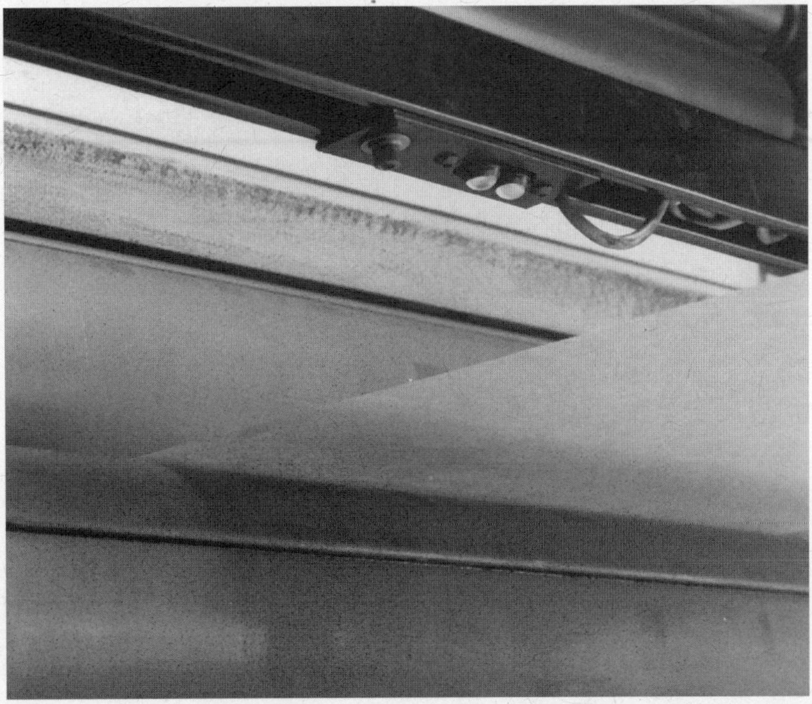

eye. The web prevents light from reaching the eye; otherwise, the press would be stopped. Another web break detector operates pneumatically. A jet of air is blown at the web. On the other side of the web is a pressure-sensitive switch that is activated when the air jet strikes it.

Many web break detectors are not fail-safe. For example, a system that consists of a signal source (light) on one side of the web and a receiver (photocell) on the other side employs the web to *prevent* the completion of a circuit. Should the light source or photocell fail, the system will not shut itself down because it cannot respond. One detector system that eliminates this problem has the light source and photocell mounted on the same side of the web. The light from the source strikes the web at an angle and reflects into the photocell. The web *maintains* the circuit. The press continues running only if the circuit is complete, which requires the presence of the web plus a properly functioning signal source plus a properly functioning receiver.

A strip rewind, although uncommon, is a particularly dangerous form of web break. With a strip rewind, only a portion of the full width of the web is coming from the press. The missing portion of the web is wrapped up on one of the blankets. A strip rewind often starts as a tear on one side of the web but does not cause the entire web to break. If for any reason web break detectors are not monitoring the edge of the web that is missing, the break detection system will not sense the problem. Unless the press is stopped manually, the paper will accumulate on the blanket and damage the blanket and printing unit. This illustrates an important concept of web break detectors: they should always be mounted so that they protect or monitor both edges of the web.

Web break detectors should be mounted in pairs at each appropriate point along the press, one detector at each side of the web. They should be set no more than 3–4 in. (75–100 mm) inside the edges of the web, and when web widths change, their proper placement should be a routine part of makeready.

Many detector systems also incorporate web severing devices that immediately cut off the web on signal of a web break. These prevent excessive paper from wrapping up in a printing unit — a particularly useful feature on large, fast presses with a relatively long stopping time.

Mechanical web break detectors also sense any decrease in tension. The tail end of the break need not run under the

Web anti-wrap system, which is installed between the last printing unit and the dryer to prevent web wrap-ups on the blankets of the last printing unit in the event of a web break
Courtesy Baldwin Web Controls

web break detector before it senses the break. For this reason they are effective when mounted in long spans of web such as those that are generated when more than one web is run through the press.

Infrared web break detectors are easy to mount on the press, since they are insensitive to printed ink and can be mounted several inches from the web. Because they use solid-state devices as the source of the infrared beam, they perform dependably.

Remoisturizers

Dryers remove moisture from the web. Overdried paper becomes dimensionally unstable; that is, it tends to increase in size across the grain when it reabsorbs moisture. The paper also tends to accumulate sizable charges of static electricity. The best way to minimize both of these problems is to replace the moisture removed from the web during drying.

Dimensional instability can be devastating if the expansion of the sheets due to reabsorption of moisture takes place after binding and trimming. Because of the binding confinement, the expansion of sheets can create wavy edges that render the finished product worthless. A more common problem is created by uneven growth of different signatures in a heatset product, such as a magazine, after it is trimmed. If the grain of the paper parallels the backbone of the sheet, an uneven edge forms along the front of the magazine. The second problem of static electricity is not so apparent on the press unless the product is being sheeted. It does, however, make signatures more difficult to handle in the bindery operation and increases bindery waste considerably.

In any heatset operation, the web should be remoisturized. This is accomplished by physically applying moisture to the surface of the web after it is chilled. The illustration below shows a system in which chrome rollers run in the water pans, contacting the web. The units can be run individually or in pairs — one for each side of the web.

Roll applicator system to apply moisture to the web

A mixture of silicone and water is sometimes applied to the web just after it leaves the chill rolls, before reaching the folder. Silicone (in a water-based solution) is used to help prevent marking by giving the web a more friction-free surface.

Coaters

Methods of applying coatings economically and effectively have developed rapidly. Coatings can be formulated with a variety of characteristics, including high gloss, rub resistance, and oil and moisture resistance. It is not uncommon to print and apply coatings in-line.

The use of in-line coating application methods is growing for all major printing processes as a direct result of their need to reduce spoilage and the cost of materials handling, to speed production, and to increase the overall efficiency of their operations. Better control over the process and faster turnaround

In-line web coater that can apply water-based, solvent-based, catalytic, or UV coating over wet ink
Courtesy Epic Products International Corp.

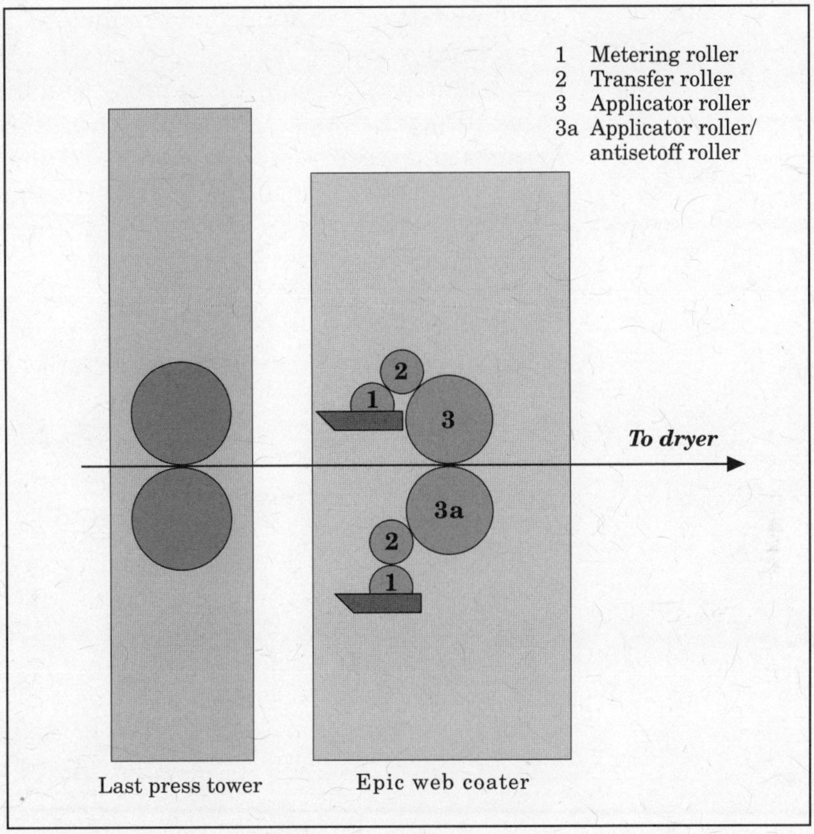

Three-roll system for coating or remoisturizing the web
Courtesy Dahlgren USA, Inc.

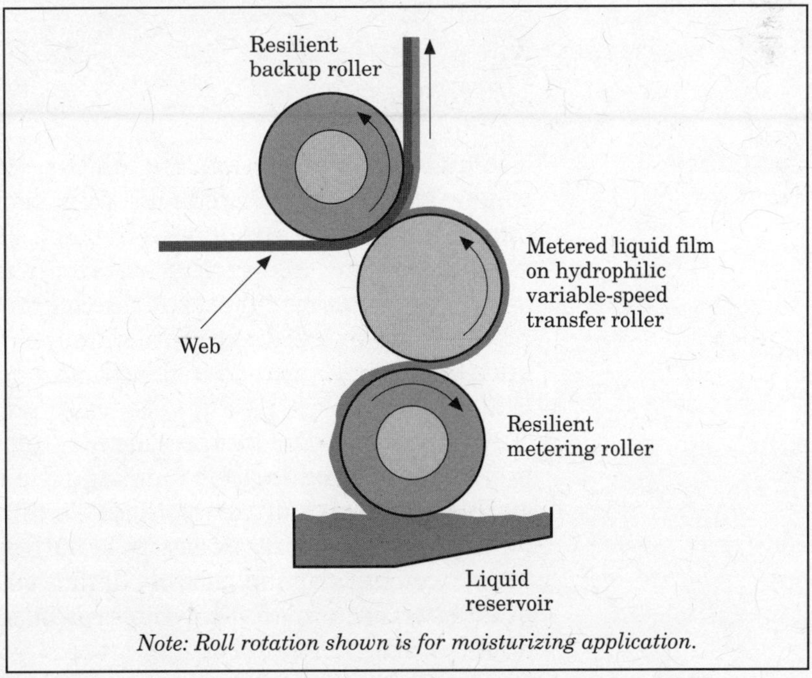

of finished goods are two additional advantages to coating substrates in-line.

In-line coaters apply a variety of coatings, including water-based, solvent-based, catalytic, or ultraviolet (UV) on all types of paper.

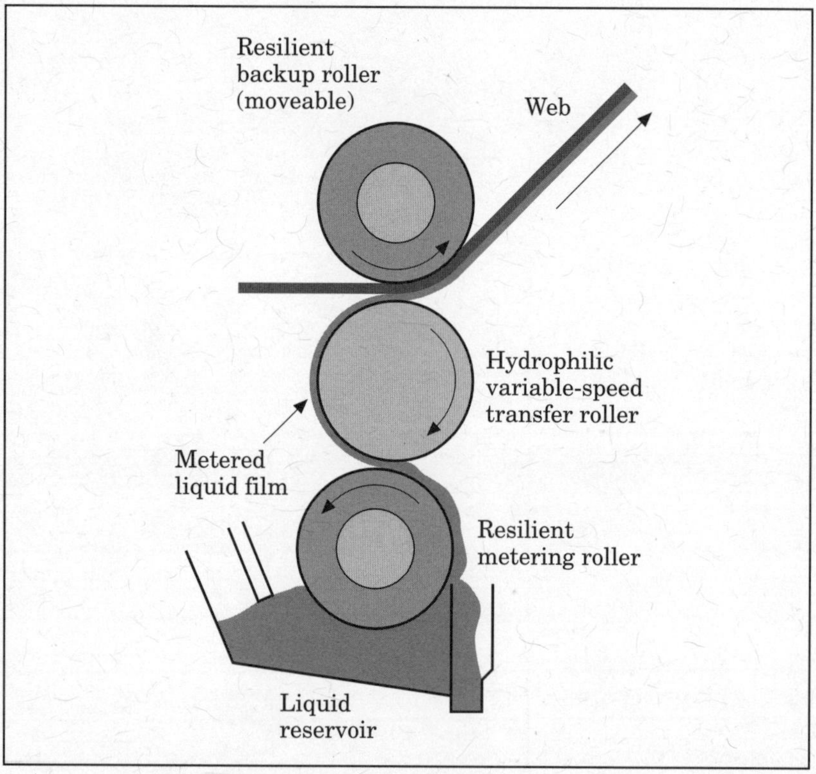

A three-roll compact coater
Courtesy Dahlgren USA, Inc.

Antistatic Devices

The buildup of static electricity in the running web sometimes causes reduced press productivity, especially in sheeting operations. As the running web meets and then separates from rollers and turning bars on the press, it picks up free electrons from these metal surfaces and acquires an electrostatic charge. In a charged web, forces of repulsion that exist between the signatures or sheets cut off a web can reduce control.

All antistatic devices turn the air immediately adjacent to the web into a conductor by ionizing the air. Antistatic devices employ electricity, ultraviolet light, and even weak radioactive fields to neutralize static charges. Devices employing radioactive elements are potentially dangerous, and their emissions must be monitored. Fabric softeners added to the silicone roll applicators also help to reduce static.

Imprinters

Imprinters are often found on presses running jobs where a small amount of copy is going to vary during the run. An example is a catalog prepared for different retailers, requiring a change in name and address for each retailer's catalogs. During the run, names and addresses can be printed on the catalogs by an imprinter that is separate from the main printing units, saving camera, stripping, and platemaking costs on each run. The imprinter is usually a flexographic unit with a rubber letterpress plate, an impression cylinder, and a simple inking system. Imprinters often carry two plate cylinders, so that one form is running while the other is being made ready, allowing for a rapid changeover.

An imprinting unit that carries two plate cylinders on which rubber plates are mounted

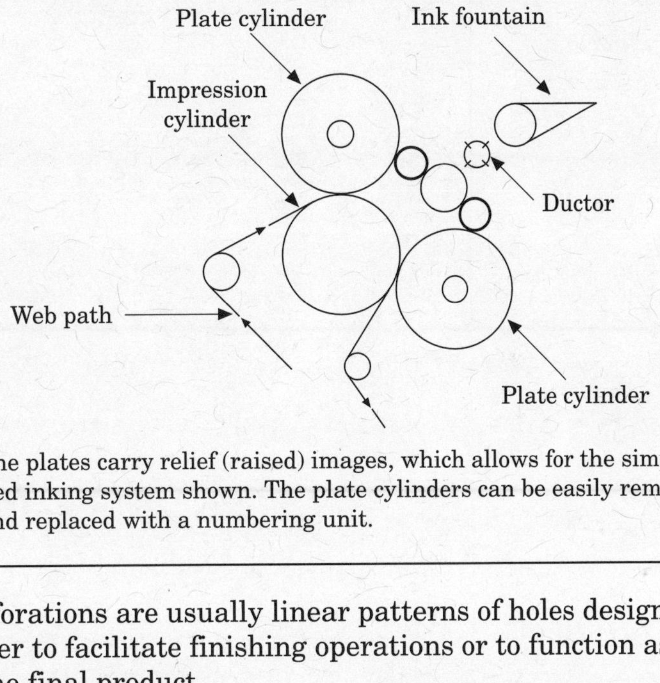

The plates carry relief (raised) images, which allows for the simplified inking system shown. The plate cylinders can be easily removed and replaced with a numbering unit.

Perforators

Perforations are usually linear patterns of holes designed either to facilitate finishing operations or to function as part of the final product.

The simplest perforating mechanism is a wheel, mounted against the roller-top-of-former. This roller perforates parallel to the former fold. On some presses, perforating across the web width is possible using a set of perforating cylinders mounted below the folder nip rollers. One cylinder carries the perforating teeth and the other a female die.

A common problem that can be corrected by perforating is the gusset wrinkle. A gusset wrinkle forms on the inside pages of a closed-head signature at the corner where the backbone fold meets the head fold. Gusseting occurs because

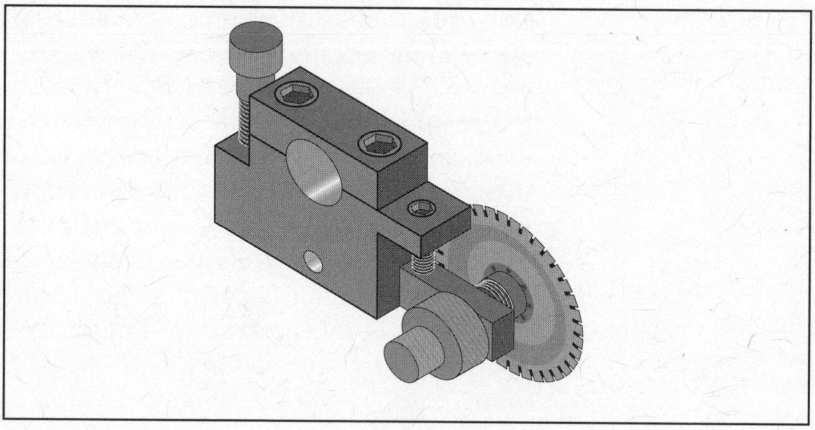

Perforating wheel in an adjustable perforating and slitting wheel holder
Courtesy RTE

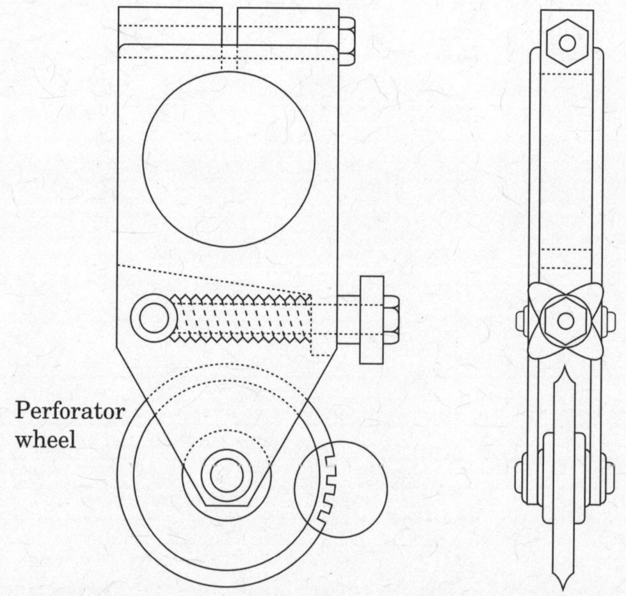

Circumferential perforators
Courtesy Heidelberg Harris, Inc.

The simplest means of perforating the web lengthwise is through perforator wheels mounted over the roller-top-of-former. Some press operators all but completely slit the web by using a slitter wheel with only a 1/8-in. (3-mm) nick taken off the edge.

the outside pages and the inside pages of such a signature are subjected to opposite stresses. When several thicknesses of paper are folded together, the outside pages of the resulting signature tend to pull back because the bend that they make has a much larger radius than that of the bend made by the inside sheets. The small-radius bend tends to push the inside sheets out at the lip of the signature. A folded signature is shown at the left in the illustration below. When the book is opened, the outside and inside pages are attached at the head of the signature. On the right, the diagram shows why the problem occurs at the place where the backbone and head folds meet: inside sheets are trying to move away from the backbone because of the geometry of the fold, but they are restrained because of their connection with outside sheets across the head of the signature.

The tendency of the inside sheets to be pushed out at the lip of the signature

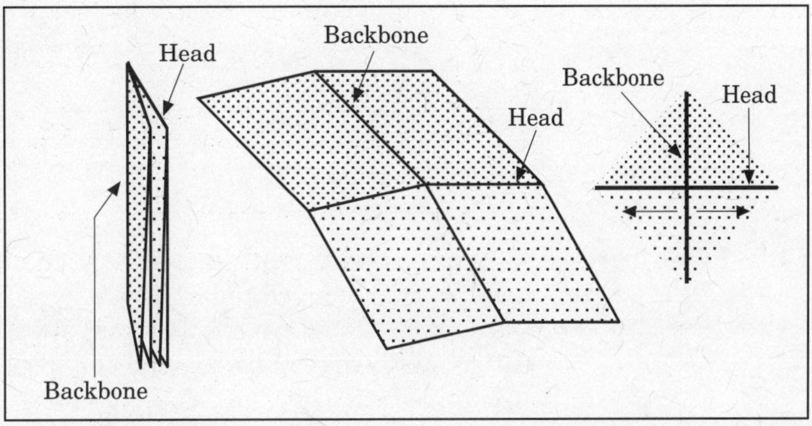

As explained previously, simple perforating along the head of the signature may relieve the strain to the point where the gusset wrinkle is no longer a problem. If, however, because of the number of sheets or the bulk of the paper, gusseting remains a problem, it can be relieved by diagonal perforation. Because of the pattern, this perforation is diecut by a hardened steel cutting head and a female die mounted in two cylinders across the backbone of the signature. The slant of the perforations readily allows movement of the inside sheets away from the backbone; therefore, the stresses that create the gusset wrinkle are eliminated.

None of the perforating techniques previously listed easily adapts to the varying patterns encountered in perforating for a tear-out. For this purpose, a steel perforating rule can be glued to one of the blanket cylinders in the proper pattern and positioned for the required perforation.

Because the unit used for perforation cannot also be used to print, most printers who perforate many jobs have separate perforating units that are mounted in the folder. These cross-perforating units have a perforating cylinder and an impression, or back, cylinder and are readily adaptable to perform various perforations.

Diagonal perforations to relieve gusset wrinkles

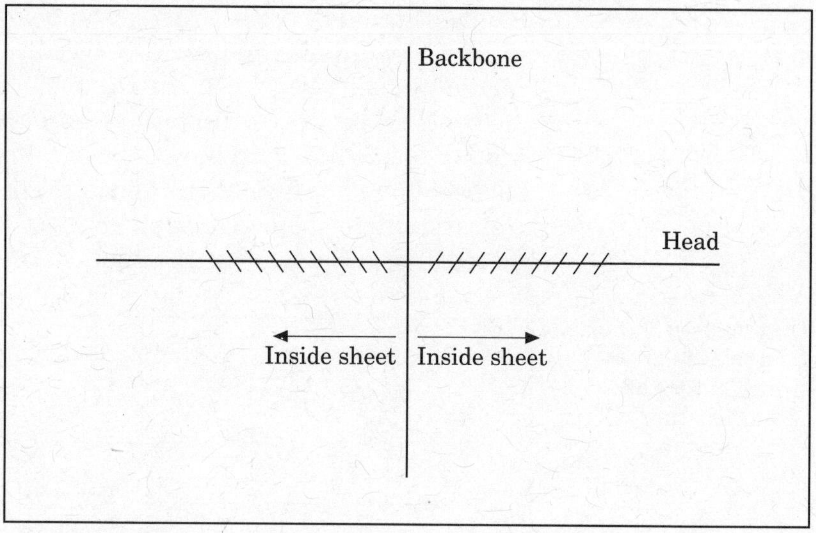

Cutoff Controls

Automatic cutoff controls precisely divide the web into signatures so that the printed images are consistently positioned. Without cutoff controls, colors may fit exactly; however, the entire image may move around the page from signature to signature because of variation in cutoff. Conventional systems can maintain cutoff within a tolerance of $\pm\frac{1}{32}$–$\frac{1}{16}$ in. (0.8–1.6 mm). Automatic controls have reduced the variation to $\pm\frac{1}{64}$ in. (0.4 mm) or less.

In an automatic cutoff system, an electric eye is set to detect a specific area of the printed form. This eye is mounted somewhere between the cutoff compensator and the cutoff knives. The control accurately measures the interval between the signal from the eye, as detected on each succeeding impression, and a signal generated by the press.

The control is connected to the compensator. If the signal from the web is received before or after the signal from the press, the web lead is increased or decreased (by moving the compensator) until the signals coincide and the web and folder are in time with each other. Proportional control should be built into these systems. Monitoring a large area of the printed form permits precise adjustment to maintain image position.

As explained in the chapter on image and web control, there is a cutoff system that does not require any compensator. In this system, positive control of web movement is maintained from the time it leaves the press until the time that it is cut off in the folder, and variations in register are eliminated.

11 Web Tension

Paper is drawn through a web offset press, creating a force known as web tension. The press operator controls the conditions under which the paper is drawn through the press. The web needs to be in a specific position relative to the blankets as it passes from unit to unit. Uniform tension and accurate lateral control must be maintained to achieve and hold register. The press operator adjusts press settings to print within close tolerances and to overcome external forces — such as blanket pull — that continuously act upon the web.

Paper characteristics greatly complicate controllability. Applying even minimal force to paper changes it dimensionally, and the change is not constant for a given paper or within a specific roll. The erratic behavior of paper under stress often results in inconsistencies in the finished product — inconsistencies due to variation in unit-to-unit register, side-lay, cutoff, and folding accuracy. Thus, the fundamental problem in web printing is controlling paper behavior through the press. The press operator, or press action such as drying and chilling, can modify web tension at various points on the press. The distances between successive points of tension are referred to as *tension spans*. Ideally, tension is uniform throughout each of these spans.

Tension-control devices act on the web in one of two ways:

- Constant-torque devices directly apply an unchanging force to the web, like the weight of the dancer roller.
- Variable-speed devices control the flow rate of the web.

Web Control Factors

Web control involves three major factors: tension, length, and the modulus of elasticity of the web. All three factors are fundamentally interrelated. A change in any one of the three must result in a change in at least one of the remaining two. Several considerations are involved:

Surface speed. When used in connection with web control, *speed* always refers to *surface speed.* As for the web itself, the distinction makes little difference: the surface speed of the web *is* web speed.

Surface speeds of the driven rollers and cylinders on the press determine web speed, which varies slightly due to slip. Nondriven idlers and angle bars only guide the web. To change the effective surface speed of driven rollers and cylinders, increase (or decrease) their circumference. Adding packing to a blanket cylinder increases its effective surface speed. Taping a chill roll to prevent wrinkling may increase its effective surface speed.

Nips between driven rollers and cylinders can greatly affect surface speeds. Hard rollers negligibly affect surface speed; surface speed at steel-to-steel nips is highly stable. Rubber compresses under nip pressures and squeezes through a nip at a faster rate than the average surface speed of a cylinder or roller. Effective surface speed of a rubber roller varies as it passes through a nip. These surface speed variations unpredictably affect web surface speed through the nip. This particular feature of nips involving one or more rubber surfaces is often encountered in the rubber-to-steel nips of some infeed metering devices and in the blanket-to-blanket printing nips.

Draw. Across a span with a nip at each end, tension can be varied by changing the surface speed of the web at either nip. The resulting difference in surface speed is called *draw* and is positive when the surface speed at the second nip is higher than at the first. Positive draw applies force to the web and increases tension. A decrease in speed at the infeed nip or an increase in speed at the output nip increases the draw and tension. An increase at the infeed nip or a decrease at the output nip reduces draw and tension.

If effective surface speed of the paper through both nips is the same, and the elastic properties of the paper do not change, tension in the span remains the same as it was in the previous span.

Slip. Web speed through a nip differs from the surface speed of the rotating rollers. Slip between the web and roller surfaces slightly slows the paper.

Slip commonly occurs at many points on the press; therefore, controlling the web is difficult. At the chill rolls, for instance, the traction between the web and the roll surface controls web speed. This traction is the result of friction. As long as there is no slip, stationary or static friction stabilizes web speed at the surface speed of the rollers. When slip occurs at the chill rolls, *kinetic* (moving) friction reduces traction; tension changes in an unpredictable manner.

Paper. Surface speed, draw, and slip are the mechanical, press-related factors that influence tension. Paper changes also effect tension changes.

As a viscoelastic material, paper reacts to pull (tension) by elongating in two different ways. Like a rubber band, paper stretches under applied force and recovers most of its original dimensions when the force is removed. Some of the change is permanent and nonrecoverable. (The recoverable elongation is referred to as *stretch,* and the nonrecoverable change is referred to as *plastic flow.)* This reduces tension control, especially in the earlier spans in the press. A series of roller-to-roller spans in the infeed create a relatively long distance between the roll and the first printing unit, more adequately conditioning the paper for printing. Higher tension in this area enhances conditioning, so that a *flat* web is delivered into the first printing unit.

Modulus of elasticity. Paper stretches relative to the amount of force acting upon it. The relationship between force and (elastic) stretch of paper is known as the *modulus of elasticity.* The modulus of elasticity depends on the paper's composition. When a paper's chemical and physical structure changes, the modulus changes and so does the paper's reaction to tension.

Bulk weight, fiber length, fiber composition, filler material, and moisture content, among other factors, all affect the modulus of elasticity. Because most of these factors can vary during the papermaking process, some variation in modulus can be expected in the roll. Devices that adjust these variations in the roll must therefore be built into the press.

Variations in modulus due to on-press processing stem from changes in the web's moisture content. Processing in the dryer radically changes the web's moisture content. Moisture picked up from the fountain solution similarly affects the web.

Varying web tension or flow rate are the means by which variations in modulus are controlled. When the modulus

Modulus of Elasticity

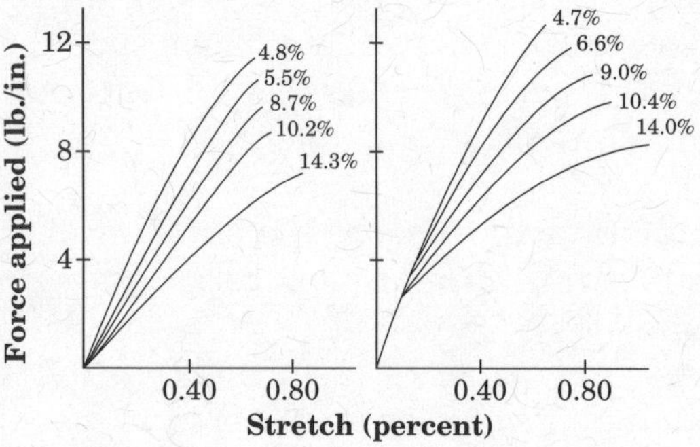

The slopes in the above diagrams represent the modulus of elasticity for different newsprint stocks. The percentage figures indicate moisture content. Both diagrams show that higher moisture content gives a lower modulus of elasticity (greater stretchability).

The diagrams below and at right show the results of two tests, each involving two different web offset papers (A and B). Each of the two papers were manufactured at three moisture contents (4%, 5%, and 6%). The tests were conducted in two plants, on two presses, by two different crews.

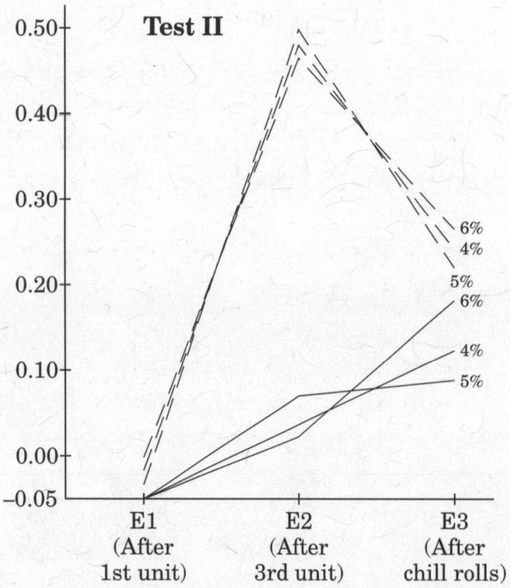

This conclusion, in turn, suggests that, *overall,* on-press influences such as press speed, variable speed settings, press water, and dryer temperature are more important in determining stretch behavior than is paper moisture content. A measure of the effect of press conditions on web behavior can be seen by comparing the readings at E1 for both tests. In Test I, all six webs gained in length between 0.10% and 0.13%. In Test II, five of the six webs actually shortened in length, from 0.02% to 0.04%. This latter effect is probably caused by the relatively high infeed tension on the presses used in Test II.

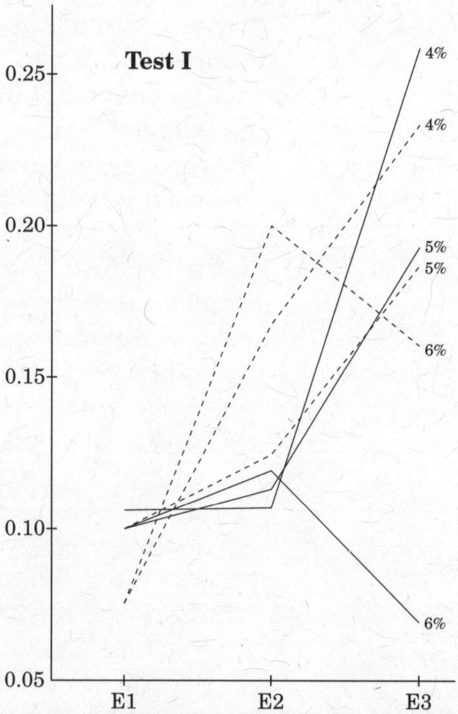

Although moisture content varied only 2% (and not the 10% shown in the newsprint diagrams), one might expect relatively consistent stretch behavior. Actually, the tests showed the paper behaved differently on the two presses. Both paper A and paper B reacted about the same to the conditions that existed during Test I. Under the different conditions of Test II, however, the two papers show no similarity in behavior. The two tests suggest that modulus of elasticity determines stretch behavior only in some cases, and, furthermore, that these cases cannot be predicted beforehand.

The effect on paper of repeated stretching
Adapted from TAGA Proceedings

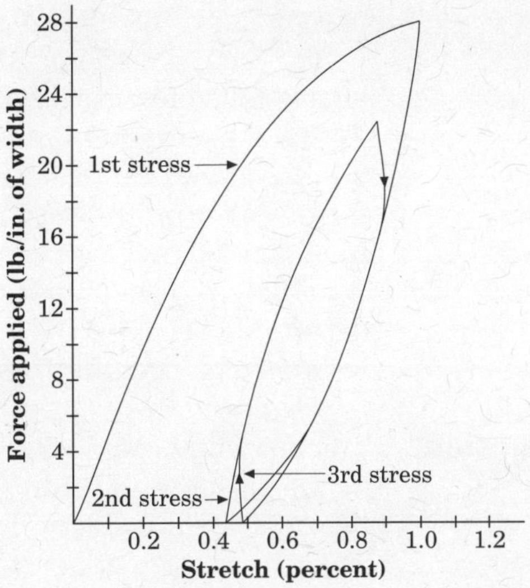

The paper was subjected to about 28 lb./in. tension, then allowed to relax. Permanent stretch was at about 0.45% of the paper's original length. When the paper was placed under tension a second time, permanent stretch increased by 0.05%. Although tension levels in this experiment are probably much higher than normal press tensions, repeated stressing on press probably produces similar results with the greatest permanent stretch at the first application of tension. The amount of permanent stretch does not change much after the second stressing, and the amount of elastic recovery is almost the same.

changes and tension is to be held constant, the flow rate must be varied. This is the function of the dancer roll and brake system. When modulus changes and the flow rate must be held constant, tension changes as the modulus changes. This occurs in the printing units.

Dryer. One point on the press where the modulus can be expected to change significantly is in the dryer. Moisture is driven out of the web and as a result the paper becomes less elastic. The same amount of tension produces less stretch in the paper after it leaves the dryer.

Paper also shrinks in the dryer. As water molecules leave the web, the fibers draw closer together and increase tension. It is not unusual for the chill rolls to run at the same speed as the last printing unit, and for all tension in this span to be supplied by paper shrinkage in the dryer.

Measuring Tension

On a press with positive (no-slip) nips, tension variations propagate in the direction of web travel only.

Slip occurs at the printing nips and the chill rolls, which allows tension variations to have some upstream effect. Actual measurement on blanket-to-blanket web offset presses shows that relatively small tension variations in the infeed carry all the way through to the folder. On the other hand, on a four-unit press, fairly large tension changes in the span between the fourth unit and the chill rolls are rarely detectable between the second and third unit and never between the first and second unit.

Setting Tensions on the Press

The foregoing provides the necessary information for arriving at the optimum tension-setting method on a web press. The needs of the infeed and press sections should be met first. Then the dryer-chill section should be balanced, and finally the delivery section. If difficulty is encountered in the last adjustment (matching the needs of the folder to the output of the press), it is common practice to go back to the infeed and attempt to change the output of the press to match the requirements of the folder. Assuming that the initial infeed settings were correct, the readjusted settings provide less than optimum performance. Control problems can be expected to continue throughout the run.

If this is commonly experienced, consider changing the folder to match press output. This can be done by changing the diameters of the nipping rollers that control web flow into the folder. An alternative method is to change press output to match folder needs by changing the blanket cylinder packing. Changes in blanket packing should be accompanied by equal and opposite changes in plate packing.

Paper Behavior on Press

Rolls of paper are wound at the mill under tension several times greater than is generated by the press. Thus, paper usually undergoes considerable elastic recovery in the infeed and perhaps beyond, in the printing units. This process necessitates long web leads (festooning) in the infeed. A long lead gives the paper more time to recover fully before it reaches the printing units, where significant elastic recovery may cause register problems.

Variations in winding tension at the mill, variations in the paper's basis weight, and rolls that are out of round or tapered produce tension variations in the roll as it unwinds. These variations can travel downstream and affect tension

The common "pyramid" infeed metering system

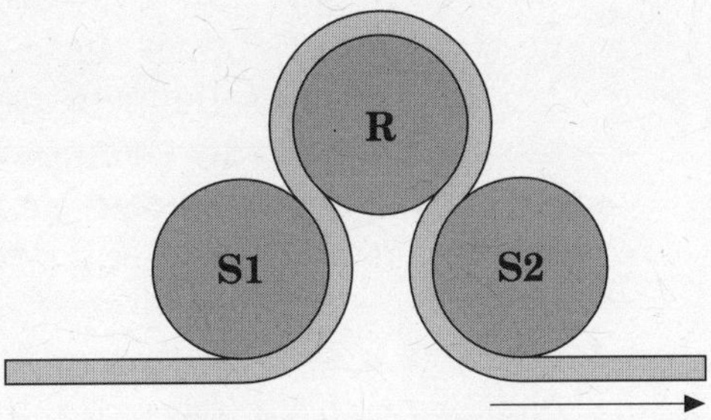

With this infeed metering system, there are two steel driven rollers (S1 and S2) and one rubber idler roller (R). The paper partially wraps the two steel rollers and almost completely wraps the rubber idler. Measurements show that the web can slip constantly on the steel rollers, because the web tracks the rubber roller (greater contact and more friction) rather than the steel rollers and because the surface speed of the free rubber roller is different than its surface speed in the nips where it is driven. Thus, the actual speed of the web is controlled by the composition of the rubber roller, the amount of pressure between it and the two steel rollers, and by the setting of the variable-speed units that drive the infeed.

The effects on web tension of various ink/water conditions set up on a four-unit press

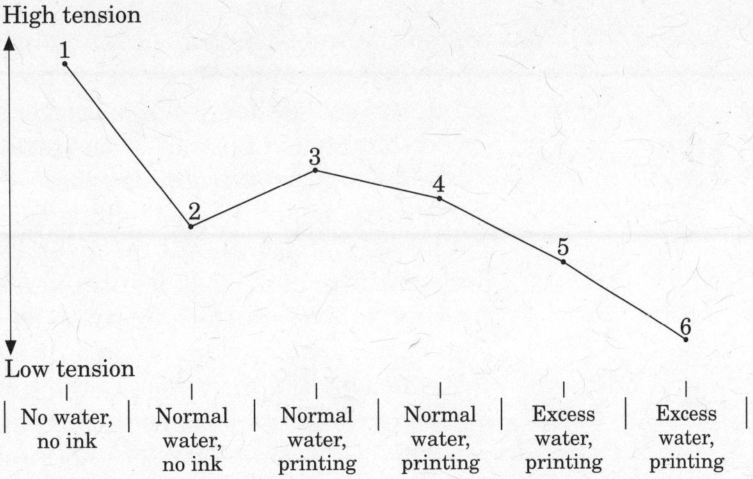

Although only a limited number of tests were conducted, they confirm the observation that press water reduces tension. Highest tension was recorded with no water and no ink being run (1) and was followed by the sharpest drop with water run and no ink (2), a condition in which maximum water would reach the paper. Tension increased at prints 3 and 4, probably due to water pickup by the ink, which reduced the amount of water reaching the paper. Running excess water when printing (5, 6) also tended to significantly decrease tension.

throughout the press, all the way to cutoff. It is the job of the dancer roller to offset these variations in the infeed; however, no dancer maintains perfectly constant tension. A tension change can pass by the dancer before it has time to react. Also, the effective weight of the conventional dancer changes through acceleration and deceleration, either as it rotates on its spindle or as it changes speed vertically. A change in effective weight is invariably accomplished by a change in dancer position; therefore, tension from the roll is adjusted to the momentary change in effective weight.

The infeed metering rollers must run slower than the blanket cylinders of the press. The web runs from infeed metering to the first printing unit under high tension, the object being to produce a taut, flat surface as the web enters the first unit.

The infeed metering rollers comprise one of the most important tension control points on the press. The rubber idler at the metering rollers offers some slip resistance, rubber giving better traction than steel. Slip at infeed metering is usually between the web and the steel rollers and not between the web and the rubber rollers.

The printing units exert the strongest, most positive control on the web. The rubber blankets provide good traction, which is assisted by pressure in the printing nips. The printing units can be thought of as establishing the nominal web speed from which tension is set throughout the press.

More slippage will occur on an in-line nonperfecting web press than on a blanket-to-blanket web press.

The tension established between infeed metering and the first unit is usually reduced through succeeding units by several forces. Press water picked up by the web increases the paper's expansion, which reduces tension unpredictably.

Blanket pull is the action of the inked blankets that causes the web to adhere to one or both blankets on the unit past the point of impression. Blanket pull tends to increase tension. The amount of pull needs to be held constant. Tension is the force that pulls the web from the blankets after a nip; therefore, high tension reduces adhesion.

Progressive packing — increasing the packing on each of the blankets of the last one or two units by 0.001 in. (0.25 mm) — builds a slight draw into the printing units. Progressive packing can increase web stability between the units.

Normally, the longest unsupported web span on the press extends from the last printing unit to the chill rolls. Because the span is so long, the web tends to corrugate (form longitudinal wrinkles) as it goes through the dryer. In extreme cases, this produces wrinkles on the chill rolls, but this can be controlled by a dryer that ripples the web.

Wrinkling on the chill rolls

On most presses, it is possible for the web to wrinkle on the chill rolls. Wrinkling begins with the web corrugating in the dryer, as shown below.

On reaching the chill rolls, the web edges tend to be drawn in toward the center of the roller, and the corrugation assumes a "mushroom" shape.

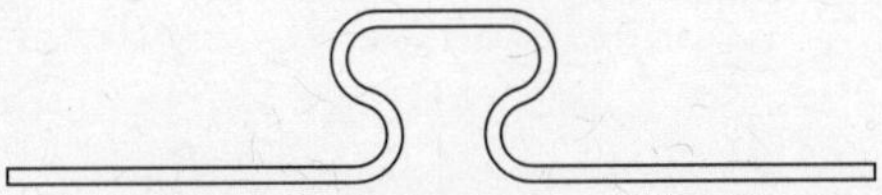

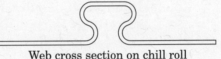

Web cross section on chill roll

As the web wraps around the circumference of the chill roll, the mushroom flattens. However, the head of the mushroom, resting as it does on the surface of the web, has a larger circumference to travel around. This creates stresses in the web that relieve themselves by splitting the paper that forms the head of the mushroom.

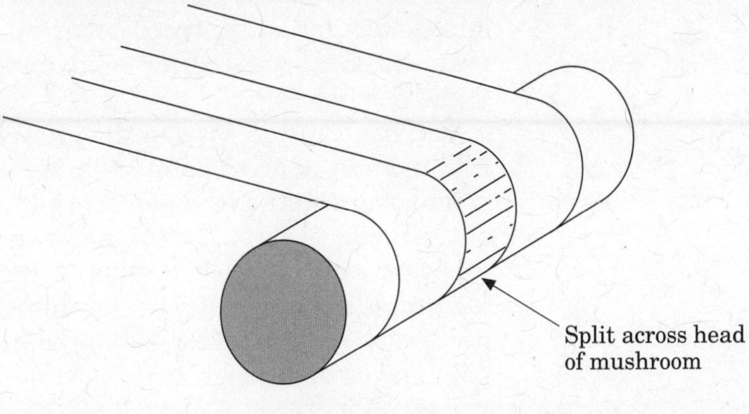

On heatset presses, a major factor affecting tension in the dryer span is web shrinkage in the dryer. The problem in controlling web tension is slip at the chill rolls. Slip can cause smearing on the chill rolls; therefore, chill roll speed should be set to produce zero slip. Chill roll surface speed should equal the effective speed of the blankets.

The effect of the dryer on many papers can cause slippage on the chill rolls. For maximum control, set the nip to pinch the web against the last chill roll and maintain constant chill roll speed.

A no-slip nip on the chill rolls can be set up through the use of air-loaded nip rollers. Air-loading makes high nip pressure attainable and permits precise equalization of pressure at each roller. Once the correct chill roll surface speed is established, it never needs to be changed. The no-slip nip and the fixed surface speed work together to eliminate shrinkage in the dryer. Conventional systems allow the length to change; tension varies in this system.

Nipping rollers in the folder have a higher surface speed than the web. The controlled amount of slip is designed into the folder and varies from press to press. Because the setting is sensitive to the caliper and finish of the web, the press operator has to acquire a feel for nipping roller adjustments. These settings must be precise, as they are critical to web control.

Alternatively, a no-slip nip may be created between the rollers below the former by air-loading the rollers. The surface speed of the nipping rollers is made equal to blanket speed by machining their surfaces to the required size. This makes the setting of these rollers easier and less critical than on conventional systems. The major advantage of a no-slip system is the ability to change from a relatively thin coated stock to a thick uncoated stock without changing folder settings.

The last tension span in the press is between the nip rollers and the press cutoff cylinder. Folder pins on the cutoff cylinder pierce the lead edge of the web, maintaining control of the uncut portion. The size and shape of the holes left by these pins indicate folder gain. If the pins tear through the lead edge, too much slip has been set into the nip rollers, and gain between these rollers and the pins is too high. Proper gain leaves holes slightly larger than the pin itself and not perfectly circular.

12 Image and Web Control

Web offset presses may measure well over 100 ft. (30.5 m) from infeed to delivery. A press of great size has to be run with the same register accuracy as a 15-ft. (4.6-m) web offset forms press. Multicolor images must print within a acceptable tolerance — impression after impression. Technological advancements and sophisticated precision equipment permit press operators to produce quality printing on a press of any size.

Image Control

As has been explained, paper can shrink and stretch on the press. From the unwinding roll to the press cutoff, the web runs through the press under tension. When put under such a stress, the paper stretches. The dampening solution picked up by the web, dryer heat, variations in moisture content, and the composition of the paper all contribute to dimensional changes.

These factors, singly or in combination, change the length of the paper or cause the web to weave from side to side in the press. This causes images to print in and out of register as they change position on the web during the pressrun. The press operator adjusts the longitudinal and lateral position of the images printed by each unit during the entire pressrun. This is accomplished by maneuvering the web, adjusting the position of the plate cylinders, or both. The aforementioned variables continuously act on the web; therefore, constant press settings do not maintain register.

Registration

Registration is the precise imposition of image elements — usually multicolor — relative to each other, so that they align exactly in final printed form. Register is a consideration from design through presswork. Intermediate procedures include color separation, film assembly, and platemaking. Each prepress operation is a potential source of misregister, which means that a job on press could be out of register before printing begins. Prepress functions and equipment must be scrupulously monitored to ensure accuracy.

Misregister frequently originates in the vacuum frame, where plates are exposed through film flats. Using standard procedures on average equipment does not ensure accurate registration.

Misregister in the vacuum frame is one of the most common, troublesome, and expensive problems encountered in web offset printing. This problem often shows up indirectly, resulting in prolonged makeready and increased waste. Standard prepress procedure is to assemble film flats that are carefully registered using a pin register system. These flats are then used in a vacuum frame to expose the four or more plates needed for process color printing. The plates are also aligned on the pins.

Each plate may not register with the others. This is not readily apparent. Thus, when misregister is discovered on press, it is a common practice to overlay the flats on the register pins over a light table to check register. The films may register on the pins; however, this does not necessarily indicate that the plates register properly or that misregister is attributable to press settings. Often, problems that occur in the vacuum frame cause serious misregister. Even when using a good pin register system properly, it is difficult to perfectly register images, simply because the film is too flexible. Three common causes of misregister in the vacuum frame are:

- The film sticks to the glass and buckles or distorts during vacuum drawdown.
- The platemaker uses improper pins in the vacuum frame.
- The film expands or contracts between exposures.

As the rubber blanket on the vacuum frame is drawn against the glass, the film (or flat) contacts the glass and tends to adhere. As the vacuum drawdown continues and air is removed, the punched edge of the film and pins are drawn tightly against the glass. The vacuum holds the film flat and plate tightly between the blanket and the glass; therefore, a buckle may develop near the pins as the film is not stiff enough to overcome the frictional force between it and the cover glass. Often, this distortion causes misregister, as shown in the following illustration.

Film distorting near register pins, a cause of misregister

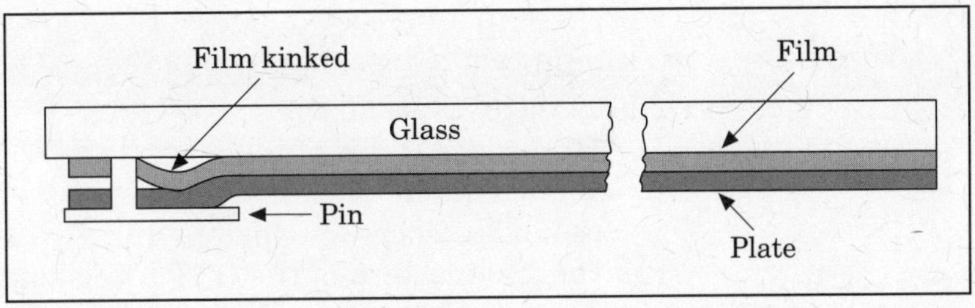

The buckle in the film would not cause misregister if films on subsequent exposures were drawn to the glass in exactly the same manner; however, film randomly responds to vacuum pressure. Thus, the film first contacts the glass and adheres in different areas on different exposures to cause misregister. Uneven vacuum, static electricity, or vacuum frame leaks contribute to unpredictable and uncontrollable drawdown.

Follow this procedure to test the vacuum frame for repeat register capabilities. Adhere register pins to the vacuum frame base in a position that corresponds to the holes in the film flats and plates. Place a plate on the register pins. Position a GATF Register Test Grid over the plate. Make four separate exposures; between each exposure, open the vacuum frame, remove the grid, and then replace it on the pins. After vacuum drawdown, make the next exposure.

Tape pattern used to test the vacuum frame for repeat capabilities

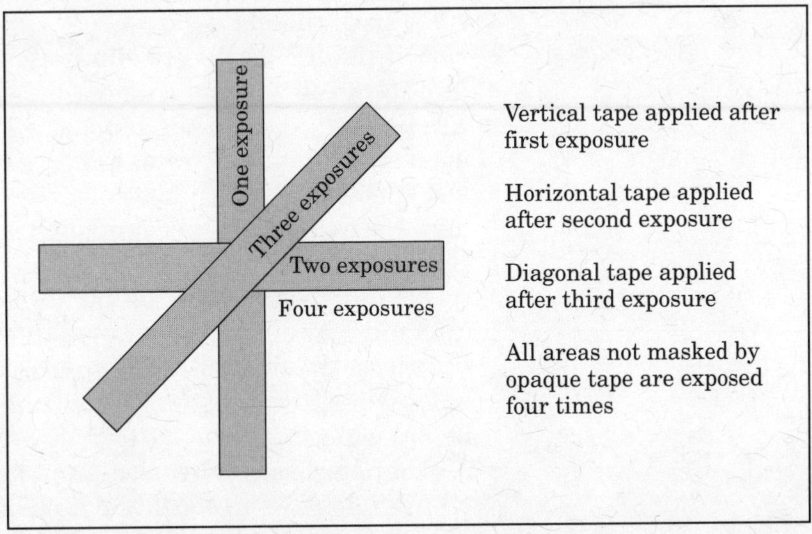

After the first exposure, place four pieces of opaque tape vertically on top of the glass, one in each quadrant. After the second exposure, place pieces of opaque tape horizontally

across the vertical pieces on the vacuum frame glass. After the third exposure, add pieces of tape diagonally across the previously taped areas.

Unmasked areas of the plate have received four exposures. Compare the image areas under the tapes to the background areas. Differences in density or line width, or multiple images of the grid pattern of the GATF Register Test Grid indicate misregister.

Some recommended procedures to use for obtaining good register in the vacuum frame are as follows:

- Be sure to use pins that fit tightly in the holes in both the plate and film. Ideally, the holes in the lead edge should be as far apart as practical.
- Do not use pins that are tapered or beveled. The film can draw against the glass and move around in the area that is tapered.
- Make sure that the pins are of the proper height, so that the film cannot move up and down significantly on them. Punch films far enough away from image areas to prevent halation.
- Be sure to maintain the vacuum pump according to the manufacturer's instructions. Most vacuum pumps should be flushed out every two months. All vacuum hoses and inlets should be unobstructed and in good condition. The vacuum frame should be several inches larger on all sides than the plates.
- Use antistatic devices to eliminate static charges.
- Maintain the vacuum frame seals. Blanket rejuvenators can be used to clean the seals and keep them soft. Damaged seals should be replaced.
- Use 0.007-in. (0.178-mm) polyester base sheets to resist distortion and achieve complete drawdown.
- Register can be improved by drawing down the vacuum frame in two stages. If the vacuum is kept below 10 in. (254 mm) for about 1 min. after the film is drawn against the glass, the film will slide against the glass more easily and give better register. Full vacuum should be reached before exposing.
- A grid negative can be used to make multiple exposures on a single plate to check the accuracy of step-and-repeat machines.
- Another means of improving register is to bleed off the vacuum (or interrupt the pump) for a few seconds after the film has been drawn against the glass. This allows

the film to slip against the glass before full vacuum is applied.

- Where register is critical or there is a chronic register problem, a tail pin should be used to prevent tail-end whip. This should be an oblong hole in the center near the tail edge of the plate. The plate and flat should be punched with the same punch. The same system should be used when stripping flats.

A hole punch system with tail punch to prevent tail-end whip
Courtesy Ternes Register System

- The vacuum frame glass and the film or flat should be kept clean and free of any sticky material. Depleted fixing solution may leave a deposit on the film that causes it to adhere to the glass.
- A clear plastic overlay on top of the film increases the number of sliding surfaces and improves register slightly.
- Misregister on some vacuum frames can be caused by excessive heat buildup in the frame. Be sure that the exhaust fan is operating properly and that the vent or exhaust is not clogged on flip-top units. The top can also be left in the vertical position between exposures for faster cooling.

Register Marks

Most printers use multipurpose register marks on the form to obtain backup register and folding accuracy. Usually, the register marks are short lines in the trim areas of the signature.

These marks require great accuracy in all prepress operations. If the press operator is going to rely on these marks during the pressrun, the image must be square on the plate before the plate is bent and mounted.

The “A” marks in the accompanying illustration are helpful in locking up the plate on the cylinder. When the “A” mark on the leading edge is lined up with the “A” mark on the trailing edge just across the gap, the plate is mounted with the image square to the cylinder. By scribing a mark on the center of tail edge of the plate cylinders and matching the “A” marks with the scribe mark, the press operator easily centers the plate from side to side on the cylinder. Usually the “A-A” line is the line of the former fold. Check the actual fold against these marks to measure former fold accuracy.

Register marks

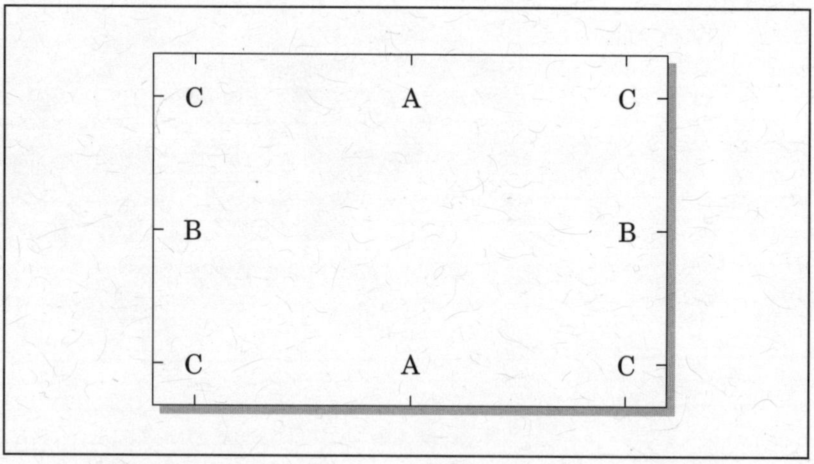

The first jaw fold is made along the “B-B” line. Misalignment of the first jaw fold is an error in cutoff. Thus, the “B” marks serve as a guide to adjust the cutoff compensator.

Many shops put the “C” marks on all four-color process work. These marks provide a simple visual reference that indicates which colors are printing long or short. See the following section on relative print length.

Backup

Backup involves the proper positioning of the image on the top side of the web relative to the image on the bottom side. Backup is established between the top and bottom couples of the unit that is the most stable. Depending on your color sequence, the center unit becomes the reference unit for all other printing couples. Once this unit is in register and backup is acceptable between the top and bottom couples of this unit, all other couples of the press are adjusted in reference to it. This will ensure proper backup at all times.

A high-quality plate bending device (bending fixture) and proper plate bending are as critical to accurate register as image placement is during platemaking. Poor bending produces plates that print tilted images, because the plates are askew on the cylinder.

A plate bending device

Unless the plate or the plate cylinder can be skewed (as it can be on some presses), no amount of circumferential and lateral movement will bring the image into register. On the other hand, skewed plates or skewed cylinders lead to either plate cracking or pressure differentials. The only acceptable solution is the proper positioning of the plate images and proper plate bending.

Color Register

Full-color reproduction of an image requires the use of four (sometimes only three) specially matched inks. Register of the successive colors is necessary to reproduce detailed images. Color register is achieved by fitting all colors to a designated color. Thus, the press operator always has two sets of colors to register for each multicolor web run: one on the top and one on the bottom.

Color register is maintained by moving the plate cylinders in each unit. The plate cylinders can be moved in two directions: circumferentially (forward and back) and laterally (toward the operator side or toward the gear side). Either movement can be made independently of the other and when carried out in combination can, within limits, bring any point into register.

On older presses, these adjustments are made manually at the unit. On newer presses equipped with remote control consoles, they are made through small motors mounted on each printing couple. On these presses, each printing couple is controlled by a separate circumferential and lateral control on the master panel. With some digitized systems, controls are shared by more than one printing couple.

The CCD scanner of the Quad/Tech Register Guidance System V mounted on a MAN Roland Lithoman III press
Courtesy Quad/Tech International

Relative Print Width (Fan-out) and Relative Print Length

Standard practice for platemakers is to center register marks down the length and across the width of an image. In maintaining register, the press operator strives to overprint these marks precisely as each successive color is printed. Register marks along the image length may align perfectly, while the marks across the width are out of alignment, and vice versa.

Infrequently, this results from inaccurate placement by the platemaker. Usually, this situation results from the expansion or contraction of color images independently of one another. *Relative print length (RPL)* and *relative print width (RPW)* designate the direction of variation. RPW is commonly known

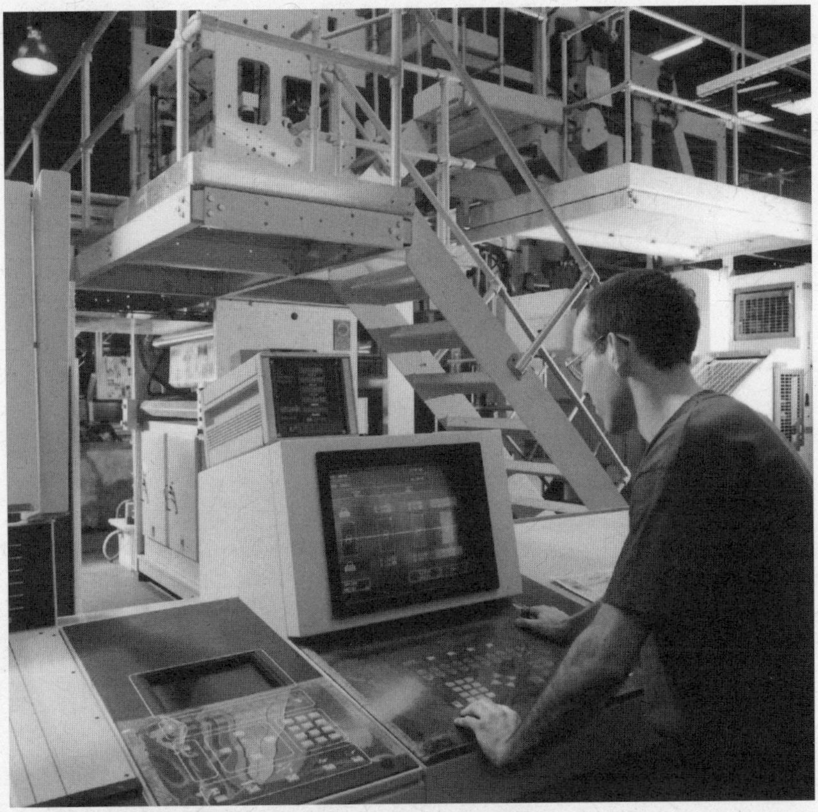

Quad/Tech Register Guidance System V in operation on a Heidelberg-Harris M-3000 press
Courtesy Quad / Tech International

as *fan-out. Relative print size* refers to the size of one color image compared to the size of another color image. The concern is not that the image has enlarged or contracted overall. Most jobs have margins that allow the image length to increase by approximately 0.012 in. (0.30 mm). RPL and RPW are concerned with relative dimensional changes — in other words, unequal changes — among color images. For example, a length difference of 0.012 in. (0.30 mm) between the magenta and cyan images prints visibly out of register. In this case, the images have not increased proportionally.

RPW (fan-out) refers to variations in size of the different colors as measured across the web. Fan-out is the result of the web width increasing as it passes through the units. Image width changes if web width changes after printing. One of the characteristics of fan-out is that the amount of variation from signature to signature is small. GATF research indicates that ±0.001 in. (±0.025 mm) on a 35-in. (889-mm) form is the normal range of variation for as many as fifty consecutive signatures. Fan-out usually decreases at higher press speeds. If the amount of fan-out does not distort the image beyond acceptable limits, the press operator can minimize its effects by moving the plate cylinders to split the difference and equalize misregister on both sides of the image.

Controlling Fan-out

Publication printing produces individual pages; fan-out can be controlled by stepping out the images on the second, third, and fourth plates.

Bustle wheels are commonly used devices that control fan-out. They are rigidly mounted on the press and set to project into the underside of the web just prior to entering the printing unit. When the wheel is forced up into the web, the resulting tent-like deformation of the web draws the edges together. The wheels shown in the illustration below can be finely adjusted by hand screw on the bottom. Bustle wheels should be mounted so that they always run true in the direction of web travel. It is important that the wheels do not

Bustle wheels

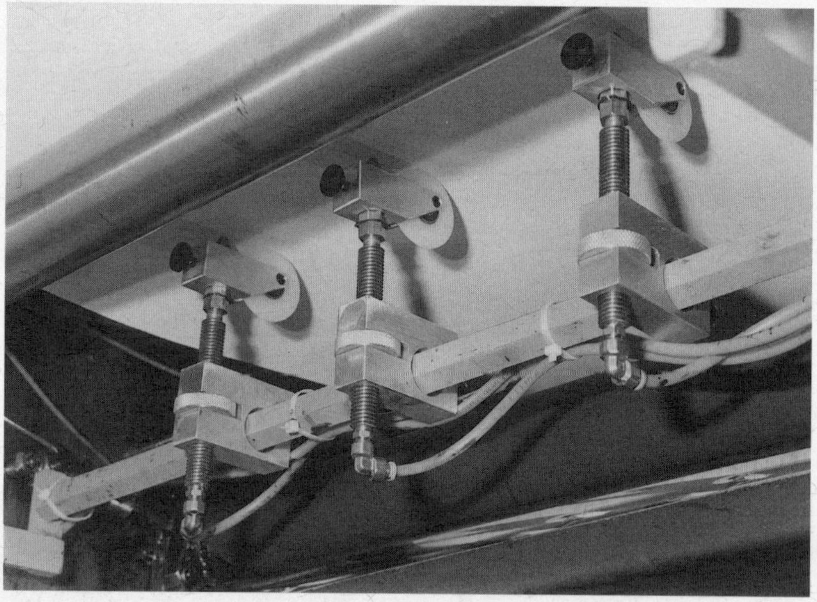

wobble; they should be mounted on ball bearings. Bustle wheels are normally 3–3½ in. (76–90 mm) in diameter and less than ¼ in. (6 mm) wide. Larger, wider wheels can be forced further into the web, allowing for greater correction from a single wheel. Two or more bustle wheels are commonly employed on the third and fourth units, where fan-out reaches its greatest proportions. Multiple wheels correct fan-out more effectively than a single wheel. Air bustles can replace the mechanical bustle wheel if ink marking may be a problem.

Bustle wheel
Courtesy Network Industrial Services, Inc.

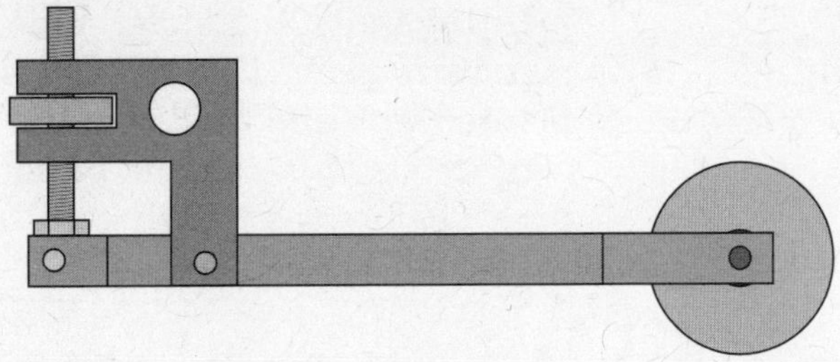

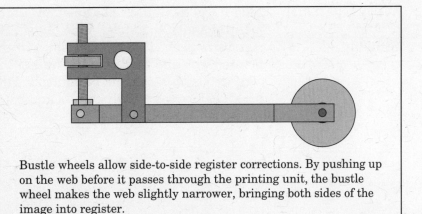

Bustle wheels allow side-to-side register corrections. By pushing up on the web before it passes through the printing unit, the bustle wheel makes the web slightly narrower, bringing both sides of the image into register.

RPW and RPL are two distinct factors. RPW (width) is paper-related, while RPL (length) seems to be press-related. RPW changes occur between units. A change on the top of the web is matched by the same change on the bottom of the web. RPL changes appear to occur within the printing couple. For example, the top magenta can print long (relative to the top black image) on one impression, while the bottom magenta is printing short — and the relationship can reverse on the very next impression. The range of variation encountered from signature to signature in RPL is much greater than that associated with RPW. Fan-out (RPW) can be controlled, while the same cannot be said of RPL.

RPL refers to variations in image size measured in the lengthwise direction of the web; however, it does not occur due to stretching. Stretch would cause the first-down color to print longer than succeeding colors, with the last-down color printing the shortest. The first- and second-down images typically contract, while the third-down image expands.

The source of RPL variation seems to lie within the printing couples, although speed settings sometimes have a strong influence. Variations in RPL on the top of the web are usually significantly greater than those occurring on the web bottom. The cause of this is not known. It is known that the tension setting at infeed metering sometimes affects RPL. Press speed also seems to have an effect, but both effects are unpredictable.

RPL can vary radically from web top to bottom, from one impression to the next, or from one unit to the next. Thus, even if the causes of the problem were well understood, the means for controlling it would not be simple.

Web Control

Side-lay

Side-lay is the lateral placement of the web through the printing units and folder. Side-lay affects the margins on the signature pages through the side margins set up on the printed web and the lay of the former fold line. For this reason, web side-lay should be controlled at two points along the press: before the printing units and before the folder.

Box tilt

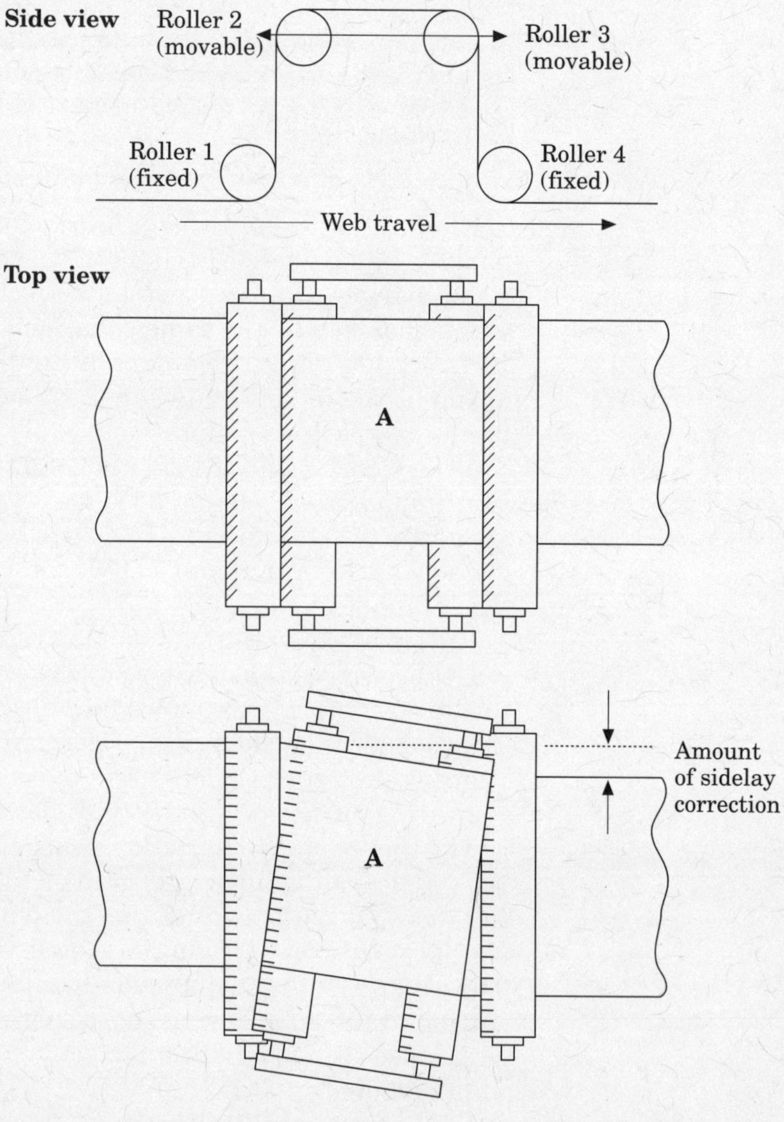

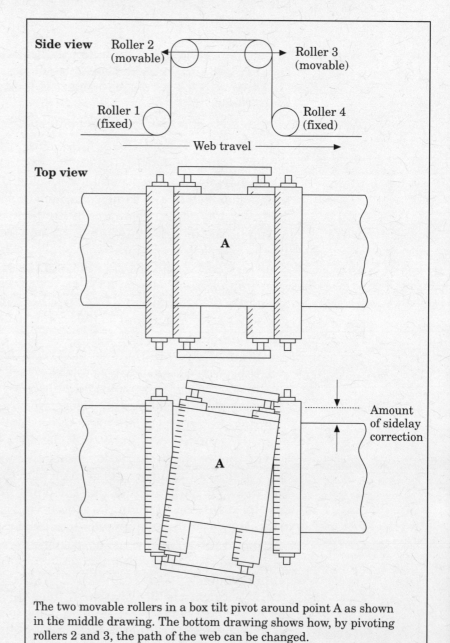

The two movable rollers in a box tilt pivot around point A as shown in the middle drawing. The bottom drawing shows how, by pivoting rollers 2 and 3, the path of the web can be changed.

The web-steering device located in the infeed controls the placement of the image from side to side on the web, and the steering device between the press and the folder registers the print to the former and chopper folds. One common web-steering device is the box tilt, which has four rollers arranged in a box shape. The first and fourth rollers in contact with the web are in fixed position, while rollers two and three can be moved in parallel and skewed relative to the other two. When the web crosses the skewed rollers, it moves to one side of roller four, relative to its position when it crossed the first roller. In this way, side-to-side position can be precisely controlled before the web enters the printing units and the folder. Other side-lay devices have three (sometimes only two) rollers. These devices should produce minimum stress in the web during correction. Wrinkles form in the web if the action of the side-lay controls generates excessive stress.

Cutoff

Like side-lay, cutoff also determines the image position on the signature. The parallel or jaw folds are always made a fixed distance back from the leading edge of the cutoff section. If the printed image in this section is improperly positioned, the signatures will be folded inaccurately.

Cutoff is controlled through a compensator roller or rollers mounted in advance of the folder. The compensator is a steel nondriven roller that can be advanced or retarded while the press is running.

Compensator roller
Courtesy Heidelberg Harris, Inc.

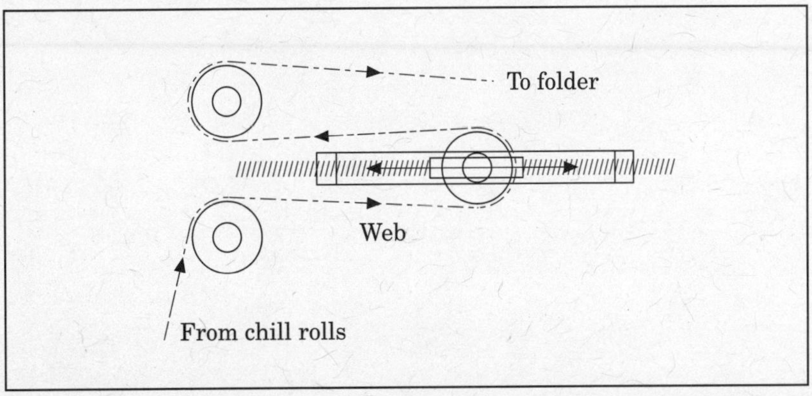

The compensator is set in accordance with signature size and creates a fixed distance between the last printing unit and the cutoff knives in the folder. This fixed distance is evenly divisible into a predetermined number of impressions — for example, ten.

The web is looped around the compensator. By moving the compensator, the size of the loop can be increased or decreased, changing the web lead so that even though signature size varies, there are always exactly ten cutoff lengths in the span.

Web-to-Web and Ribbon-to-Ribbon

Multiple webs or ribbons must properly correspond when superimposed if folding accuracy is to be maintained. Because of the variations in the paper, side-lay and cutoff must be independently maintained in each web (or ribbon).

Most ribbon folders have a full-web compensator to maintain cutoff register before the web is slit. They also carry smaller compensators to register each ribbon after the slitting operation. If the press has automatic cutoff controls, the full-web compensators are usually automatic and the ribbon compensators are manual.

An example of web-to-web register

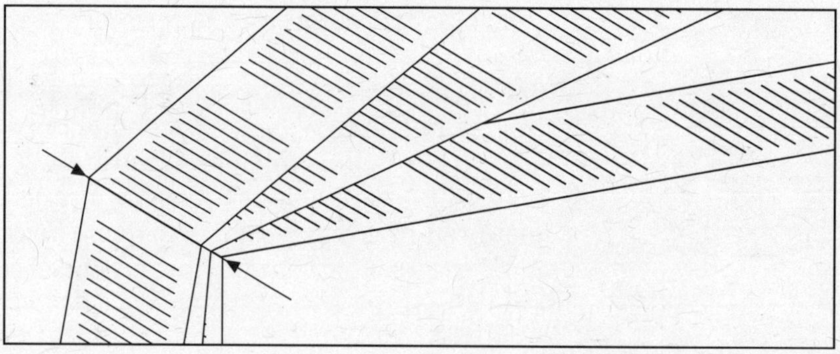

13 Test Images for Web Offset

Test images are quality control devices that, when printed, allow the press operator to evaluate print quality and press performance. These devices are specifically designed to indicate variations between an original image and the final printed image. Numerous factors contribute to print quality, and many test images may be used singly or in combination to assess press performance or control production.

Press Performance Testing

Test images that monitor press performance are those that provide information regarding the consistency and reproduction capability of the production equipment. They are usually too large to be included in the trim area of an actual job; therefore, they are printed separately as press tests.

Newspaper Test Forms. The film version of the *Newspaper Test Form* consists of several test images that enable newspapers printed by nonheatset web offset to achieve high-quality color printing. The combination of quality control devices allows press operators to diagnose press, platemaking, and image assembly problems. Target values for various printing parameters, such as tone reproduction, gray balance, dot gain, print contrast, and ink trapping, are provided. The test form was used as the basis for the SNAP (Specifications for Nonheatset Advertising Printing) test form.

A companion to the GATF film newspaper test form, the *Digital Newspaper Test Form* consists of a series of digital files that include three different 13×22-in. (330×559-mm) newspaper page layouts. The first page of the test form is dominated by four-color reproductions and quality control targets. The form also has four-color pictures and a variety of targets including tone scales, ink coverage targets, a gray balance chart, and an IT8.7/3-1993 basic color field, which is

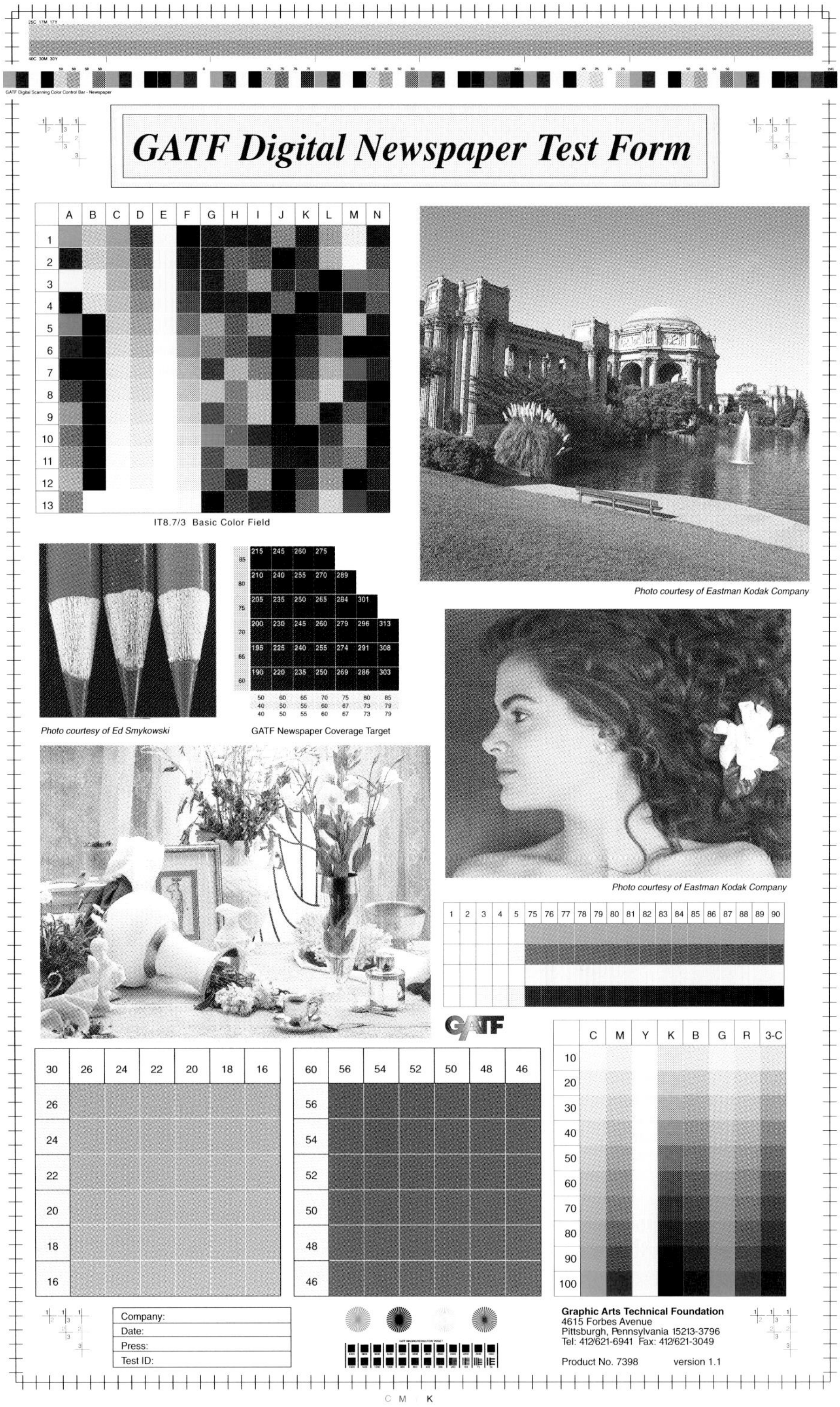

GATF Digital Newspaper Test Form
A B C D E F G H I J K L M N
IT8.7/3 Basic Color Field
Photo courtesy of Eastman Kodak Company
Photo courtesy of Ed Smykowski
GATF Newspaper Coverage Target
Photo courtesy of Eastman Kodak Company
GATF
C M Y K B G R 3-C
Company:
Date:
Press:
Test ID:
Graphic Arts Technical Foundation
4615 Forbes Avenue
Pittsburgh, Pennsylvania 15213-3796
Tel: 412/621-6941 Fax: 412/621-3049
Product No. 7398 version 1.1
C M K

a data set that allows printers to characterize color reproduction with a number of different selected colors. The test form involves the electronic prepress operations by proving GATF-corrected TIFF files in the first test page, while the second page has blank windows and uncorrected TIFF files. This gives the newspaper the chance to adjust the TIFF files in an image manipulation program and place their pictures in the blank windows. The third page is an ink gamut chart that consists of small color patches at a variety of different cyan, magenta, yellow, and black dot-size combinations.

SWOP Calibration Kit. The kit includes a set of four-color 30×40-in. (762×1016-mm) films of the SWOP Calibration Test Form, which contains a variety of QC devices and photographic images taken from the ISO Standard Color Image Data (SCID) set. It is designed to calibrate the color reproduction system to conform to SWOP (Specifications for Web Offset Publications.

SWOP Calibration Kit

Color Reproduction Guide II. The Color Reproduction Guide II helps camera and scanner operators evaluate color separations. In its printed form, the guide indicates the effects of ink, paper, and press variables, such as trapping, dot gain, density, and print contrast. Printing the Color Reproduction Guide II with the ink and paper that is to be used for an upcoming job allows the color separator to match separations to actual printing conditions. This enables the press operator to print more accurate reproductions.

Standard Offset Color Control Bars. The GATF Standard Offset Color Control Bars were designed to standardize four-color magazine proofing. Various elements of this strip — depending on available space — may be used on production runs. The complete strip provides the means of evaluating primary and secondary colors, 120- and 150-line/in. screens, tints, and gray balance. Dot gain or loss, slur, doubling, and ink/water balance may also be detected visually or densitometrically.

Plate Control Targets. In addition to controlling platemaking and proofing, the *GATF Plate Control Target* addresses the special needs of the new screening technologies, such as stochastic screening. The target includes a 0% patch on the halftone wedge, a special version of the Dot Gain Scale II©, and the ability to calculate a numerical index of sharpness. The GATF Plate Control Target consists of seven elements: a calibrated continuous-tone step wedge, a continuously variable microline resolution target, a calibrated halftone wedge, fine-screen midtone patches, highlight and shadow dot control patches, three patented Dot Gain Scale-II©s for platemaking, and a patented GATF Frequency Modulated Acutance Guide.

The continuing development of computer-to-plate technology provided the impetus for the development of the *GATF Digital Plate Control Target.* It is a native PostScript file that allows the user to monitor the output of digital systems, particularly computer-generated printing plates. The file generates a 6×½-in. (152×13-mm) target that contains a wide variety of elements that measure the exposure, resolution, and directional effects of the imaging system in addition to its reproduction characteristics.

Also available from GATF is the *UGRA Plate Control Wedge,* which contains a sensitivity guide, positive and negative microlines from 4 to 70 microns, halftone dots from 0.5% to 99.5%, and a slur target. It can be used for plotting plate reproduction curves, determining reproduction characteristics of plates at different exposures, detecting slur or doubling, and determining dot gain or loss on plates and prints.

Ladder Target. The Ladder Target is a test image that visually shows variations in the amount of slur and doubling along its length—when printed around the cylinder. Slur and doubling may be determined using a densitometer. The

Ladder Target also detects gear streaks and wash marks. The GATF Ladder Target is one of the most effective diagnostic test targets for troubleshooting the printing units.

Gray Balance Chart. The GATF Gray Balance Chart equates halftone film dot area to the requirements for gray balance by using ink, paper, and plates under production conditions. Gray balance is the desired highlight, midtone, and shadow dot percentages of cyan, magenta, and yellow required to produce neutral gray where the primaries overprint. The chart establishes empirically determined tone correction for gray balance in color reproduction.

Production Control

Test images for production control indicate print quality variations during a pressrun. They are usually small enough to fit in a trim area, or even within the printed form.

Star Target. The Star Target quickly indicates ink spread, slur, and doubling in screen rulings as fine as 2,200 lines/in. The sensitivity of this device magnifies ink spread approximately 23 times, thus press operators can easily detect any variation.

Star Target (actual size)

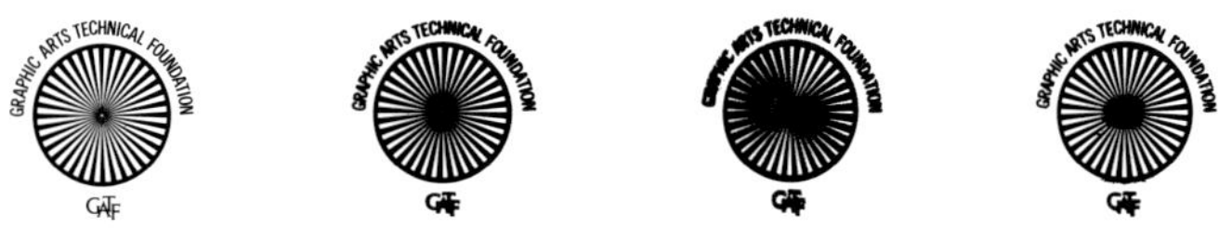

Normal | Simulated dot gain | Simulated double | Simulated slur

Color Control Bars. GATF provides the web printer with a variety of color control bars to monitor the pressrun. The typical color control bar consists of solid patches, tint patches, Star Targets, and Dot Gain Scale-IIs. These bars enable the press operator to monitor ink density, dot gain, print contrast, ink trapping, slurring, and doubling during the web pressrun.

The *GATF/SWOP Production Control Bar* was designed in cooperation with the Specifications for Web Offset Publications (SWOP) committee. This color control bar permits ink density, print contrast, and trapping measurements. It also indicates slur, doubling, and dot gain. Solid color overprints, solid ink patches, tint patches, Star Targets, and Dot Gain Scale-II©s comprise this test image, which easily fits into trim areas.

Mini Control Bar
for Web

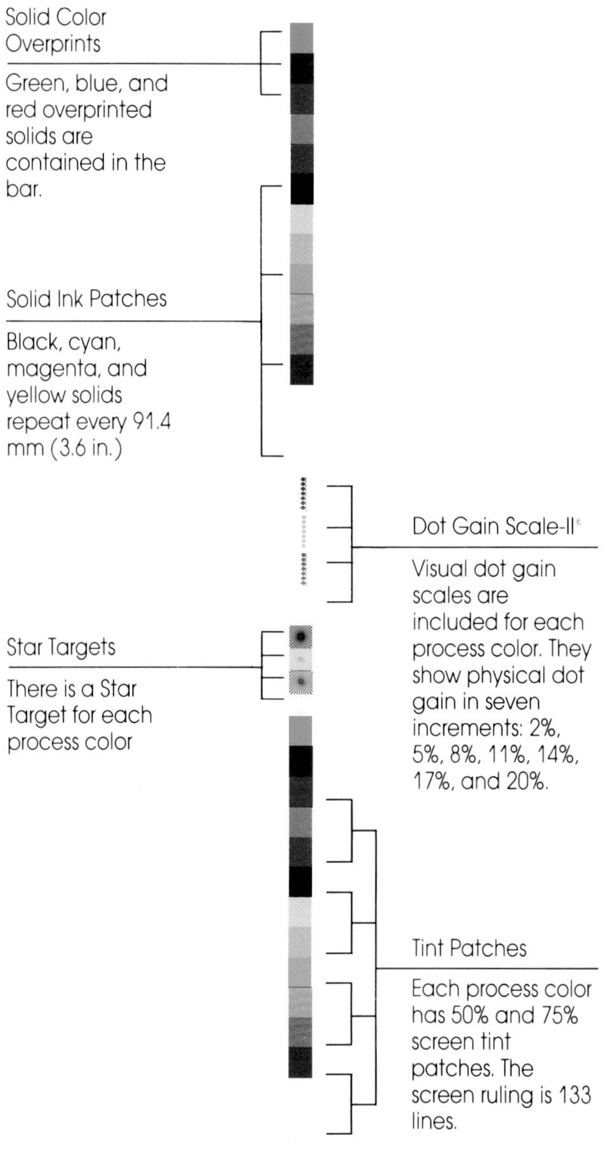
Solid Color Overprints
Green, blue, and red overprinted solids are contained in the bar.
Solid Ink Patches
Black, cyan, magenta, and yellow solids repeat every 91.4 mm (3.6 in.)
Dot Gain Scale-II©
Visual dot gain scales are included for each process color. They show physical dot gain in seven increments: 2%, 5%, 8%, 11%, 14%, 17%, and 20%.
Star Targets
There is a Star Target for each process color
Tint Patches
Each process color has 50% and 75% screen tint patches. The screen ruling is 133 lines.

The *Mini Control Bar for Web* is a smaller version of the previously described control bar but serves the same purposes in a more confined area. The design of the bar is based on SWOP specifications for magazine production.

The GATF/SWOP Production Control Bar and the Mini Control Bar for Web are just two of many color control bars available from GATF. GATF color control bars are available as film images or as digital files. Some are designed for use with scanning densitometers. Contact the GATF Order Department for a copy of the *GATF Product Catalog,* which describes and illustrates color control bars and other quality control devices.

GATF Dot Gain Scale and Slur Gauge. This device contains numbers from 0 to 9 using 200-line tints with graduated densities against a uniform 65-line background tint. On the original film, the number "2" has the same background and, therefore, is invisible at normal viewing distance. With dot gain on the plate (or prints) the fine 200-line screen dots gain proportionally more than the 65-line dots, so progressively higher numbers become invisible with increasing dot gain. On positive-working plates, the number decreases since these plates sharpen.

Dot Gain Scale and Slur Gauge, which show the effects of ordinary dot gain and slur

Sharp

Dot gain without slur

Dot gain caused by slur

Dot gain may be caused by slur; however, this gives a higher reading on the number scale. Therefore, a section of the bar contains horizontal and vertical lines that spell "SLUR" if slur or doubling occurs on press.

Dot Gain Scale-II©. The GATF Dot Gain Scale-II© shows midtone dot gain in seven increments: 1%, 2%, 5%, 10%, 15%, 20%, and 30%. A pattern of round dots and squares display dot gain when the round dots increase in size and touch the squares. The corresponding percentage that is printed below the image indicates the degree of dot gain. The scale is available in the following screen rulings: 65, 85, 100, 120, 133, and 150 lines/in. (26, 34, 40, 48, 54, and 60 lines/cm).

GATF Newsdot. The GATF Newsdot is a test image that allows the printer to monitor dot gain during newspaper production. The minute size of the Newsdot makes it applicable to jobs that have no trim area for color bars, because it is not readily apparent to newspaper readers. Dot gain is visually assessed using a hand magnifier.

GATF Newsdot

Dots on film (enlarged)

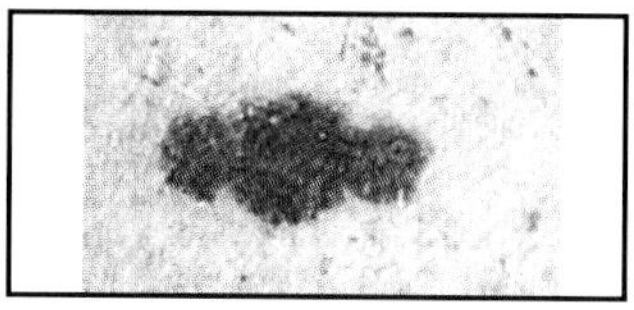

Target with excessive gain (enlarged)

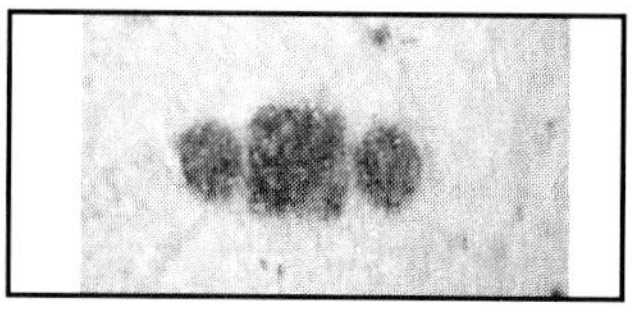

Normal target (enlarged)

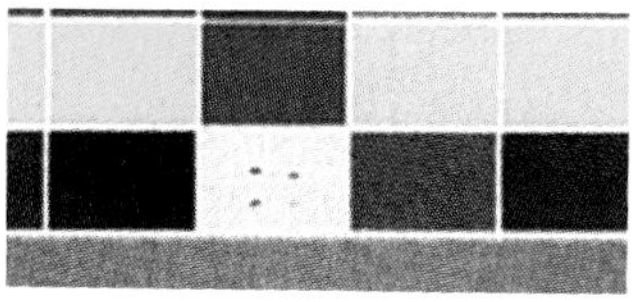

Newsdots in color bar (actual size)

Right Register Guide. The Right Register Guide indicates misregister between colors (in thousandths of an inch or hundredths of a millimeter). Upon visual inspection, the press operator can determine which way to move a specific plate cylinder to register the color printed by that plate.

Right Register Guide

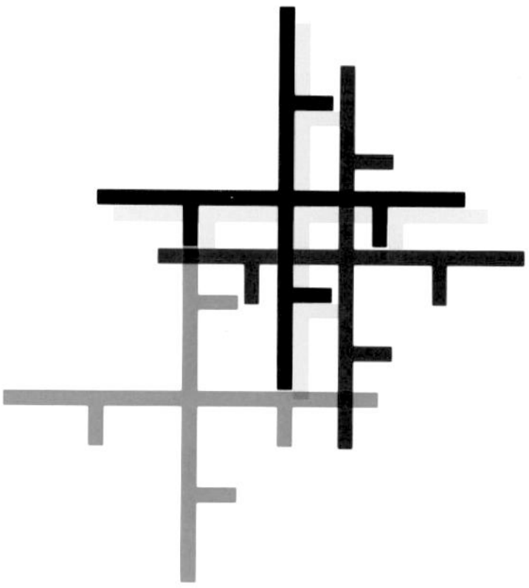

QC Ink/Water Balance Strip. The "QC" strip is a test image that indicates variations in ink-film thickness, ink/water balance, and dot quality. The press operator compares inspection sheets to the OK sheet to detect any differences in the size of the image and nonimage areas of the printed strip.

14 Makeready

Makeready is the series of operations by which the press is changed over from one job to the next. Makeready ends when salable signatures are coming off the delivery tapes. Increasing efficiency during makeready can save a printer thousands of dollars per year.

The press crew's duties during makeready differ from plant to plant. In some plants, the crew is responsible for retrieving and bending plates, transporting paper to the roll stand, and obtaining job specifications from management. A more efficient procedure puts the materials the crew needs at their fingertips when makeready begins. If the plates are to be bent at the press, they should be brought to the press and bent while the preceding job is running. Good preparation for makeready means having all necessary materials at the printing units at the time they are needed. Plates should be bent and packed, blankets laid out and ready to be mounted on the press, and packing cut to the appropriate size. Paper, ink, and fountain solution should be ready. If there is to be a color change, washup materials should be waiting at the press.

Usually, two people work as a team to change plates and blankets, a procedure that is most efficient if another crew member can hand the plates, blankets, and packing to the two people working at the units. This means that the people changing plates and blankets remain at the units, saving time and effort. Makeready time is further reduced if all the plates and blankets on each unit are changed before proceeding to the next unit.

Makeready efficiency is enhanced by crew members that work as a team. Each member of the crew should be fully occupied during makeready. The head press operator should organize the crew, using each most advantageously.

Crew members should be qualified to perform their assigned duties. For example, the head press operator should be responsible for the makeready on the most difficult side of the web and the second press operator for the other side of the web. Each is responsible for the ink lay, ink/water balance, and register on their side of the web.

Many press operators keep notebooks in which they list press settings and other information that might be of value on unusual jobs in the future. Notebooks can provide information that may eliminate an hour or more of trial-and-error experimenting. If all press operators on different shifts work together and collect common data, everyone benefits.

Makeready: What Is Minimum?

With the total cost of makeready for a sixteen-page press in excess of $500,000 per year, printers realize that it is necessary to look at makeready as a separate function. An ideal makeready for a four-color, high-quality job should run no more than 10–12 min. per plate and should generate no more than 1,000 waste signatures, as opposed to recorded makereadies of 30–45 min. per plate with waste in the area of 8,000–10,000 or more. The main cause of a long makeready is the time required to achieve acceptable image quality and to obtain accurate register.

Image quality. For many years, the average printing plant has performed final color correcting in the pressroom. The printer should understand that if the *separations* from which plates are made have been *adjusted for the press*, the ink, and the paper to be run on the job, the image on the plate will be exactly correct to produce the image desired on the paper. With such images on a set of plates, the ink fountains can be either automatically or manually preset with precision; the press operator should only have to establish ink/water balance. Color correcting should take place before the job has reached the pressroom. Customers should approve a proof, and everybody involved in prepress proofing must ensure that the proofs are matchable on the press.

Register. For many years, web printers have struggled with prepress register systems that were designed around the adjustments available to the sheetfed printer. These systems have never produced the accuracy required by web offset. To ensure that plates do not crack on the press, the plates have to fit the plate cylinders perfectly. This requirement means that the images on the plates must be in register with the bends provided by the plate bending device. Today, several companies offer total register systems: systems that carry from the original copy through all of the processes required to make separations and plates and that finally ensure that the image is in register with the bends in the plate. All of these systems are capable of ensuring that circumferential register is held very closely on the press. Furthermore, adding pins to the cylinder ensures that the side-to-side register is also maintained on the press cylinders. Such a system can ensure that the printed images will register to within a few thousandths of an inch.

With the previous two parameters under control, the remaining makeready functions consist of presetting the ink fountains, mounting the plates on the press, starting the press, and adjusting register during the time that ink/water balance is being achieved. This assures short makereadies with minimal waste.

Makeready: The Infeed

If there are any outward signs that a roll of paper may create running problems on the press (for example, a torn wrapper), the roll should not be mounted and run during makeready. At this stage, the press operator has enough responsibilities, and the roll tender should select the best rolls. Potentially troublesome rolls should not be run until after press conditions have suitably stabilized.

Preparing the New Roll

Careful attention to makeready at the infeed can go far toward ensuring a smooth start-up and run. The roll tender should closely inspect each roll before mounting it on the press. The roll should be round. Out-of-round rolls have a higher incidence of web breaks.

A roll with end wrapper removed

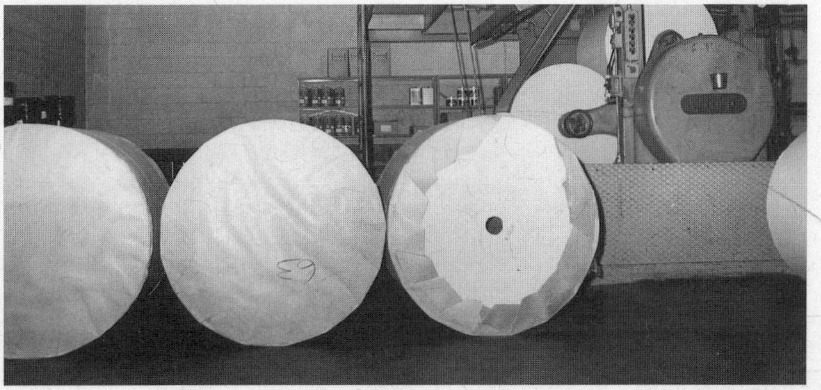

End wrappers can be removed some time before the roll is mounted. The tightly wound edges are relatively impervious to atmospheric humidity.

Check for nicked sides and torn wrappers. A torn wrapper, even without damage to the roll underneath, indicates potential trouble. Most wrappers are moisture-proof to preserve the natural moisture content of the web (about 5%). Usually, the first part of the roll to dry out in storage is the surface near the tear. The result is uneven running tension. The best practice is to leave the body wrapper on until just before the roll is prepared for splicing.

Finally, the roll tender should check for defective roll cores. A roll with a deformed core wobbles while running, causing problems with all but the most sophisticated infeeds.

Although most roll tenders leave as little paper on the core at the time of splice as is possible, many slab off a considerable amount of paper from the outside of the new roll before inspecting it for damage. A fairly small depth of paper removed from the outside equates with a good deal of waste left on the core. For example, slabbing ⅛ in. (3.2 mm) from the outside of a 40-in. (1,016-mm) roll generates 1.25% weight loss. The accompanying illustration shows the size of a roll that would result if the same amount of slab waste were wound onto an empty 4-in. (102-mm) core. As can be seen, a ⅛-in. (3.2-mm) depth of paper off the outside of a 40-in. (1,016-mm) roll produces a butt roll 6 in. (150 mm) in diameter. The effect is even more striking as the outside diameter of the roll increases. A roll tender should be encouraged to

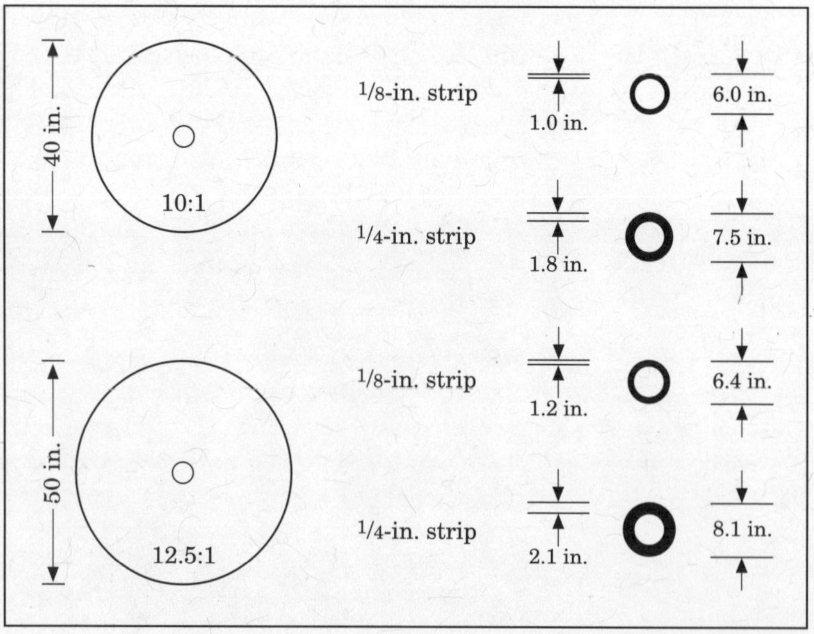

The size of roll that would result if a given amount of slab waste were wound onto an empty core with a 4-in. (102-mm) outside diameter

save paper wherever possible and should understand that the greatest savings are realized by conserving paper on the outside of the roll.

Running Rolls by Machine Position

Press performance is improved by running rolls in a specific order. When paper is manufactured, it comes off the paper-making machine in wide rolls. A 15-ft. (4.6-m) machine roll can be slit into five 36-in. (914-mm) rolls, and the printer is advised to run all the rolls from the same machine position together. There is also an advantage to making ready with the most uniform rolls, saving uneven rolls for later in the pressrun. A check of incoming rolls may show highly uniform center rolls, while center back rolls have a soft spot near one side. If the remaining rolls appear normal, the best order for running these rolls would be all the center rolls first and the remaining roll positions run second, third, and fourth as sets. Running rolls according to their machine position minimizes tension and register problems. This improvement is especially apparent during splicing.

A paper machine roll before slitting, showing the nomenclature for press roll position

Nomenclature varies slightly, depending on the number of rolls slit from the machine roll.

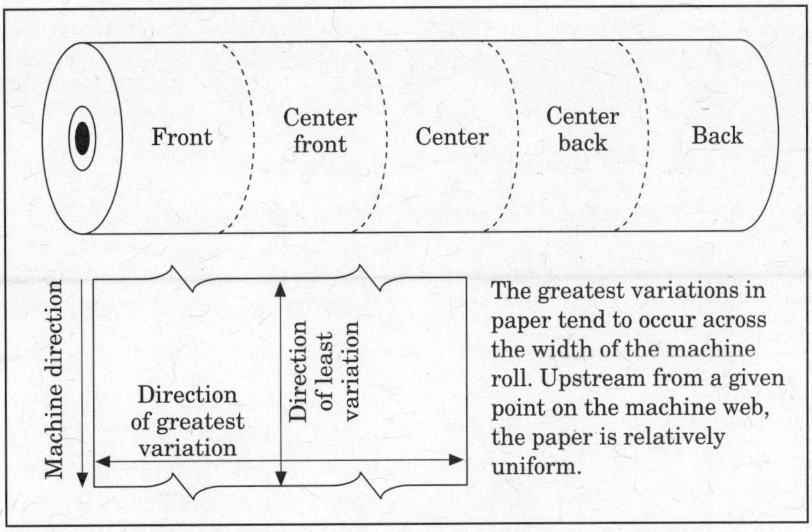
Front
Center front
Center
Center back
Back
Machine direction
Direction of greatest variation
Direction of least variation
The greatest variations in paper tend to occur across the width of the machine roll. Upstream from a given point on the machine web, the paper is relatively uniform.

Some papermakers color-code each roll according to its machine position by either banding or adding color labels. Such color markings make it easy for the printer to store the rolls according to the machine position and bring them out to the press as sets. All manufacturers include roll position information on the roll card that accompanies each roll. The following illustration shows the TAPPI recommended system for sequence roll numbering. In the recommended numbering system, complete information about the roll is recorded. This includes the month of manufacture, the log number, and the reel position. It is the reel position that is used to group the rolls together as sets to minimize disturbances while running.

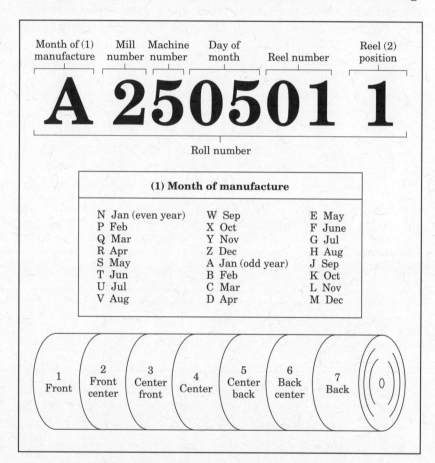

TAPPI recommended roll numbering system

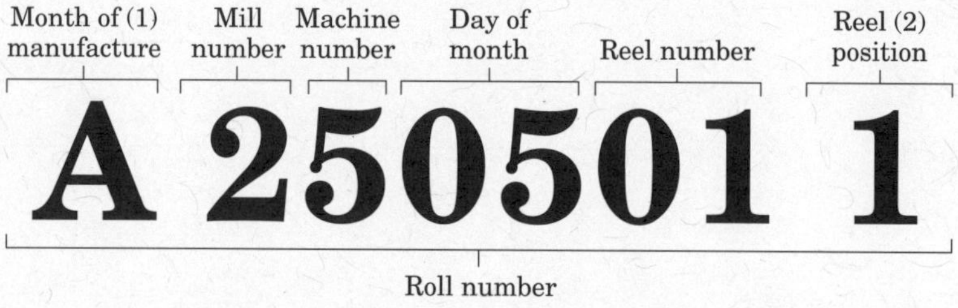

(1) Month of manufacture		
N Jan (even year)	W Sep	E May
P Feb	X Oct	F June
Q Mar	Y Nov	G Jul
R Apr	Z Dec	H Aug
S May	A Jan (odd year)	J Sep
T Jun	B Feb	K Oct
U Jul	C Mar	L Nov
V Aug	D Apr	M Dec

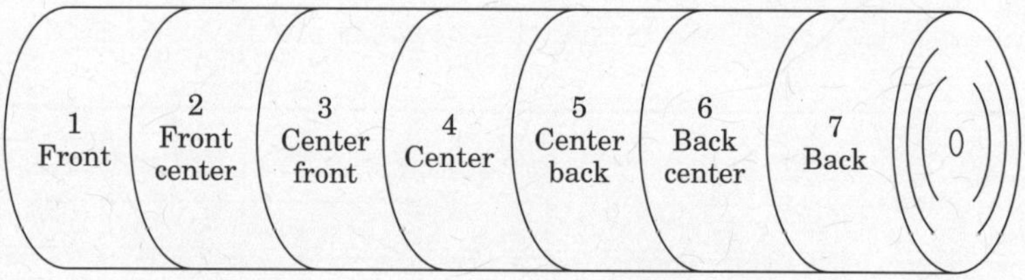

Mounting the Roll

When properly set up and run, the paper is *drawn* from the roll by the infeed metering rollers. The action should be as smooth as possible. With a conventional infeed (using a dancer roller connected to the reel brake), a smooth paper feed is achieved with a properly adjusted brake and a tight linkage between brake and dancer. The brake should be adjusted so that the dancer runs (on the average) in the middle of its stroke. This means that the dancer tends to run low on a full roll (more torque generated by the tension in the web requiring more braking) and high (less torque) when the roll is nearly depleted. A brake in poor condition may require adjustment as the roll decreases in size. An uneven feed indicates a faulty linkage, nonuniform braking, or an out-of-round roll.

When mounted, the roll should be aligned to prevent contact with the semidried ink on the edges of the blankets. Misalignment of the new roll temporarily increases the effective width of the web, causing it to run in this dried ink, from which a web break may result. This can occur regardless of whether automatic side-lay controls are in use.

Increase in web width if splice is not registered

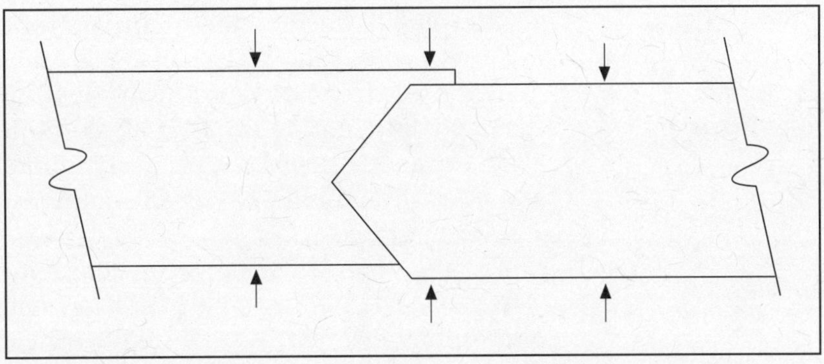

Automatic Splicers

The roll tender should mount a new roll on press without removing the wrapper or preparing the splice until the running roll is nearly expired. Dust and humidity can adversely affect the paper and reduce the adhesiveness of the splice tape.

On synchronous splicers, the lead edge of the new roll should be carefully cut to the proper V-shape. This shape is necessary to the proper functioning of the paster tabs. The splicer manufacturer prescribes the proper shape for the splice, and each roll should be prepared according to these requirements through use of a template. Adhesive — either tape or glue — should be applied exactly as specified by the manufacturer.

On many flying pasters, the new roll is driven by belts or a roller to bring it up to press speed just prior to splicing. The roll tender should make sure that the new roll rides against the drive mechanisms with little or no slippage. Missed splices can result from improper contact.

On splicers employing photoelectric eyes, the roll tender should routinely check the surface of the eye for accumulated paper lint and dust. If ignored, this material can block out the eye and prevent it from functioning properly.

Makeready: The Printing Units

During makeready, most of the crew's time and effort is spent on the printing units. Numerous preparatory steps precede every job. All have to be executed with precision and care, including washup.

Washup solvents are either one-step or multistep. Multistep solvents involve the successive applications of two or more separate solutions. They require the use of water, which is essential for removing gum accumulated in the inking system. Multistep solvents are customarily used for washups more complete than those performed in an ordinary makeready. It is advisable to follow the manufacturer's instructions on storage, agitation, and quantities of two-step solutions.

Routine Washups

Routine washups usually involve a simple, one-step solvent. The solvent cuts the ink film on the rollers, making it more fluid for easy removal. A properly applied one-step solvent removes the buildup of varnishes and resins on roller and blanket surfaces.

To remove the ink, a washup device is attached to the press. After use, the blade and pan of the washup device should be thoroughly cleaned. A washup device can thoroughly clean the rollers; however, the press operator should visually inspect the inking system rollers to ensure that they are completely clean.

Reconditioning Washups

The previously described simple washup applies to makereadies not involving color changes. At least once a week, and if ink color changes, the crew should wash up the press more thoroughly. A good reconditioning washup permits changing from black to yellow with no problem of residual color. Special attention should be given to the roller ends where ink builds up and dries. (**Warning:** Do not perform this operation while the press is running.)

The durometer of rollers should be checked regularly (once a month) and the information used to determine whether the rollers require maintenance. If the roller exceeds the recommended maximum durometer, remove it from the press and put it through a reconditioning wash. If this fails, the roller should be reground; if this fails to restore it to usable form, the roller should be re-covered. *Usable form* means that the surface of the roller is soft and velvety and the durometer is within the press manufacturer's specifications.

A reconditioning washup follows basically the same procedure as that for a regular washup, except that a multistep solvent is used instead of a single-step solvent. While the actual solutions vary, all multistep solvents perform the same functions. One solution cuts the dried ink and liquifies wet ink, throwing pigment particles into a chemical suspension.

These particles then carry down through the rollers to the washup device. Water is then used to break down dried gum. Between each step, or in a separate final step, the inking system is rinsed to remove all traces of these solutions.

On most presses, at one end of the ink fountain is a throw-off handle that either raises the fountain roller away from the blade or drops the fountain and blade away from the roller and holds them apart for easy cleaning. A solvent-soaked rag is used to remove the remaining ink from the fountain. All parts of the fountain that contact the ink should be thoroughly cleaned. Good washup routine includes cleaning the edge and as much of the underside of the blade as can be reached.

The copperizing of steel inking rollers on older presses is often made part of the reconditioning washup. Copperizing solutions deposit a thin layer of copper on the roller and make the roller more resistant to stripping. Copperizing requires that the roller be very clean; therefore, the crew should perform this operation during the reconditioning washup. The surface of metal rollers on most new presses have a "Rilsan" (nylon 11) plastic coating that helps to reduce roller stripping and eliminates the need to copperize the rollers.

Multistep solvents must be used in their correct order, because they are designed to work in a specific sequence. The press operator should never substitute for any of the multistep solvents.

Reconditioning Rollers

Multistep reconditioning washups can cut roller maintenance by a factor of three or four; however, rollers still require periodic reconditioning. The durometer reading of the roller is the cue.

Press operator screwing the 1-kg weight into the top of the durometer before using it to measure roller durometer *Courtesy Pacific Transducer Corp.*

Monthly readings should be taken on all rubber rollers in the inking system; if the durometer has risen above the set point, the rollers should be removed from the press for reconditioning. The rise in durometer indicates glaze on the surface of the roller or the effect of the materials that have penetrated the roller surface.

Recondition rollers by thoroughly scrubbing them with the recommended solvents to break through the glaze. The illustration shows a scrubber that is used to remove glaze from blankets and rollers. Products like this effectively scrub the surface of the roller without depositing any troublesome byproducts in the inking system.

Press operator using hand blanket scrubber

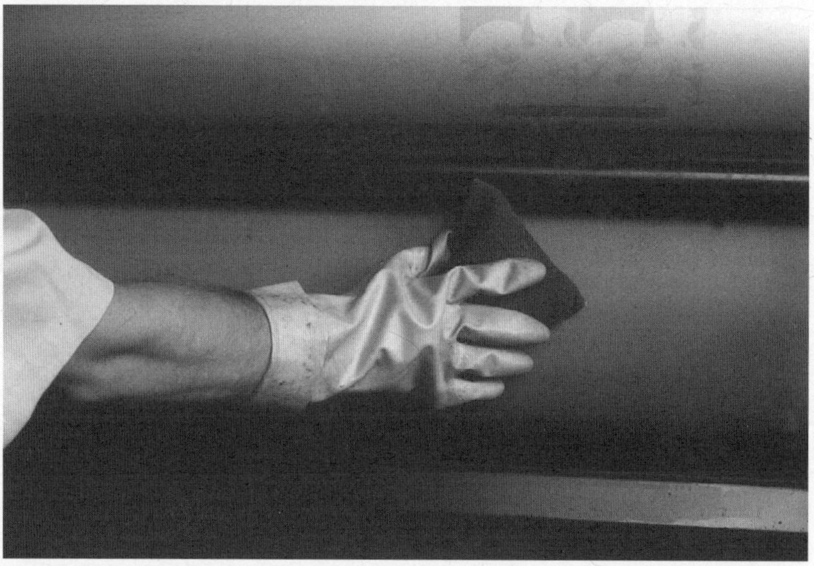

If reconditioning fails to lower the durometer of the roller into the acceptable range, the roller has to be reground. In regrinding, the roller has a surface layer cut off and is then polished. This process normally restores the roller. If regrinding fails, the core must be stripped and re-covered.

The Dampening System

Ordinarily, ink solvents are not used to clean the dampening system, though they can be used to clean some paper coverings. Cloth covers retain ink solvents and should be cleaned only with suitable detergents, then thoroughly rinsed.

Changing cloth covers is time-consuming; therefore, the crew should have an extra set ready to go on press at all times. The dirty rollers can then be cleaned and changed during the pressrun. Although cloth covers probably give the

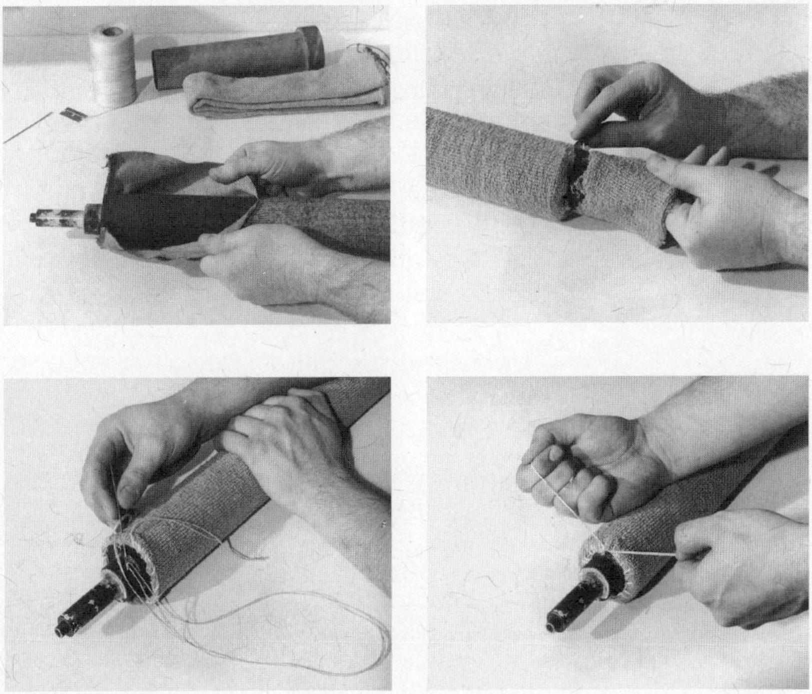

Changing a cloth dampener cover

The old cover is first slit and removed. The new cover is pulled over the roller and trimmed to the proper length. The ends are sewn with heavy cord. The cord is pulled tight and tied so that the ends of the cover are snug against the roller ends.

longest press life, care must be used in mounting them. The seam should be straight, the cover uniformly tight along the roller length, and there should be equal amounts of overhang at each end. When tied, the ends should be flat, not rounded.

By comparison, paper sleeves are much easier to change. When removing a covered roller from the press — whether the cover is cloth or paper — the press operator must be careful not to reverse the ends of the roller when remounting. A reversed roller rotates in the opposite direction, and a paper sleeve or cloth cover becomes baggy.

Switching dampener covers changes the running diameter of the roller. When new covers are put on the press, roller settings should be checked and adjusted as necessary.

Most dampening systems today have a bareback water form roller. This bareback water form roller usually has a softer durometer than the other inking form rollers. Generally, a roller with a durometer of 20 seems to work much better than a hard roller. Water seems to split better with a softer durometer. Urethane rollers seems to be more hydrophilic than rollers covered with Buna-N. On jobs with very light ink coverage, however, many printers have found that paper sleeves or a molleton or cloth dampening cover on the water form roller seems to work better than a bareback roller. If ink emulsification buildup is occurring between the water form roller and the oscillator roller, perhaps covered form rollers will help to resolve some of those problems.

Winding of paper-strip dampener covers

Variations in the amount of overlap can hamper control of dampening.

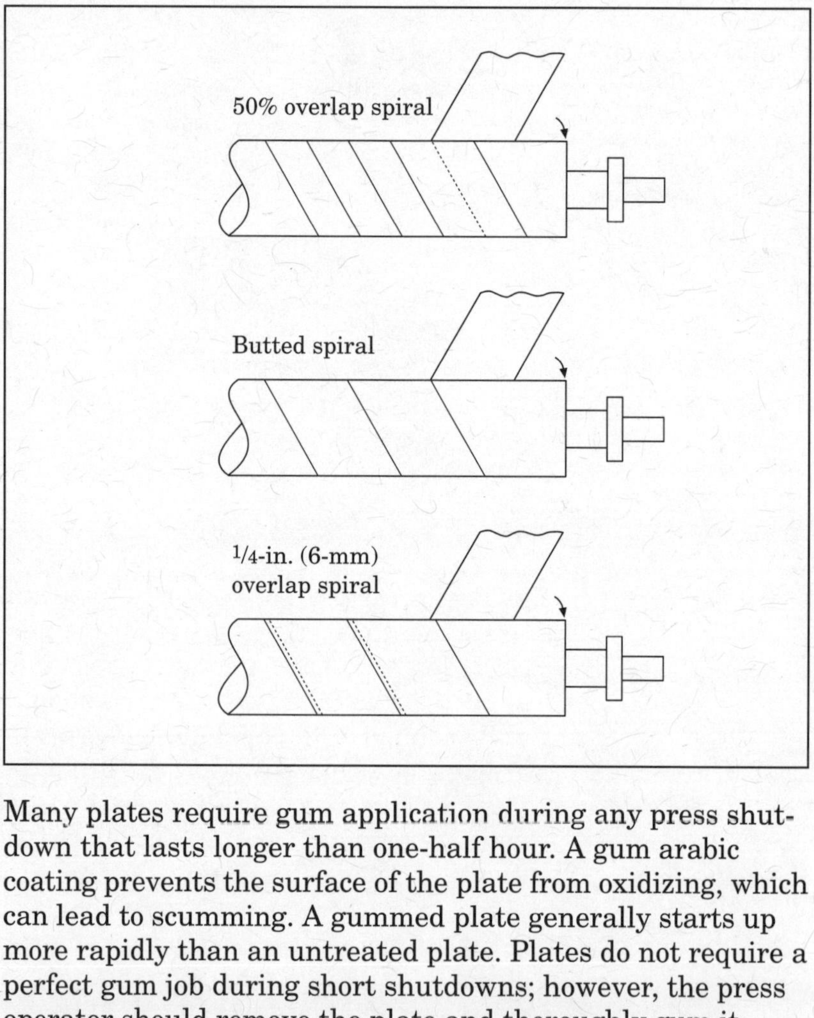

Preparing the Plates for Storage

Many plates require gum application during any press shutdown that lasts longer than one-half hour. A gum arabic coating prevents the surface of the plate from oxidizing, which can lead to scumming. A gummed plate generally starts up more rapidly than an untreated plate. Plates do not require a perfect gum job during short shutdowns; however, the press operator should remove the plate and thoroughly gum it before storage.

There are some materials that are essential for cleaning and preserving press plates: gum arabic, asphaltum, and solvent. Combinations of asphaltum and solvent are commercially available as plate washout solutions. There is no substitute for gum arabic other than commercial synthetic gums.

Gum arabic in an 8° Baumé solution is used to make the nonprinting areas on the plate water-receptive. The solvent removes ink from the image, and the asphaltum provides a nonhardening ink-receptive surface on the image area of the plate.

Usually, the plate is first wiped over with a gum sponge while still on the press. The entire surface of the plate should be rubbed down. The gum should be quickly and neatly applied over the plate. Gum is applied in a solution with a high water content. In reasonable amounts, it will not cover the greasy image areas of the plate still carrying ink. When excessively applied, gum can adhere to image areas in such a thick coating that it becomes impervious to solvent and asphaltum. Plates sent to storage in this condition invariably print gum streaks when rerun.

After the gum is lightly sponged over the press plate, it is buffed with a soft, damp cloth. When wet gum gets near an inked image area on the plate, it tends to back away. Unprotected background areas next to the image gradually become sensitized during storage. The soft cloth rubs the gum tightly against the image and prevents this. If the cloth is too damp, it may thin the gum and allow the washout solutions to penetrate the gum. This can cause scumming and should be avoided.

The nonprinting areas of the plate are now protected by a dry film of gum. There is nothing on the image areas but ink. At this point, the plate is wiped down with solvent to remove the ink from the image areas. Asphaltum is then rubbed over the entire surface in a thin, smooth coating to act as a preservative and a grease-attractive layer for the image. The plate should be covered with paper to protect it from scratches.

Storing the plate in an area away from water and moist air keeps it in good condition indefinitely. When rerun, the plate is washed with water to cut through the asphaltum and the gum underneath, loosening them from the surface.

Preparing the New Plate

A few press lockups require accurately cut plates. Most, however, allow for some variation in plate size and squareness.

Generally, it is a good idea to use plates that fit across the entire width of the cylinder body. This helps to prevent water and chemicals from working their way in behind the packing and plate.

After removing an old plate, clean the plate cylinder body and wipe off the bearers. During running, dirt, oil, ink, and various chemicals can collect and build up in both places.

Inspect the front of the new plate for scratches and other imperfections that may produce printing defects. Also check the back; dirt or platemaking chemicals not removed by the platemaker can cause problems and should be removed.

Check the surface for bumps and dents. If any are found, attempt to flatten the plate. If this does not work, get a new plate.

Bend a plate on a plate bending device. Usually supplied by the press manufacturer, plate bending devices are designed specifically for a particular press lockup. Plates are bent to conform to the circumference of the cylinder body as well as the radii at the gap. Should the bends be too far apart or too close together, the plate is likely to crack on the press. Improper bending is a cause of plate cracking. If the plate fits the cylinder properly, it cannot crack. Eventually, it will wear out.

Register

One of the major differences between registration on sheetfed offset and web offset presses is the fact that web plates, because of their bends, do not lend themselves to being twisted on the cylinder. The accompanying illustration shows the precision required in maintaining register between the image and the bends due to the fact that cracking results if the plate is not mounted on the cylinder according to the bends.

Because of these requirements, it is exceedingly difficult to maintain the register required for quick and efficient makereadies. Assuming that the prepress operation has been

Movement required to throw two points out of register a given amount

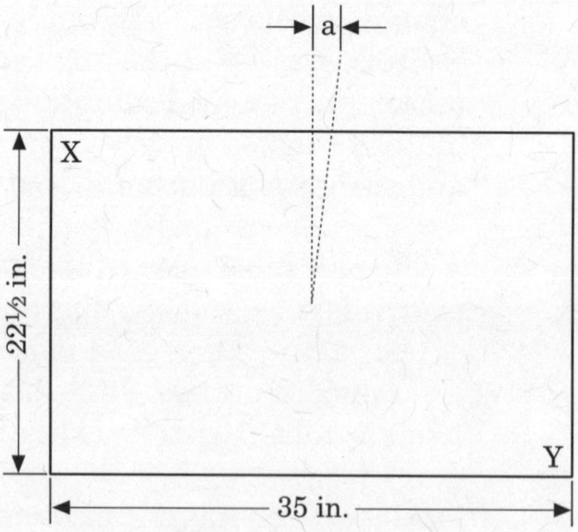

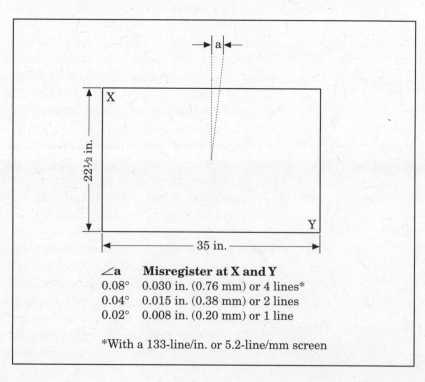

∠a	Misregister at X and Y
0.08°	0.030 in. (0.76 mm) or 4 lines*
0.04°	0.015 in. (0.38 mm) or 2 lines
0.02°	0.008 in. (0.20 mm) or 1 line

*With a 133-line/in. or 5.2-line/mm screen

revised to provide precision film assembly, it is necessary that great care be taken during bending to ensure that the register established between the plates is not disturbed during the bending operation.

The accompanying illustration shows a punching system that employs a round hole and a slot. The punched plate is fitted to pins that are in fixed positions on the plate bending device. First, fit the slot over its corresponding pin. Then, align the round hole with the other pin. The previously fitted slot maintains front-to-back register while allowing exact lateral positioning relative to the round hole. Mount the plate carefully on the pins so as not to distort the dimensions of the slot and round hole.

Punched plate with a round hole and a slot

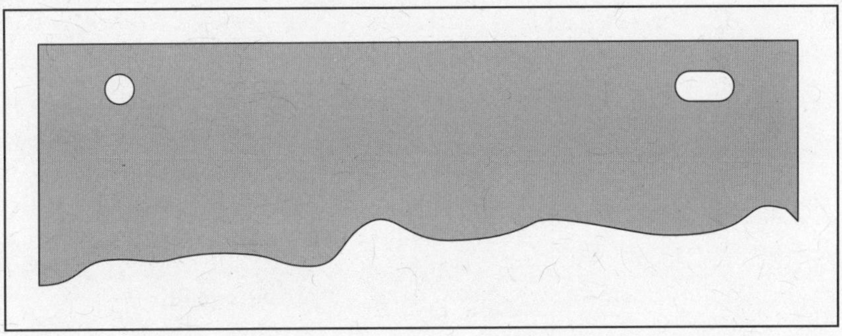

A properly bent plate meets the following requirements:

- The distance between the two bends must correctly match the distance around the plate cylinder body from gap to gap (including packing). If the bends are too close together, the plate will fail to fit snugly against the cylinder and will crack at the tail edge.
- The distance between bends must be the same from side to side across the plate. That is, the bends must be parallel to each other to make the plate sit squarely on the cylinder. If not, cracking results if the plate is shifted to square the image with the cylinder.
- An acute angle bend is put on the plate's leading edge. The angle and shape of this bend are critical if the plate is to be held firmly. Plates bend differently, depending on the speed of the bending. Power-operated plate bending devices eliminate this variable. If the angle is either too small or too large, it will cause cracking at the lead edge.
- The lip put on the plate at the trailing edge should be precise. If the trailing edge bend is too long, the plate

will touch the reel rod in the lockup. This prevents the plate from being pulled tight against the cylinder. Too short a trailing edge bend may cause the plate to slip out of the lockup.

Critical dimensions in plate bending

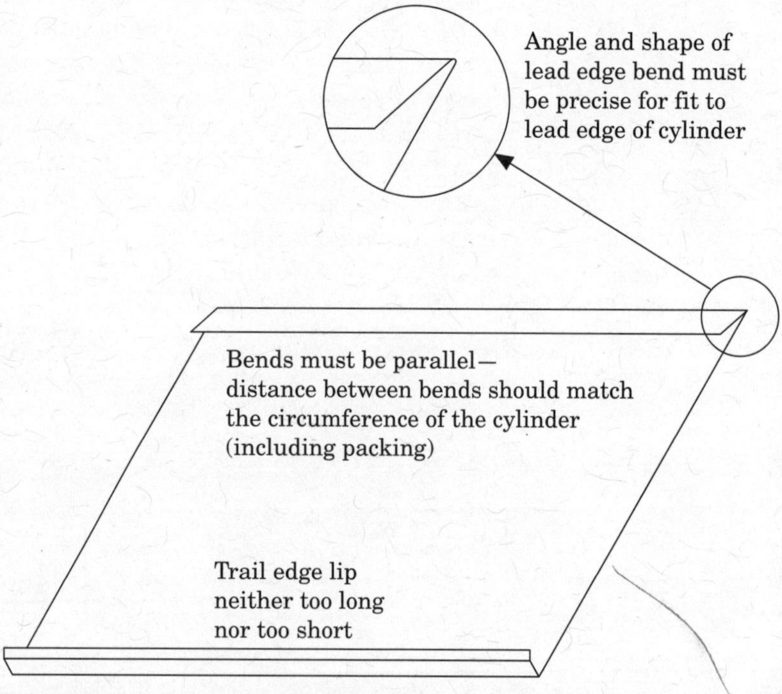
Angle and shape of
lead edge bend must
be precise for fit to
lead edge of cylinder
Bends must be parallel—
distance between bends should match
the circumference of the cylinder
(including packing)
Trail edge lip
neither too long
nor too short

Note: On presses with lockups requiring square-cut plates, bends must be parallel to the plate edges.

To ensure proper bending of plates, a plate bending device should meet these requirements:

- It should allow adjustment of the distance between bends.
- It should have a pin register system to ensure accurate register of the image to the plate bending device and a vacuum hold-down to maintain control of the plate during clamping and bending. These two features help to prevent misregister of the plate image to the bends, which can result in an image skewed on the plate cylinder.

Metals bend according to the amount of force applied, the rate at which it is applied, and the radius of the bend. To ensure uniform bending, these factors cannot be allowed to vary except to accommodate for a change in either plate thickness or metal.

Packing the Plate

Most web presses require a plate to have a packing sheet underneath the plate so it comes up to the manufacturer's recommended height to print and transfer the inked image to the blanket to complete the process of printing.

Any material having enough dimensional stability and uniformity of thickness to raise a plate (or blanket) to proper height and keep it there can be used for packing. Unfortunately, few materials meet these requirements. Probably the most common material currently used is specially manufactured kraft paper. Kraft paper is a highly calendered (smoothed), water-resistant paper with negligible compression. It is made in a variety of thicknesses so that the press operator, by choosing the right sheet or sheets, can create nearly any packed height that is required. Kraft packing paper is manufactured to reasonably close caliper tolerances, which is extremely important to the press operator.

Packing paper is usually attached to the plate to make it easier to simultaneously insert and position both plate and packing on the press. There are several ways to attach packing. Quite often, oil is applied to the back of the plate. The packing is then laid on the plate back, sealing the plate and packing together. During running, the oil helps to prevent the plate cylinder body from rusting and repels water that otherwise creeps under the plate and softens the packing. Grease may be used instead of oil; however, it must be spread thinly and evenly to prevent lumps that cause uneven pressure between plate and blanket. Paste or glue are more likely to lump than are oil or grease, so adhesive is usually only applied at the lead edge. This allows the trailing edge of the packing to slightly move in response to the changing physical forces encountered during mounting.

Packing paper, however, does not offer the ultimate dimensional stability on press. Polyester (e.g., Mylar) or similar plastic is much tougher and is coming into wide use as a packing material under plates — especially frosted polyester. Polyester also has a high resistance to lithographic chemicals. It is more expensive than kraft paper but, with reasonable care, can be reused. Some polyester sheets come with a crack-and-peel adhesive backing, which works well in adhering it to the plate cylinder. Some press manufacturers offer kits that allow press operators to "semi-permanently" mount the plastic packing material with spray adhesive to the plate cylinder. This method is particularly helpful if numerous plate changes are made per shift. The press operator must carefully adhere the polyester to the plate cylinder by slowly smoothing out the polyester to prevent wrinkles or air bubbles between the polyester and the plate cylinder. Once the plate cylinder has been covered with the polyester, the ends of the polyester can be trimmed off at the gap with a razor blade to eliminate the possibility of dog-earing at the corners when plates are being installed or removed. Using polyester reduces makeready time and, in the long run, costs less than throw-away packing paper. With proper care, the polyester could last as long as three to six months. Keep in mind, however, that if you have to print long or short on a particular unit, the polyester on those cylinders has to be removed, the cylinders have to be cleaned, and the cylinders have to be repacked with a different thickness of paper packing.

Packing is usually narrower than the plate on each side, so that it doesn't draw fountain solution in under the plate where it can damage the packing. Packing should extend exactly to the cylinder gap at the trailing edge. If the packing protrudes into the gap and hits the reel rod of the lockup, it may back out and wrinkle under the plate.

Mounting the Plate

Movements on the plate cylinder are limited; therefore the initial positioning of a newly mounted plate must be accurate.

The plateroom often sends the plate to the press with a covering sheet attached. Remove it only to mount the plate. The covering sheet protects the plate from scratches and contamination.

The leading edge of the plate and attached packing are first locked into position. A scribe mark at the exact center of the tail edge of the cylinder permits alignment with a center-of-image mark put on the plate by the platemaker. The platemaker should put center marks at the leading and trailing edges of the plate. The press operator can then match these marks across the narrow cylinder gap, a procedure that helps to ensure accurate register.

The press unit is then put on impression and the cylinder slowly turned to the trailing edge. The plate should fit uniformly tight against the cylinder. A space between the cylinder body and plate indicates that the plate was improperly bent and will probably crack during the pressrun.

The trailing edge of the plate is then inserted into the lockup and tightened, the press unit is taken off impression, and the tightening completed. Torque wrenches should be

TRUPAK Plus™ magnetic packing gauge, which is used to measure the height of the plate or blanket in relation to that cylinder's bearers
Courtesy Lithco, Inc.

used to uniformly tighten blankets. The press operator then uses a packing gauge to make sure that the plate is packed to the proper height in relation to that cylinder's bearers.

Blanket Packing and Mounting

Before packing and mounting a new blanket, clean the body of the cylinder and wipe the bearers to remove any dirt, oil, ink, or other chemical residue.

First, lock the lead edge of the blanket into place. Insert the blanket packing underneath the blanket and work it slightly into the cylinder gap; this holds the packing in place and prevents it from creeping while the press is running.

The blanket packing should extend all the way around the cylinder, from leading edge to trailing edge. This ensures complete plate-to-blanket and blanket-to-blanket contact all around the cylinder, and maximum printing area on the form.

Packing can be cut to various widths. Many shops cut blanket packing to web width, because ink and gum build up on blanket edges beside the running web. Since the blanket edges are slightly lower, the paper is less likely to run into one of these tacky buildup areas, which would probably break the web. Packing cut to web width or less reduces this possibility.

Cutting packing to web width also prevents inks from mixing when different colors are run in the top and bottom halves of the same printing unit. Packing blankets wider than the web allows the bottom color to spread into the top ink train and the top color to spread into the lower ink train. This interchange occurs just beyond the edges of the web.

Scoring the exact center of the blanket cylinder aids in placing blankets and packing. By marking the exact center of blankets and packing, the press operator can match the cylinder, blanket, and packing marks and accurately center blankets and packing with minimum effort.

Packing cut slightly narrower than the blanket and to web width

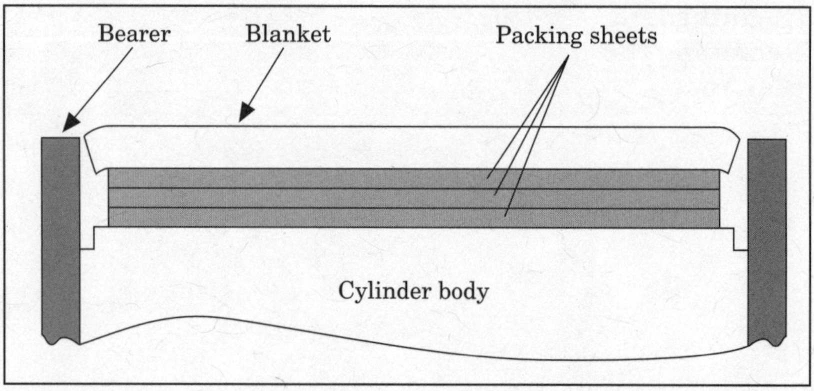

Once the lead edge of the blanket has been locked in the press, the cylinder is slowly turned to the trailing edge. During this time, the press operator stretches the blanket by the tail edge. The blanket is locked into the trailing lockup and pulled tight. Because of possible variations in the elastic properties from one blanket to the next, a torque wrench is the only means for achieving truly consistent results in blanket tightening.

At this point, tension on the blanket is probably about 50 lb./sq. in. (350 kg/m^2) of cylinder width. Blankets should stretch a small amount after a short initial run; they should then be retorqued.

The press operator then uses a packing gauge to make sure that the blanket is packed to the proper height in relation to that cylinder's bearers.

Press operator mounting a packed blanket

Cleaning and Removing the Blanket

Blankets remain on the press from one job to the next, and they are washed after each pressrun. Since blankets are expensive, every possible impression should be gotten out of them. However, if blankets wear out in the middle of a long run — especially on a four-color job — the savings realized by running used blankets are quickly negated by the cost of downtime. The press operators should track blanket performance to determine how many impressions may be printed by a given blanket. This information and the length of the next pressrun dictate whether the press operator should run used blankets or switch to new ones before start-up.

During the washup, ink is removed by means of a solvent. Specific solvents are designed for washing blankets. They should have a high solvency power for ink and other compounds picked up by the blankets during printing. They should have no damaging effects on the resiliency or printability of the rubber. They should be nontoxic and have a flash point above room temperature, yet not so high as to prolong evaporation. Before deciding which solvent to use, consult the blanket and roller manufacturers. Once the ink is off, the blanket is washed with water to remove gum residue. The blanket may now be removed from the press for thorough cleaning prior to storage.

The illustration on the next page shows what happens to blankets when exposed to different solvents. It can be seen that some solvents have an extreme effect on blankets while others have little or no effect.

Inappropriate solvents contain benzol, toluol, or acetone, which damage natural rubber. Do not use solvents like kerosene and mineral spirits, which have a high boiling point and take a long time to dry. Chlorinated hydrocarbons like perchloroethylene, carbon tetrachloride, and trichloroethylene damage rubber and are highly toxic.

The chemistry in UV inks can also cause blanket swelling and can affect certain rubber characteristics. Therefore, the blanket that is ordered must be "UV compatible" so that swelling is minimized. Rollers must also be UV compatible so swelling of rollers is minimized.

Selecting and Preparing the New Blanket

Blankets are usually shipped in tubes, an excellent place to store them until needed. Keep blankets in a cool, dark place; heat and sunlight can deteriorate them.

Select a blanket that is thick enough to run with minimum amount of packing. Single-ply, two-ply, three-ply, and four-ply

Swelling of a 0.075-in. (1.90-mm) blanket caused by exposure to various solvents for 5 min.

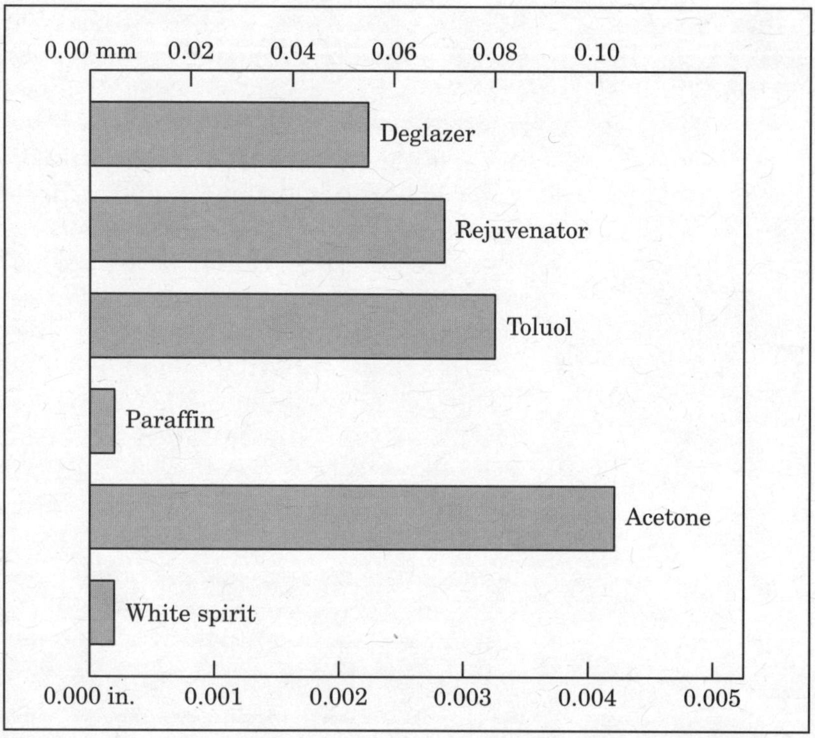

blankets are available. Single-ply blankets are approximately 0.035–0.038 in. (0.89–0.97 mm) thick. Many of them have a sticky-back for use on nonperfecting presses. Two-ply blankets are 0.050–0.053 in. (1.27–1.35 mm) thick. They can be sticky-back blankets, or they can be locked up in reel rods on presses. Three-ply blankets, which are the most popular, come in thicknesses between 0.064–0.070 in. (1.63–1.78 mm). Four-ply blankets are approximately 0.010 in. thicker than a three-ply — e.g., between 0.075 and 0.080 in. (1.91 and 2.03 mm) thick. The thickness of blankets for a particular press must correspond to the cylinder undercut, which is designated when a press is ordered. Putting a four-ply blanket into a three-ply blanket lock-up device is difficult because the bars are thicker than the reel lock-up device.

The blanket width should run from gutter to gutter. This helps to prevent chemicals and other contaminants from working under the blanket during running.

Blankets come in different colors, which at one time were codes indicating hardness. This is no longer true. Most blankets are described as *compressible* or *noncompressible,* which describes their reaction to pressure. Durometer tests provide inadequate measures of blanket hardness, because the rubber layer is too thin. Readings are also affected by the relative compressibility of backing materials.

Quick-release blankets have rough surfaces that reduce the tendency of the paper to adhere to the blanket. However, as the roughness of the surface increases, the blanket's ability to reproduce fine dots with great precision decreases.

Blankets usually come with their thicknesses marked on the back. This figure may be accurate, but it does not give enough information to the printer. A single figure stamped on the back of the blanket does not ensure uniformity of the blanket. The printer and blanket supplier should establish the acceptable nonuniformity of a given blanket. Uniformity of ±0.001 in. or ±0.002 in. (±0.025 mm or ±0.05 mm) refers to the specified thickness of an entire shipment of blankets. The printer and supplier should also agree on the acceptable overall variation for any given blanket. The device most commonly used to measure blanket thickness is the Cady gauge, which is a spring-loaded deadweight micrometer. The model used for measuring blankets should have a wide foot on the bottom of the device.

Check each blanket using a standard procedure. Measure all four corners of each blanket to locate the lowest thickness. This measurement is used to compute the required packing. The difference between the lowest and highest readings should not exceed the agreed-upon tolerance. A single blanket of nonuniform thickness creates pressure variations and unevenly transfers ink.

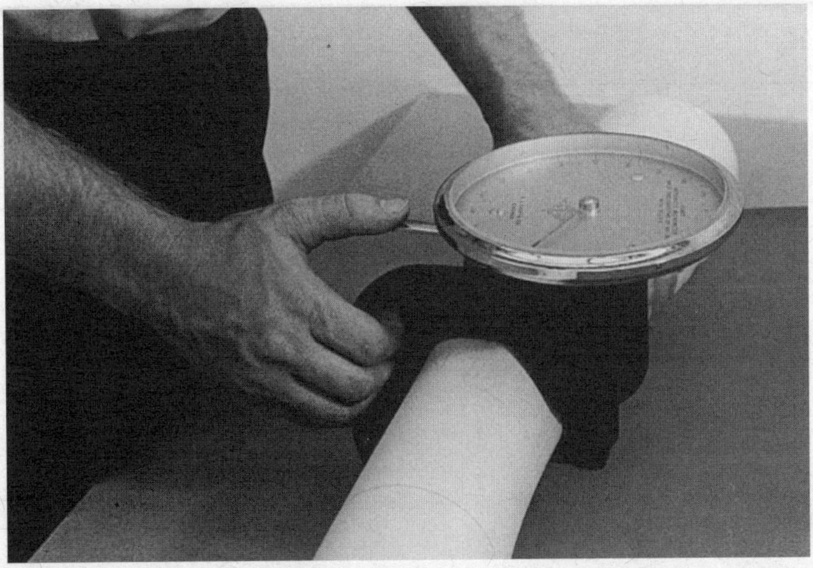

Press operator using a deadweight bench micrometer from E. J. Cady & Co. to measure blanket thickness

Dimensionally stable blankets provide consistent print quality. If a blanket stretches or compresses excessively during running, the printed image enlarges or squeeze pressure reduces to a level that is inadequate to completely transfer printing ink.

The most stable blankets compress 0.001 in. (0.025 mm) or less, even after several million impressions. The compression-pressure ratio describes the amount that a blanket compresses relative to the amount of pressure applied to it. Blankets should uniformly compress over a wide range of pressure. Blankets that are less sensitive to changes in packing perform more predictably on the press.

Makeready: The Dryer and Chill Rolls

One crew member should periodically inspect the nozzles in the dryer during makeready. Contact with wet ink can create a buildup that clogs these openings. Uneven drying and, in the case of some hot-air dryers, loss of web control (web flutter) can result. Some installations require heating experts to periodically clean the dryer box and exhaust stack.

The surface of the chill rolls should be inspected. Remove ink buildup on these rolls with solvent; then, thoroughly remove the cleaning agent.

Dryer and chill roll temperatures are determined by several factors. The amount of web surface covered by ink directly affects dryer temperature. Heavy coverage requires more drying energy than light coverage. A 20-lb. increase in paper basis weight requires a substantial increase in dryer temperature, because the dryer has to heat a larger volume of ink and paper. Finally, dryer temperature is directly related to press speed. Faster moving webs must be dried at high heat. Conversely, slower web speeds require lower dryer temperatures. Drying is a function of time and temperature.

The dryer should be run at the minimum temperature so as not to drive moisture out of the web. Excess heat causes the paper to crack when folded. Printed books with below-normal moisture content often gradually pick up atmospheric moisture, which creates wavy page edges. Heavily coated webs with heavy ink coverage can be especially difficult to dry properly. Blistering occurs when dryer heat vaporizes moisture inside the web more rapidly than it can escape because of heavy coating and ink coverage, both of which reduce the porosity of the web.

After the dryer evaporates the solvent from the ink, the web enters the chill roll section. In order for the chill rolls to set the ink, sufficient solvent has to be removed in the dryer and the surface temperature should be 90°F (32°C) or lower. Otherwise, marking in the delivery section of the press results from the materials in the ink that are meant to remain on the surface of the web.

To counteract this problem, check the temperature of the web coming off the chill rolls before adjusting dryer controls. If the temperature of the web is sufficiently cool coming off the chill rolls, the ink film contains too much solvent and the dryer temperature should be increased. If the web is warm coming off the chill rolls, the marking is likely due to insufficient cooling. In this case, reduce the dryer temperature. If this does not eliminate the marking problem, it may be necessary to slow down the press and reduce the dryer temperature to increase the effectiveness of the chill rolls.

Press operators should run the dryer at the minimum temperature to flash off the solvents in the ink. This temperature could be as low as 250°F (120°C) web exit temperature or as high as 300°F (150°C) web exit temperature. Most operators operate the press in the "web temperature mode," which means that the web temperature is set and monitored by an external infrared pyrometer that reads the temperature of the web as it exits the dryer.

The lens of the external infrared pyrometer has a tendency to get dirty, and it must be cleaned periodically, perhaps monthly, so that the pyrometer will accurately read the web exit temperature.

Sometimes, when the lens gets dirty, the pyrometer gives a false reading of the web exit temperature because the lens does not clearly see the web exiting the dryer because of the buildup on the lens. As a result, the internal temperature of the dryer can rise significantly, thus causing the web to exit at a much higher temperature than desired. With higher web exit temperature, the surface gloss of the paper (usually coated paper) begins to suffer — all because of a dirty lens on the infrared pyrometer.

Makeready: The Folder

The press operator should remember when adjusting the folder that *gain* is built into most folders. Gain means that each successive operation in the folder occurs at higher surface speed, so that the paper is subjected to a steady drawing force as it moves through the folder. Folders can have a gain factor anywhere from zero to 2% or more.

Adjusting the Former

Three or four trolley wheels at the top of the former are usually spaced across the width of the web. The nip pressure on each of them must be equal. One roller pressing harder than the others pulls the web to the side with the greater nip pressure. The simplest way of equalizing nip pressure is to insert strips of paper under each trolley roller and test them for drag.

The position of the former nose relative to the web guide rollers partially determines how accurate and wrinkle-free the fold will be, and whether the ink will smear at the former nose. This position is set by a long metal rod behind the former board. One end of the rod is linked to the folder frame and the other end to the former nose. Both ends are threaded so that when the rod is turned, the nose moves out and away from, or down and into (between) the web guide rollers. The starting setting should be marked, so that the nose can be easily and accurately returned to its original position.

To accurately determine the correct angle of the former board, the press operator can conduct a slit test of the full web running down the former board. With the idle former rollers in the correct position and nips accurately set to pull the web into the folder, the operator replaces the center trolley wheel with a slitter wheel and allows the full web to be cut into two ribbons.

If the two ribbons separate by more than approximately ⅛ in. (3 mm) as they pass over the tip of the nose, the tip of the nose is too high, or too far forward, and it is not accurately supporting the full web with the former board. Only the tip of the nose is holding the web out and not at the correct angle. The consequences include wrinkles and draws coming down the backbone of the signature at the tip of the former board. These can also contribute to gusseting that will occur as the folding process continues into the tucker blade. If the two ribbons separate by more than ⅛ in., the press operator adjusts the threaded rod to lower the tip of that nose until the two ribbons come closer together, within 1⁄16 (1.6 mm) to ⅛ in. If the tip of the nose is too low, the two ribbons will overlap each other as they go past the tip of the former board nose. In this case, the press operator adjusts the threaded rod to raise the tip of the nose to get the same 1⁄16 or ⅛ in. of separation between the two ribbons. Once this is accomplished, the nose can be locked into position. At that point, it should never need to be adjusted again, and it should be at the perfect angle. The operator may want to put

Major operating adjustments on the former board
Courtesy Solna Web USA, Inc.

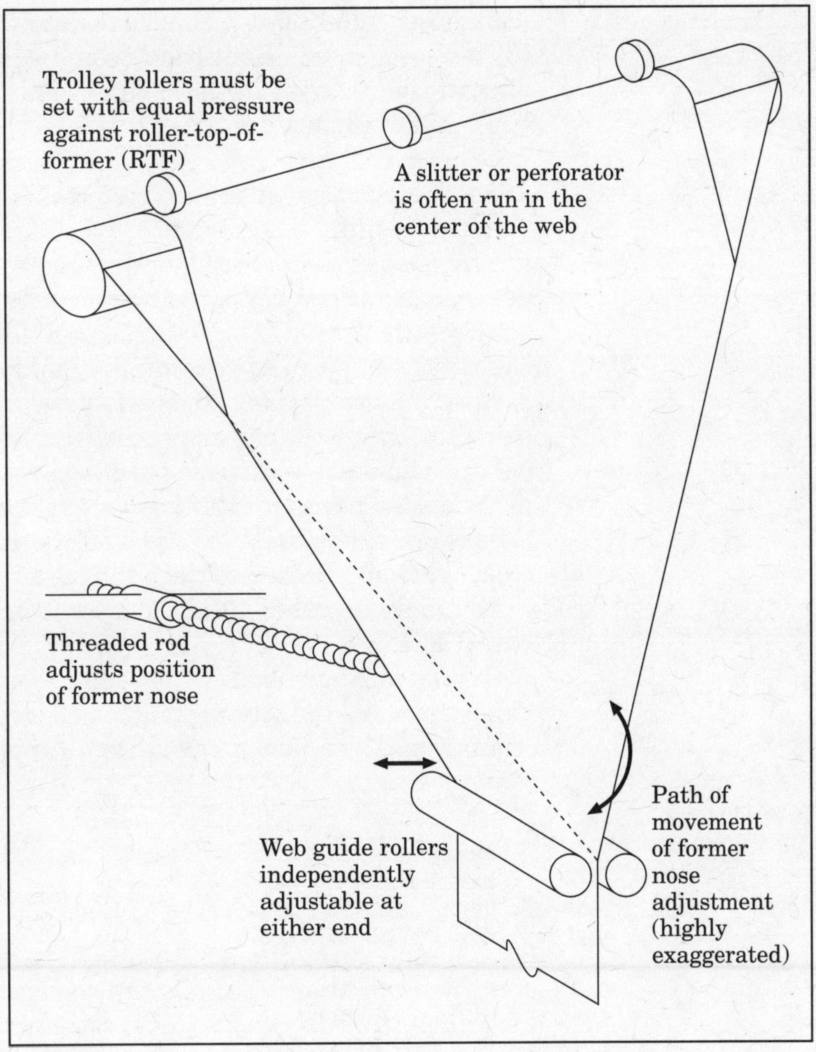
Trolley rollers must be set with equal pressure against roller-top-of-former (RTF)
A slitter or perforator is often run in the center of the web
Threaded rod adjusts position of former nose
Web guide rollers independently adjustable at either end
Path of movement of former nose adjustment (highly exaggerated)

a protractor on the former board to determine the angle at which it was set.

Accurately set web guide rollers provide wrinkle-free folds. They can be set farther apart or closer together and are adjustable at both ends.

The front-end adjustment of the web guide rollers is made by tearing a strip of paper from the roll to be run and folding the strip in half. To this doubled thickness of paper is added 0.015 in. (0.38 mm) of thickness. Strips from packing sheets are suitable for this. Insert the entire sandwich between the rollers at the front end, and adjust the rollers until there is a firm drag on the strips. This provides an initial setting from which to adjust. The back ends of the web guide rollers are set in the same way, but the doubled-up strip is used without the additional 0.015 in. (0.38 mm) of material. The web should run fairly tight through the back end of the rollers.

The Nip Rollers

The nip rollers perform the vital job of drawing paper into the folder cutoff. Their surface speed is slightly higher than that of the press in order to meet the paper feed requirements of the folder. Feed rate at the nip rollers is controlled by varying the pressure between the rollers. Too much pressure can produce slack between nipping and cutoff and probably cause cutoff variations. Too little pressure (excess slippage) causes the pins to tear out of the web.

Nip rollers are set to one sheet less than the total thickness of the folded paper to run through this point in the folder. The rollers are set so that there is a firm drag on the test thickness. To ensure adequate paper feed, set the nip rollers a little too tight rather than too loose. Pressure can always be eased off later.

Setting the back ends of the nip rollers a little tighter than the front holds the web tight against the former and prevents wrinkling. More tension can also be applied to the outside

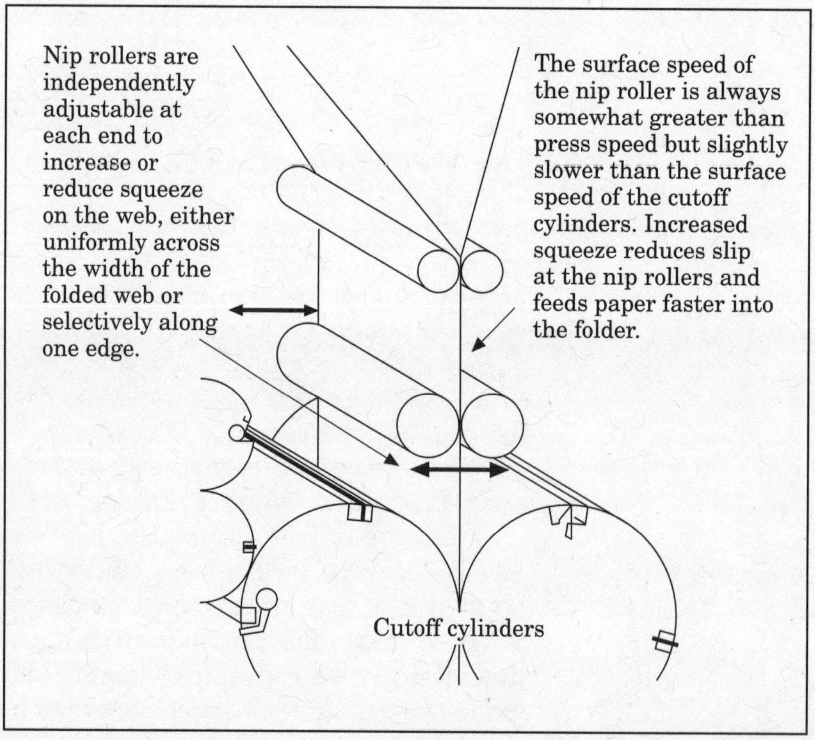

Nip rollers are independently adjustable at each end to increase or reduce squeeze on the web, either uniformly across the width of the folded web or selectively along one edge.
The surface speed of the nip roller is always somewhat greater than press speed but slightly slower than the surface speed of the cutoff cylinders. Increased squeeze reduces slip at the nip rollers and feeds paper faster into the folder.
Cutoff cylinders

Major operating adjustments on the nip rollers
Courtesy Solna Web USA, Inc.

edges of the web going over the former than to the center going over the former nose. The center is where wrinkling, tearing, and smearing can occur. The best approach is to start with uniform pressure on the roller, from front to back, and then experiment to find the settings that produce the least wrinkling.

Cutoff

The cutoff knives extend into a slotted, female die on the opposing cylinder at the moment of cutoff. If the female die is filled with a rubber material that absorbs the shock of the cutoff blade, the problem of blade adjustment is less critical. On many folders, however, the female die is a simple slot across the face of the cylinder. In this case, adjustment becomes critical. Repeated contact between the knife blade and the sides of the slot wears out the blade.

Setting the cutoff blade is not required during every makeready, but the setting should be checked when problems arise or when cutting knives are changed. Set the blade by eyesight while slowly turning over the folder. Check the blade setting by placing tape across the slot at two or three different positions along its length, then turning the cylinder over again and observing where the tape was cut. The knife should be set slightly closer to the leading edge of the slot than to the trailing edge. This procedure can be 100% effective if the press operator also performs a running check on the cutoff adjustment with the aid of a strobe light.

Sometimes, the entire knife box assembly has to be moved. The impaling pins slip into holes in the knife box; therefore, whenever the knife box is moved, the press operator should ensure that the pins align with these holes. When adjusting the release of the pins, the timing should be such that the pins retract and release the sheet as the folding jaw closes.

When the press is running at idling speed, it is normal for alternate signatures to tear out of the pins. This occurs because the folder is starved for paper at very slow speeds, and tension on the alternate signatures is excessively high. This does not indicate improper adjustment on the folder, unless the problem continues at running speeds.

Jaw Fold

The key to clean, accurate, parallel folds is the proper adjustment and timing of the tucker blades and folding jaws.

The tucker blade protrudes from the surface of the cylinder, usually about ⅛ in. (3 mm). On all folders the height of the blade is adjustable to some extent, as is its position on the

Major operating adjustments on the folding jaws and tucker blades

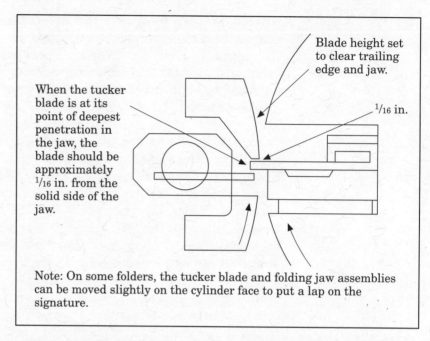

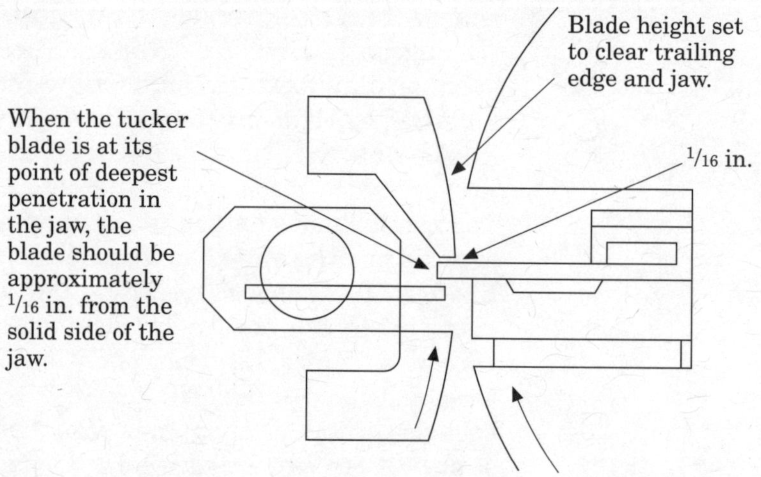
Blade height set to clear trailing edge and jaw.
When the tucker blade is at its point of deepest penetration in the jaw, the blade should be approximately 1/16 in. from the solid side of the jaw.
1/16 in.

Note: On some folders, the tucker blade and folding jaw assemblies can be moved slightly on the cylinder face to put a lap on the signature.

cylinder. The height of the blade should be adjusted with close regard for the entry of the tucker blade into the fully opened jaw. If the height of the blade is excessive, contact with the folding jaws quickly damages the parts and the paper running through them.

The blade should never be set so that it touches either side of the jaw. Allow for the paper thickness that will pass between the blade and the jaw. At the point of its deepest penetration into the jaw, the blade should be set slightly closer to the fixed trailing face of the jaw than to the movable jaw. Close settings against the movable leading face will probably result in loose folds, cracked folds, and wipeout. **Wipeout** is the removal of the inside fold on the face of the tabloid signature. This is caused by the tucker blade not being set at the correct position as it comes out of the marriage between the moveable and solid jaw cylinders. Most press operators cover the tucker blade with the thinnest available Teflon tape to allow the slippage of that tucker blade out of that fold, so that the inside fold does not follow and pull out with the tucker blade as it continues on to the next stage of folding.

Chopper

The folding rollers located under the chopper table should be set first. A large piece of stock to be run is folded to one sheet less than the thickness that will go through the chopper.

When testing the two rollers for drag, check for uniformity of tension from end to end on the rollers.

Adjusting the timing of the chopper blade requires that the headstops have approximately a 9⁄16-in. (14-mm) gap between the signature head as the chopper blade touches the quarter fold. The chopper blade inserts the backbone of the signature into the center of the knurled position on the nip roller. Setting the chopper blade too low can cause the blade to withdraw the signature from between the rollers as the blade retracts.

Major operating adjustments of the chopper folder

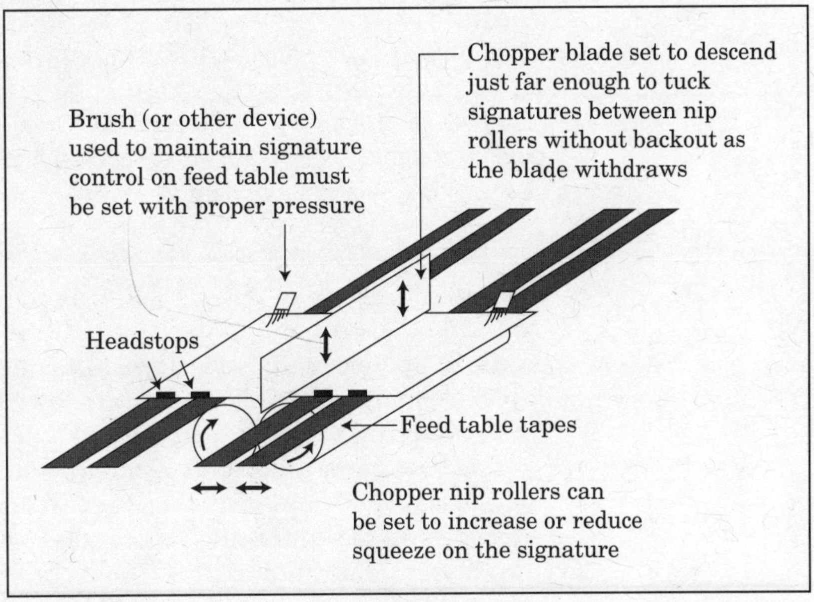

Chopper blade set to descend just far enough to tuck signatures between nip rollers without backout as the blade withdraws
Brush (or other device) used to maintain signature control on feed table must be set with proper pressure
Headstops
Feed table tapes
Chopper nip rollers can be set to increase or reduce squeeze on the signature

Scoring the signature along the intended fold line can improve folding accuracy. Applying a line of moisture along the fold line complements the scoring procedure. Scoring, unlike perforation, is applicable to jobs that are to be sewn or saddle-stitched. A water-glycerine mixture can also help, but it must be used with caution. Such a mixture acts as a plasticizer and can permanently soften the paper. Moisture applied to the chopper fold lines softens the web and improves the accuracy of chopper folds.

Perforators

Perforators are used in folders for two reasons. Sometimes, the finished job calls for a tear-out. The simplest and quickest way to provide for this is to perforate on the run. The second, and more common reason, is to help with folding accuracy and to prevent wrinkles on the inside of the signatures where the head and back meet. These wrinkles are called gussets.

There are two basic perforator designs. *Circumferential perforators* slit the paper in the direction of web travel. Usually, circumferential perforating is performed by a wheel mounted against the roller-top-of-former. *Cross perforators,* on the other hand, perforate the web across its width. This perforation is executed by a set of rotating cylinders below the nip rollers. One cylinder carries the perforating teeth and the other acts as a die for the teeth.

A circumferential perforator wheel set at the top of the former perforates the web lengthwise, usually along the former fold line. Once set and centered, this perforator should not be moved. If the web begins weaving to either side as it crosses the former board, the web guide rollers should guide the perforation back into proper position. This perforator wheel can also be replaced by a slitter wheel that slits the web into ribbons.

Running Makeready

Running makeready begins with the press start-up and ends with the delivery of approved signatures. During this period, work tempo picks up because the paper running through the press is being wasted. The point is to keep this waste down by completing the running makeready as soon as possible.

The press operators' chief concerns at this time are attaining a proper ink/water balance, setting color to a specified density and maintaining it, adequately drying the web, and gaining and maintaining control of the running web in terms of register.

During running makeready, the press operators have to quickly decide whether a given problem requires a press shutdown. Each moment of hesitation increases paper waste.

Inking up the Press

Before webbing the press, the press operators start up the printing units. Ink and water levels are roughly set before running makeready begins. The ink-feed profile across the press is established through adjustment of the fountain keys relative to the form to be printed. This can be judged by looking at the lighted profile on the console or the amount of ink on the fountain roller. Before starting to print, keep the ink level fairly low. This allows the press operator to increase ink feed to the *minimum* needed for good color. Inking up at the same, consistent speed provides close control of the amount of ink introduced into the roller train.

Starting the Press

When ready, the press is put on impression and given a short burst at running speed to check folder and tension settings. This test is usually not necessary if the previous job ran successfully with a similar web-up and comparable paper. The paper used during this test is pure waste, so, if settings are found to be far off, stop the press to make adjustments. Waste must be held to the absolute minimum. Under most conditions, tension is adequate if the web runs fairly tight without weaving from side to side in the press. Additional adjusting will be required during the pressrun.

Running makeready is usually accomplished at a relatively low speed. The speed should be high enough to fire up the dryer. Otherwise, wet ink tracks on the chill rolls, the former board, and the folding cylinders.

The plates are inked after the press and dryer are started. The next step is to put the press on impression, *after* ink and water are on the plate in their correct relative amounts. Too much of either can lead to a web break.

Sometimes, the impression pressure is inched on, especially to accommodate a lightweight coated stock. The half-set ink on the rollers from inking up is now on the plate and blanket. Easing up to full impression allows the web to pull this tacky ink off the blanket little by little rather than all at once and helps to avoid web breaks and coating pick.

As the speed of the press slowly increases, the web may tear out of the pins in the folder cutoff. One remedy is to increase the infeed, chill-roll speed, or both, and run more paper through the press. When the press seems to be running properly and the paper no longer tears out, the infeed setting can be reduced to maintain web tension. A second method is to increase the nip roller pressure, forcing more paper into the folder. This setting, too, can be backed off once the press is running properly. It is usually necessary to increase the squeeze only at the front or the back of the nip rollers.

Ink/water balance and color are rarely up to standard at the beginning of the pressrun, because the ink and water films are purposely set too light. The press operator starts setting ink and water by cutting back on the water until the plate has caught up and is carrying as much ink as the rollers deliver. The units still print weakly at this point. Add just enough water to stop the *catch-up* and allow the press to run for a while. Add more ink followed by just enough water to stop *catch-up*. If color still is not strong enough, repeat this process. The press should always be running on ink/water balance with *minimum ink* and *minimum water.*

Starting the Run

During running makeready, the press runs at approximately 400 ft. (122 m) per min. Once the signatures are okayed, makeready ends and the press operator eases the press up to running speed. There should be no drastic increases in speed during this time. Rather, the increase from makeready to running speed should be gradual. A major reason for this procedure is to keep register and color under control and reduce spoilage. No signatures need be lost in going from makeready to running speed.

Check for proper tension at cutoff by inspecting the holes left by the pins. There should be enough tension on the web to slightly tear the paper at the pins. Too much tension causes the pins to tear out of the paper, while too little tension shows little or no tear behind the holes.

This check is meaningful only if the pins are properly timed in the first place. If they retract too slowly, the pins hold the paper and take it in one direction while the folding jaw also grips the paper, taking it in the opposite direction. The result looks as if the web is under too much tension; in other words, the pins tear out of the sheet. Likewise, if the pins retract too fast, the paper runs free in the folder, causing erratic folding. There is still another factor to be considered, the height of the pins. Pins set too high do not fully retract from the paper and tear out, giving the appearance of too much web tension, improper timing, or both. Most manufacturers supply gauges to set the folder pins and tucker blades to the correct height.

Holes left by the cutoff pins, indicating the amount of tension present at the cutoff

Round holes indicate insufficient tension. Long slits indicate excessive tension. Proper tension is evidenced by slightly elongated holes.

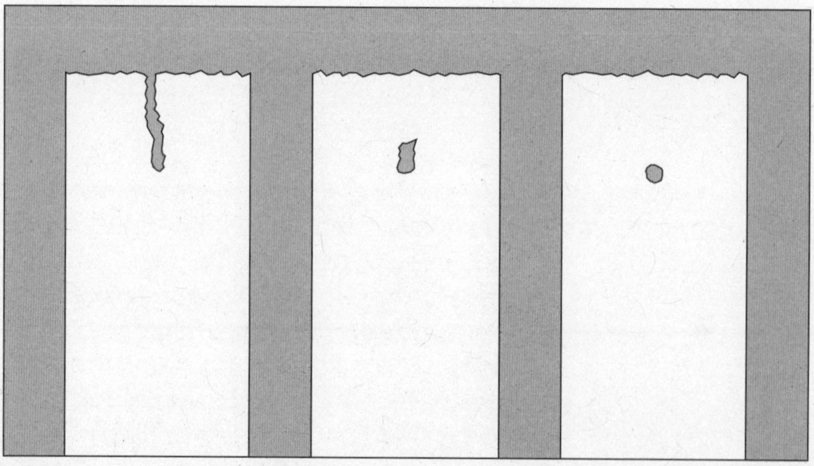

The most important factor affecting the length of makeready is the quality and register of images on the plates as mounted on the press cylinders. If the quality is unacceptable — that is, the images on the plate are not the images that are to be printed on the paper — then, the press operators have to adjust color. Likewise, improper fit and/or misregister extend makeready. If the quality and register are good, then makeready should not exceed 15 min. per plate regardless of how difficult the job is. Under these conditions, it is to be expected that makeready waste can be kept down to 1,000 signatures or less.

It is difficult to pinpoint the speed at which makeready should be carried out. Most dryers fire at about 8,000 or 9,000 impressions/hr. (IPH), and in many plants the press is held at that speed until salable signatures are coming out of the delivery.

At a running speed of 8,000 IPH, a web of 50-lb. coated paper costing $1.00/lb. on a sixteen-page press runs at a cost of about $11.34/min. Multiplying this out, 20 min. of running waste costs about $227 for paper alone. Some stocks cost less, but it can readily be seen that in terms of dollars and cents, the waste factor is something a press crew cannot afford to ignore.

Once salable signatures are delivering, the press is raised to running speed in a series of steps. Depending on the job being run and the characteristics of the press, these increases may range from 2,000 IPH to as much as 5,000 IPH. After each increase, the ink/water balance is restored (if necessary), the tension readjusted, and finer settings are made on the folder. If something goes wrong after any one of these increases in speed, and waste is being produced, slow the press to the previous level and work from there. Once the problem is corrected, increase to running speed. *The objective is to continue to produce salable signatures at all times.* Increasing speed in relatively small increments keeps the press under control and thus avoids waste production.

An Alternative Makeready

If the quality of the job and the fit required are not high, a high-speed makeready may prove to be more economical. With this system, the press is quickly taken up to running speed and a few hundred signatures are run. The press is then shut down and adjusted to the actual printed signatures. After this, the press is brought up to running speed, and salable signatures should be coming out of the delivery.

15 Monitoring the Pressrun

A press must run continuously and efficiently at high speed to achieve maximum productivity; however, a press running at top speed is not necessarily productive. If a press runs steadily at 30,000 impressions/hr. all day, it will produce more than one running at 40,000 impressions/hr. with occasional shutdowns. Every stop leaves surplus water and/or ink in the press, throwing off the ink/water balance. A long stop may result in a dried-out dampening system. At start-up, the press generates spoilage until ink/water balance is restored.

Sometimes, web tension suddenly changes for no apparent reason, throwing off register or folding accuracy. Possible causes are mill splices and changes in mill winding tension that surface as the web unwinds on the press. Waste due to mill splices can be minimized if the roll tender watches for splices and warns the press operator when they are about to go through the press. Most paper-induced tension variations can be completely controlled by a constant-tension infeed.

Blankets must transfer a clean sharp image during the entire pressrun. Several factors affect blanket performance. Some paper coatings readily build up on the blanket (piling), which reduces print quality. Often, the only recourse is to wash the blankets frequently during the run. Some presses are equipped with automatic blanket washers that retard the rate of buildup. A press without automatic blanket washers should not be washed on the fly. The savings in time and paper that might be realized from washing during running are not worth the risk of personal injury or mechanical damage.

Heatset inks can begin to set during the pressrun. The ink becomes less workable due to solvent evaporation caused by heat generated in the inking system. Water-cooled ink oscillators help to control this by limiting temperature increases in the inking system. If the press is not so equipped, use inks with solvents that have relatively high boiling points. Such inks yield their solvents less quickly and remain stable on the press; however, they dry more slowly. Ink that sets on the rollers is not properly formulated for existing conditions.

Cost of Waste and Makeready

Waste and makeready costs vary from one printing operation to the next, depending upon numerous variables. Controlling these variables can greatly reduce the expense generated by waste and makeready.

The following example illustrates the cost of materials and time for one 35-in. (889-mm) web with a 23-in. (584-mm) cut-off. Running a single web, this press consumes approximately 2 lb. of ink per 1,000 signatures. Press time is charged at $425/hr. Makeready averages 2.51 hr. and generates 4,178 waste signatures.

Net press hours per year total 5,318. This represents 277 working days, running 24 hr./day. Twenty percent downtime is figured for maintenance, repairs, and delays.

The press in this example prints 79,911,000 impressions per year, averaging 21,800 impressions per hour (iph)— 20,000 signatures are good. The average pressrun takes 4.95 hr., thus producing 99,000 good signatures. Makeready and printing take 7.46 hr. Available press time allows 713 jobs to be printed.

Paper cost (e.g., $3,056,000) can be determined by dividing total impressions per year (79,911,000) by 1,000; then, multiply by the weight of 1,000 signatures (e.g., 85 lb.); multiply this value by the cost of the paper being run (e.g., $0.45/lb.). Add 3% for wrapper, core, and strip.

Ink costs $1,200,000/year if every 1,000 signatures consumes 2 lb. of ink that costs $7.50/lb.

Working with the previously prescribed parameters, the *cost of 1% of waste* totals $58,000. Total *cost of makeready* for this press totals $920,000/year. Therefore, decreasing 713 makereadies by one minute each saves $6,100/press/year. Furthermore, reducing 713 makereadies by 1% saves an additional $9,200/press/year.

Downtime

Stops in the middle of the pressrun are sometimes unavoidable; however, they are always costly. Studies have indicated that average run intervals are between 0.8 and 1.8 hr., depending on the plant. Stop intervals average between 0.4 and 0.7 hr., also depending on the plant. The average figures are about 1.3 hr./run interval and about 0.55 hr./stop. These figures indicate that between the OK sheet (start of production) to the end of the job the press is running only about 70% of the time. Every plant should have a program aimed at extending the length of the run interval and reducing the length of the stop interval. Improving either figure increases the amount of good signatures produced per running hour.

Reduce downtime by anticipating the stop, assigning specific duties to crew members, and bringing the required materials to the press in advance.

When the press is stopped, immediately gum the plates if it appears that the shutdown will exceed 30 min. (depending on the plate). The plates must be gummed properly to prevent gum streaks in the image areas, which would require additional stops to clean the plate. When restarting the press, some press operators increase speed incrementally while adjusting register and color. If plates blind during the run, rub them with the solution that is recommended by the manufacturer.

Wash blankets as needed to maintain image quality. Several successive jobs may be printed without washing the blankets in between pressruns. The duration of downtime also dictates whether or not blankets should be washed. Manually washing blankets between every pressrun consumes valuable time and reduces productivity. Ink may set on the rollers during makeready. Spray solvents on the rollers to overcome this problem.

Run Length

Web offset printers often encounter discrepancies between run length and final signature count in the bindery. Jobs that come up short in the bindery require rerunning to make up a shortage, which generates an unnecessary expense.

Some pressrooms normally run 2–3% more signatures than the job order calls for just to prevent such a shortage. The cost of such a practice can be estimated by using the figure of $40,000 as the cost of 1% of press production per year. In other words, for a single press, a standard overrun of 3% represents a cost of $120,000 each year. The discrepancy between pressroom and bindery counts is aggravated in most plants, because neither count has been established as accurate. This makes it difficult to locate the cause of the waste.

Historically, two counters attached to the press drive have tracked total count and good count. With this system, the good counter should be turned on and off with the change in production of good and bad signatures. Because of the

Denex laser counter

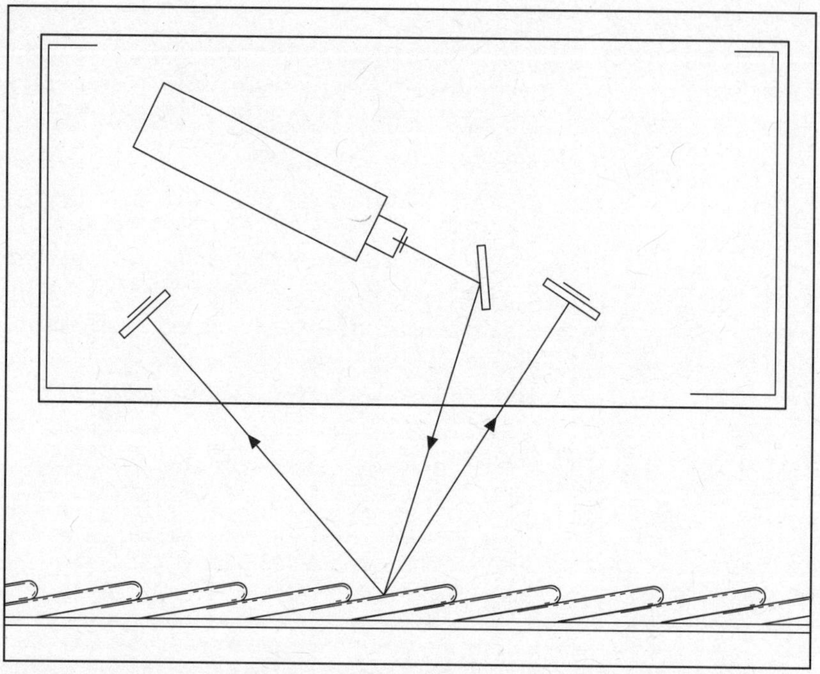

pressures of production in the pressroom, this has never been a satisfactory counting method. There are other common but often overlooked practices that cause errors in counting. First, signatures totaled on the good counter are used as inspection sheets. These signatures are usually discarded. With three or four people on the average crew inspecting signatures, this can become a significant source of inaccurate counts.

A second source of shortage — usually the most important source— arises when bad signatures are thrown out while the counter is running. Catch-ups, off-register and/or poorly folded signatures, and other problems account for numerous signatures that are wasted. Often, these are not accurately accounted for by turning off the good counter. Furthermore, signatures may be discarded by the jogger who is collecting them from the delivery.

All of these items create inaccurate counts coming off the press. Each by itself is probably small enough that it could be ignored; collectively, they represent a significant cause of shortages. Counters that track individual signatures in a delivery stream should be mounted far enough into the delivery system that they avoid any waste signatures, signatures that have been removed for inspection or splices, or other unused signatures.

Automatic counter
Courtesy Automation, Inc.

In addition to a counter, scales are used to weigh stacked and bundled signatures that are unacceptable. A group of signatures previously recorded as good signatures can be taken off a skid and put on the scale and accurately counted. This count would then either be subtracted from the good count or added to the print order count. There are other systems on the market that, when used properly, guarantee an accurate count of good signatures. Such a system gives the printer a source of accurate count and indicates the sources of waste occurring after the press. If you are frequently going back to the press for reruns due to shortages, you need to reevaluate your present counting system.

If bindery spoilage allowances have been figured into the count, there is no need to overrun. The bindery needs only the signatures called for on the print order.

Regardless of the accuracy of the counting procedure used, unforeseen bindery problems can still cause the job to come up short. For this reason, seconds — signatures produced at the end of running makeready before the counter is turned on — are saved in many shops. Usually, seconds are only slightly off register or off color. Seconds, sometimes called salvages or substandards, can be especially useful if the job has several sections to be bound together. Simply by saving a few hundred sections, the bindery may finish a job that otherwise may have been short in only one of the sections. Seconds are often used for makeready in the bindery set-up.

Record Keeping

Records are necessary for the analysis and control of any business. This is especially true for a business that is as complicated and difficult to analyze as printing. In the past, records had to be maintained manually. Fortunately for the printer, computer-controlled data recording systems accurately monitor production on web presses.

If it is necessary to keep manual records, use data forms that are simple to complete. *The press operator's main function is to run the press.* Little time is available to track production performance. The data sheet on page 227 was developed by GATF for gathering information in the pressroom. Wherever possible, the data is entered by merely making a check mark. All of the required information is printed on the form. The exception is quality level, and normally such extended information would be printed on the back of the data sheet for easy reference.

The shaded squares at the top of the job data sheet show that record keeping can be simplified by clarifying the degree of accuracy of information. For example, the last two squares in the areas for showing the number of makeready signatures, good signatures, and the gross count are shaded. This was done because the data only has to be accurate to the nearest 100. When the press crew fills out the information, there is no requirement that they divide the count by 100 and show only the significant figures required. On the other hand, if a person is entering the data into a computer, he or she can be instructed that the information in the shaded areas is to be ignored. The design of the form should lend itself to accurate use. A job data sheet can be used to provide the following information:

- Press production capabilities.
- Cost of running poor quality paper. When this information is relayed to the sales force, jobs requiring these papers may appear less frequently.
- Productivity obtained when using paper with excellent runnability. Relaying this information to the estimator can give the shop a competitive advantage on many jobs.
- Crew efficiency. A good reporting system indicates specific areas in which the crew needs help.
- Consistent figures that may be used to estimate future jobs.
- Excessive white waste. This is pure spoilage. These parts of the roll (wrapper, strip, and butt) never get printed.
- Press problems and mechanical or electrical weaknesses.

JOB DATA SHEET

Plant ______ Year 19 ☐☐ Month ☐☐ Day ☐☐

Job Number ☐☐☐☐☐ Press Number ☐☐

Makeready Hours (to nearest tenth)
Makeready Signatures
Running Hours (to nearest tenth)
Good Signatures
Gross Count (incl. makeready)

Total paper — Pounds
Transit Damage — Pounds
White Waste — Pounds
Paper Costs (cents/lb.) — (nearest tenth)
Basis Weight (pounds) — 25 × 38—500 sh.

Paper Finish
1 ☐ Offset (Book)
2 ☐ Newsprint
3 ☐ Supercalendered
4 ☐ High Bulk
5 ☐ Embossed
6 ☐ Other Uncoated
7 ☐ Dull Coated
8 ☐ Gloss Coated
9 ☐ Coated—One Side
10 ☐ Other—Coated

Type of Plate
1 ☐ Photopolymer—Neg
2 ☐ Photopolymer—Pos
3 ☐ Bimetal—Neg
4 ☐ Bimetal—Pos
5 ☐ Trimetal—Pos
6 ☐ Wipe-on Al.—Neg
7 ☐ Presensitized—Neg
8 ☐ Presensitized—Pos
9 ☐ Other

Type of Blanket
Conventional
1 ☐ 3-Ply
2 ☐ 3-Ply—Quick rel
3 ☐ 4-Ply
4 ☐ 4-Ply—Quick rel
Compressible
5 ☐ 3-Ply
6 ☐ 3-Ply—Quick rel
7 ☐ 4-Ply
8 ☐ 4-Ply—Quick rel

9 ☐ Other

☐ Blankets Changed (during makeready)

Number of:
☐☐ Webs
Press Units Used
☐☐ Plates (originals, do not include makeovers)

☐ Split Fountains (0, 1, 2, etc.)

Job Frequency
1 ☐ Plate Change
2 ☐ Multiple Form
3 ☐ Weekly
4 ☐ Monthly
5 ☐ Every 2 Months
6 ☐ Every 3 Months
7 ☐ Every 4 Months
8 ☐ Every 6 Months
9 ☐ Annually
10 ☐ One-Time Job

Job Folding
1 ☐ Double Former
2 ☐ Combination Folder
3 ☐ Ribbon
4 ☐ Ribbon—Interleaved
5 ☐ Ribbon + Former
6 ☐ Sheeter
7 ☐ Two Folders

Paper Changed (from last job)
1 ☐ No Change
2 ☐ Change Paper (type, brand, or basis weight)
3 ☐ Changed Width (or number of webs)
4 ☐ Changed Paper and Width (or number of webs)

Perforation
1 ☐ No Perforation
2 ☐ Running Perforation
3 ☐ Cross Perforation
4 ☐ Running and Cross Perforation

Paste
1 ☐ No Paste
2 ☐ Job Pasted on Press

Folder Change from Last Job
1 ☐ No Change
2 ☐ Minimum Change (tabloid to chop)
3 ☐ More Difficult Change
4 ☐ Change from Folder (or sheeter) to Folder
5 ☐ Change from Folder to Sheeter
6 ☐ Make Change That Requires Machinist

Accuracy of Fold
1 ☐ Not Important
2 ☐ Average
3 ☐ Important
4 ☐ Critical

Sheets Okayed By:
1 ☐ Production Dept.
2 ☐ Quality Control
3 ☐ Art Department
4 ☐ Salesperson
5 ☐ Customer

Total Ink Coverage
1 ☐ 0–50%
2 ☐ 100% (±50%)
3 ☐ 200% (±50%)
4 ☐ 300% (±50%)

Spot Color
☐ Number of Plates with Spot Color (0, 1, 2, 3)

Quality Level
1 ☐ See Separate Sheet
2 ☐ for Definitions
3 ☐
4 ☐
5 ☐

☐ No. of Products Delivered

☐ No. of People Used on Crew

	1st Shift		2nd Shift		3rd Shift	
1st Operator						
2nd Operator						
3rd Operator						

- Areas for improvement.
- Waste and the reasons for it during makeready and the pressrun.
- Damaged paper rolls. Relay this information to the manufacturer.
- Bad splices. Automatic pasters must operate at 95% efficiency or higher to be economical.

The following two illustrations show two approaches to record keeping. Many other items may have to be recorded in order to determine the cause of reduced production or increased waste; for example, the frequency that blankets had to be washed during the run of a given paper, the mechanical

A form for recording both numerical and verbal information, with emphasis on the identification of paper and press problems

WEB PRESS RECORD FORM

Press no. ______ Press operator ________________ Date ______________
Customer ________________ Issue ____________ Job no. ____________

Time:

At start of makeready ____________ a.m. / p.m. Form no. ____________

At end of run ________________ a.m. / p.m. Imposition style __________

Impressions required ________________ Press speed __________ IPH

Counter Reading: Strip waste ____________

Total counter at start of run __________ Printed waste __________

Total counter at end of run __________

Job counter at end of run __________

Paper: Code no. ________ Roll no. ________ Record all stops

Roll damage: ______________

Performance of paper on press (circle most applicable number)
(worst) 1 2 3 4 5 6 7 8 9 10 (best)

Web breaks during run ____________

Location of break Reason for break

Plates: No. of plates required for normal job ___ Excess plates needed ______

Reason for excess plates ____________________

Quality: Of pressrun (circle most applicable number)
(unacceptable) 1 2 3 4 5 6 7 8 9 10 (excellent)

Comments and Problem Areas: (continue on other side if necessary)

A record keeping form that emphasizes quantitative information regarding production

PAR-WEB OFFSET REPORT FORM*

Press Mfgr. ______ Rated Speed ____ IPH Auto Pasters ____ Roll Stands ____ Perfecting Units ____ Type of Folder ____ Cutoff ____ Width ____

Job. No.	Type of Makeready	Type of Paper	Chargeable Hours				Standard Hours	Non-chargeable Hours	Percent of Productivity	Makeready Impressions	Net Good Impressions	Run Average Per Hour	Gross Run Impressions	Run Spoilage Percent	Paper Consumed Pounds	White Waste	
			MR	WU	Run	Total										Pounds	%

*All data will be treated confidentially.

Courtesy Web Offset Association, Printing Industries of America

troubles encountered on the press, and downtime. Record the cause and duration of downtime and the amount of time successfully run between stops. Reducing stop intervals and increasing running time can greatly increase production per running hour.

Computers

Computerized monitoring devices attached to the press record most of the information required to analyze the printing operation with little or no effort on the part of the press crew. These systems immediately provide press performance information, and the crew can make the necessary adjustments to maintain print quality.

Controlling quality is beyond the computer's capability. Quality is generally not measurable; however, by measuring and adjusting individual printing parameters, the press crew can control quality. One problem is that quality characteristics can be interrelated. For example, quality might be improved by increasing sharpness and increasing density. However, increasing sharpness may decrease density. The two characteristics are not independently controllable.

Furthermore, specific printing parameters may be controlled by several methods. For example, if the density on a job decreases while the press is running, there is not enough ink on the paper. The press operator could increase the ink film thickness; however, a loss of density is often caused by excessive water. In this case, the ink feed and water should be decreased at the same time. Computers only provide data; the press crew must interpret the information, evaluate press performance, and adjust press controls.

16 Paper

Web offset printing papers include newsprint, offset, coated free sheet or groundwood, and super-calendered. The surface of web offset papers should resist picking and be relatively free of dust and lint. The paper should resist moisture, thus preventing fountain solution from loosening the surface fibers or coating pigment. It must also exhibit good ink receptivity and high holdout.

Raw Materials

The principal raw material for producing paper is cellulose fibers, short and threadlike structures obtained mainly from wood. There are four chief sources of cellulose fiber: softwoods, hardwoods, secondary (recycled) fiber, and *rag,* usually composed of textile cuttings and cotton. In addition, synthetic fibers are used for some specialty papers. Softwood and hardwood pulps are most commonly used in web offset papers. These woods are transformed into the pulps used in the papermaking process.

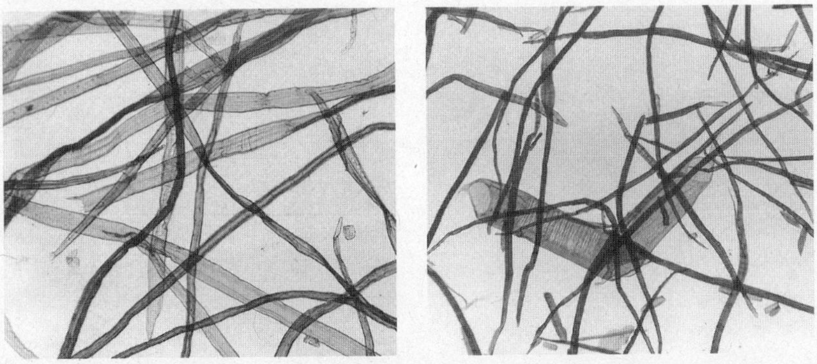

Softwood *(left)* and hardwood kraft fibers before beating, magnified 90×
Courtesy Institute of Paper Science and Technology

In addition to fiber, printing papers generally contain sizing materials, mineral filler, and coloring matter. Sizing may be added internally, externally, or both. Internal sizing is intended to give the paper the desired water resistance. Surface sizing controls the absorption of printing ink, reduces the picking of surface fibers, and may serve as a preliminary treatment for subsequent coating of the paper.

Mineral fillers are added to the fiber before the sheet is formed to improve smoothness, ink receptivity, opacity, and color. They also reduce strike-through, a condition whereby ink penetrates the paper and shows up on the other side. Fillers also improve the ink receptivity of offset papers. Paper that has been sized but not filled may not accept printing ink quickly enough for good initial setting, especially at high press speeds. Fillers also reduce dot distortion and show-through, which is a lack of opacity in paper that allows the image to show through to the reverse side of the sheet. Fillers improve the brightness (whiteness) of paper, and pigments may sometimes be added for colored papers.

Papermaking

Most printing papers are made on fourdrinier machines. A mixture of pulp and water (furnish) flows onto the wire — a continuous, moving screen through which water drains — leaving the fibers in a thin sheet or web. The fibers align

A fourdrinier machine, viewed from the dry end
Courtesy P. H. Glatfelter Co.

Optireel, which is used in the reeling process on paper machines
Courtesy Valmet Paper Machinery, Inc.

with the moving wire, which determines the *grain direction*. The web transfers from the wire to a continuous felt blanket that carries it to the steam-heated dryer cylinders. Each side of the paper is designated as either the *wire side* or the *felt side*.

The wire and felt sides exhibit different characteristics, and print quality may vary from one side to the other. Twin-wire machines form the paper *between* two wires; thus, the resulting web has two wire sides.

Surface-sized paper is made by passing the partially dried web between two rollers that apply the solution of sizing material. The size press is located in the dryer section of the machine.

After being dried, the paper web is calendered between polished steel rollers to give it the desired smoothness. It is now *machine-finish* (M.F.) paper.

Supercalendered paper is made by running machine-finish paper through the supercalender, a machine consisting of alternate polished steel and compressed paper or cotton rollers running together under high pressure. It compresses the paper and increases surface smoothness and gloss.

Coated papers are stocks that have received mineral application, usually clay, to improve their printability and appearance. They are available in a variety of finishes. Coatings improve pick resistance, ink holdout, and overall print quality. Usually, paper is coated on two sides (C2S). Labels and some specialty products are only coated on one side (C1S).

A supercalender

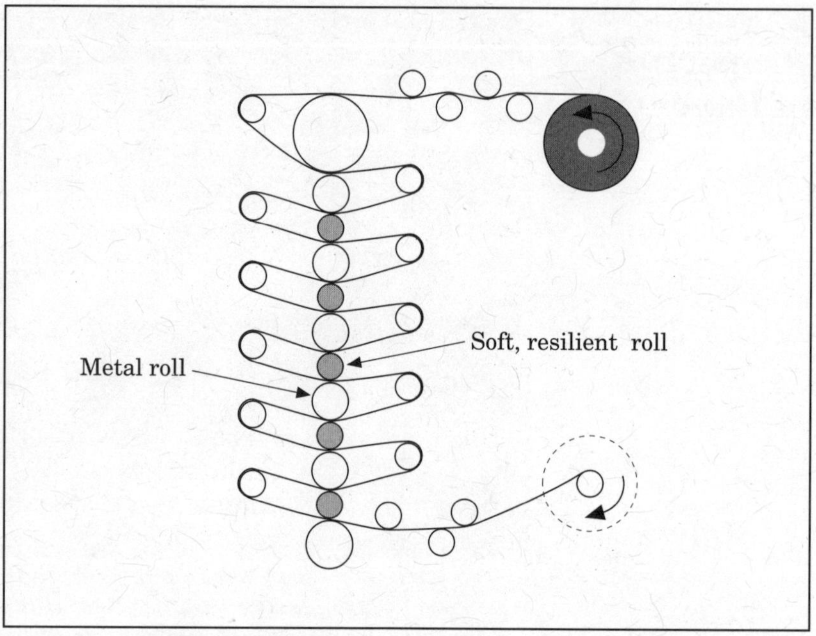

Offset newsprint is a low-grade paper used mainly to economically produce a large quantity of newspapers by the offset method. Most newspapers were formerly printed by letterpress; however, offset lithography prints much finer and better halftones, thus lending itself to the wider use of quality pictures and color in news and advertising. The web offset presses designed for newspaper printing generally do not have dryers. The inks dry entirely by absorption and oxidation.

Paper Finishing

Paper machines vary in width. The widest web is over 300 in. (7,620 mm), but most printing papers are made on 100- to 200-in.-wide (2,540- to 5,080-mm-wide) machines that produce what is called a parent or log roll. This roll is slit to the needed width either at the dry end of the paper machine or in a separate operation. Rolls of the slit paper are wound on cores or reels for use directly on web presses.

It is during the paper finishing operations that two important aspects of quality control—namely, elimination of physical defects and maintenance of moisture content—can either be emphasized or neglected. It has been stated that 50% of the mechanical troubles in paper are either caused in the finishing room or can be reasonably eliminated there. Automatic optical and electronic systems are used to detect and eliminate flaws such as holes and dirt.

Physical Properties of Paper

Paper is a porous material in which the pores or voids sometimes amount to half its total volume. Its structure is determined by the materials used in its manufacture and by the forces that enter into the papermaking operation. Important physical characteristics of paper are thickness, strength, and surface quality. Other structural characteristics that are of importance to the printer include grain, two-sidedness, and density.

Grain

Grain is a characteristic of all machine-made papers. It results primarily from fiber alignment during the formation or drying of the sheet. The fibers tend to align themselves parallel to the direction traveled by the wire of the paper machine. On all roll papers, grain direction is lengthwise on the web, parallel to the direction of web travel. The effects of grain on paper properties are as follows:

- Paper tears and folds more easily in the grain direction than across the grain.
- Paper exhibits greater stiffness and higher tensile strength in the grain direction.
- Paper absorbs or gives off moisture with changes in atmospheric humidity. When in contact with a wet blanket, passing through a dryer, and running in contact with chill rolls, it expands or contracts more in the cross direction than in the grain direction.

Two-Sidedness

Because paper is first formed on the wire screen of a paper machine, its two sides are different in structure. The bottom

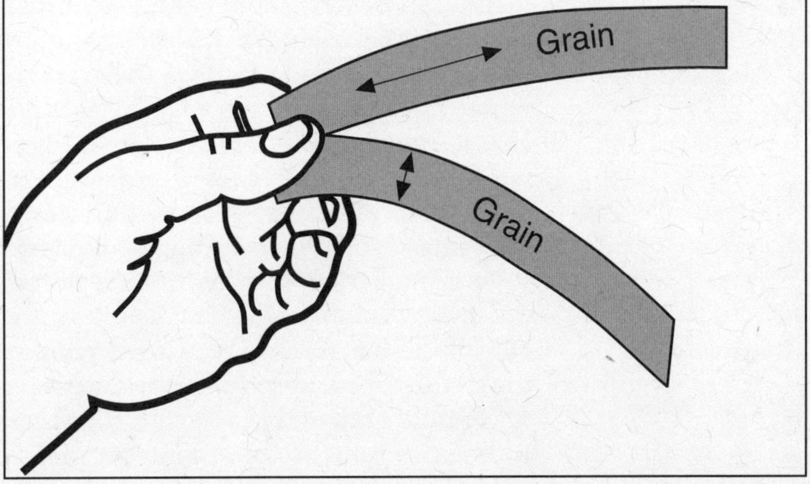

Paper cut in the direction of the paper grain *(top)* and across it

Paper is stiffer in the direction of the grain than across the grain, and folds are cleanest when made parallel to the grain direction or wire side has a porosity somewhat different from that of the top or felt side and is somewhat different in composition. The fibers on the wire side line up more completely in the machine direction than those on the felt side.

Thus, the finished sheet is two-sided. The wire side of uncoated paper has an open structure, contains less size and filler and fewer short fibers, and has a more pronounced grain. The felt side has a closer structure and less grain, because the fibers are more completely interwoven. The sophistication of modern papermaking machines has greatly reduced two-sidedness. Both sides of the stock manufactured on conventional machines print equally well. As previously stated, paper made on a twin-wire machine has two wire sides.

Density

Density is the weight of paper relative to its volume. Dense papers are compact and their fibers are strongly bonded together. Surface-sizing and supercalendering also increase density. In soft, bulky, porous papers, individual fibers can swell or shrink without so much change in the overall dimensions of the sheet. The dimensional stability of paper, therefore, closely relates to density. It is related to the amount of change in the dimensions of a sheet for a given change in its moisture content.

Nonuniform density in a web can cause tension variations. Especially in uncoated stocks, uneven density can also lead to nonuniform ink absorption, which appears most noticeably in solids and halftones (mottle).

Color

Paper can be made in almost any color. Process color reproduction, however, should employ white paper, because any color in paper reduces the color gamut of the reproduction. The colors affected most are those complementary to the paper color. Blue sheets reduce the clarity of yellow, and red sheets cause green to appear gray. Slight variations from white (blue-white, cream-white, or pink-white) may still produce acceptable results; however, they are visibly discernible. As white a sheet as possible is necessary to get the maximum color gamut from any given set of process inks.

Brightness

Brightness of paper is measured with a blue wavelength (457 nm), which provides a value indicative of the degree of bleaching. Optical brighteners that increase blue-light reflectance contribute to contrast in the printed subject—

provided that the colors are limited to blue and black — and therefore to brilliance, snap, and sparkle. Brightness reduces the color gamut of yellows, reds, and greens. Variations in brightness detract from print quality, most noticeably in large areas of halftone tints.

Whiteness

Whiteness is the degree of reflectance, in *uniform* amounts, of red, green, and blue light. White objects are highly reflective. Conversely, black objects reflect little or no red, green, and blue light, although the reflectance — or the lack thereof — may be uniform.

Reflectiveness

Paper reflects light superficially and internally. Some of the light that falls on the white areas in printed halftones penetrates the paper, where it is scattered. Part of the scattered light is trapped behind the halftone dots.

As a result, the white areas between dots appear lower in brightness than large white areas under the same illumination. Deeper light penetration increases light scattering. This results in increased contrast in the highlights and decreased contrast in the shadows. In addition, all tone values are darkened. Low contrast means lack of brilliance, snap, sparkle, and clarity of detail.

Mineral filler and coating pigment reflect more light than cellulose fiber, prevent the deep penetration of light, and yield higher halftone contrast.

Opacity

Opacity, the extent to which light transmission is obstructed, controls show-through of printed matter. Show-through is the lack of opacity that allows the printing on the reverse side of the sheet to be seen through the stock. Excessive show-through reduces contrast and detracts from print quality.

Show-through is different from strike-through. Strike-through is excessive penetration of ink through the sheet.

Smoothness

Smoothness describes the continuous evenness of a paper's surface. Smoother paper surfaces require thinner ink film to attain adequate coverage. A thin ink film promotes better rendition of tones, greater sharpness, and clarity of detail.

Gloss

Gloss is the property of a paper surface or a printed ink film determined by the degree to which specular reflection exceeds diffuse reflection. High-gloss papers are desirable for some applications but inappropriate for others. They enhance the brilliance and intensity of colors but are objectionable for reading matter because of glare. Paper gloss has an important effect on the gloss or finish of printed ink films. When identical ink films are printed on papers of equal ink absorbency, the ink gloss is always higher on the glossier paper.

Performance Requirements of Web Papers

Papers used in web offset come in a wide variety of classes and finishes. Their basis weights range from about 17 lb. to more than 100 lb. — basic size 25×38 in. (25–148 g/m^2). Heavier weights can be run but do not handle well in folders and are usually delivered in sheets. Heavier-weight coated papers are also more prone to blistering. Lighter-weight papers are difficult to run because of their lower tensile strength and lower stress resistance. For satisfactory performance in web offset, papers should meet the following basic requirements.

Flatness

Webs should be flat enough to pass through the printing nips without wrinkling or excessively distorting. Flatness is only in part achieved through proper press settings. Webs with wavy edges and baggy centers sometimes show up on the press. The problems are usually the result of varying moisture content or basis weight in the web. These webs can be substantially improved on the press by increasing the distance traveled and the tension between the roll and the first printing unit.

Moisture Content

Web stress is constant on the press when tension settings have been completed. The forces applied to the web stay the same during the pressrun. As the web picks up moisture from unit to unit during the pressrun, its dimensional stability changes. Tension must be adjusted to maintain register.

Nonuniformity in moisture content is more frequent across the web width. Variation in this direction can result in one or both edges of the web running tight while the center runs baggy or vice versa. This can lead to localized misregister, wrinkling, and doubling in the loose parts of the web. Modern infeed tension control devices improve the runnability of such a roll by subjecting it to maximum pre-stressing before it reaches the printing units. Alternatively, the web may be run through the longest possible lead in the infeed under the high tension.

Moisture content should be as uniform as possible throughout the roll. It should also be as high as possible — but within web paper specifications. The dryer drives most of the moisture out of the web. Dry paper cracks easily in the folder, and delivered signatures are extremely dry. If a bound book has low moisture, it will pick up atmospheric moisture, turning the edges wavy. Remoisturizing restores adequate moisture content to uncoated paper, ensuring that the delivered signatures remain dimensionally stable. This process also reduces static electricity in the web.

Note that many of the sheetfed printer's concerns about conditioning paper to pressroom atmosphere do not apply to the web printer. If wrappings are left on the roll as long as possible, atmospheric humidity has little effect on roll moisture content. The edges of the roll are tightly wound and relatively impervious to atmospheric moisture.

Moisture Resistance

Fountain solution weakens the coatings of some papers, especially in four-color process work. Material from a weakened coating can be picked off and cause print defects or blanket piling.

Internal Strength

Because web papers that run on blanket-to-blanket presses are printed on both sides simultaneously with thin films of high tack inks, they are subjected to forces that can cause internal rupture or delamination. Delamination occurs when the web adheres to both blankets past the point of impression in an S-wrap.

S-wrap and delamination

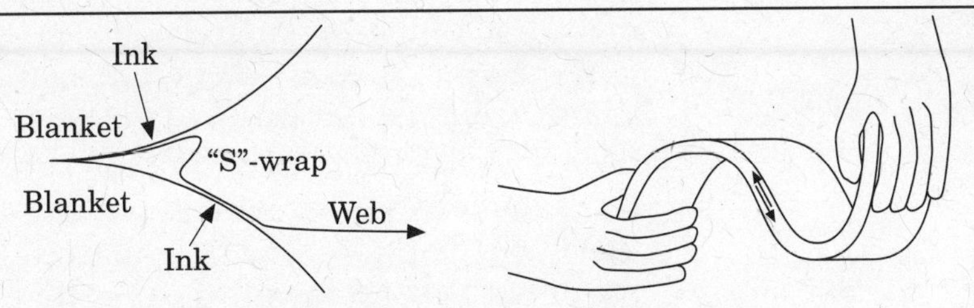

A web can wrap on both the top and bottom blankets at the same time. Delamination is associated with this type of S-wrap. In the right-hand drawing, the part of the paper between the two bends is under particularly high stress.

Delamination, unlike blistering, occurs on one side of the paper only. It is long in the press direction and ragged in appearance. Delamination occurs in the printing units of blanket-to-blanket presses. The effect can be cumulative on multicolor printing.

Dimensional Stability

In printing, the paper web is under tension all the way from the roll to the cutoff. Uniform mechanical stretch is necessary for good register and requires uniformity of fiber density and paper moisture content.

Paper Printability

Printability is the characteristic of paper that is directly related to the quality of the images printed on it. Physical and optical properties of paper and its surface affect tone and color reproduction, smoothness of print, and therefore the appearance of the printed reproduction. Diverse papers provide varying degrees of fidelity in tone and color, contrast, smoothness of halftones and solids, and clarity of detail.

The attractiveness of a printed reproduction depends on the nature of the original and the end use of the printed piece. Some subjects such as portraits, greeting cards, or abstract art appear more attractive when reproduced with the soft effects obtainable on a rough vellum stock. Other subjects such as machinery, furniture, or food illustrations, requiring sharpness and clear detail, are best reproduced on a high-finished or coated stock.

Surface Strength

Surface strength is the characteristic of paper that enables it to resist external forces — chemical and mechanical — as it passes through the printing press. Diverse papers exhibit varying degrees of surface strength.

Paper Condition

The condition of the paper rolls is important. They should be round and uniformly wound under proper tension; they should be free from soft spots, welts, corrugations, and water streaks; and they should not be *starred*. Fully protect them from the atmosphere and maintain constant moisture content throughout by proper wrapping. The wrappings should be undamaged and kept on the roll until just before it is run on the press. Several layers of paper that must be slabbed off the outside of a damaged roll represent a substantial loss.

Paper Problems

The variability in paper and printing techniques contributes to paper problems. Problems can be due to improper paper or paperboard, printing plates, inks, printing process, or any combination of these factors. Frequently, the cause may be an unworkable combination of paper and ink on the press.

Piling

Piling is the accumulation of material on the printing blanket or the plate. This buildup usually contains paper, ink, and

A Gallery of Paper Defects

Burst:
An irregular separation or rupture in the wound roll, usually shortest in the cross-machine direction.

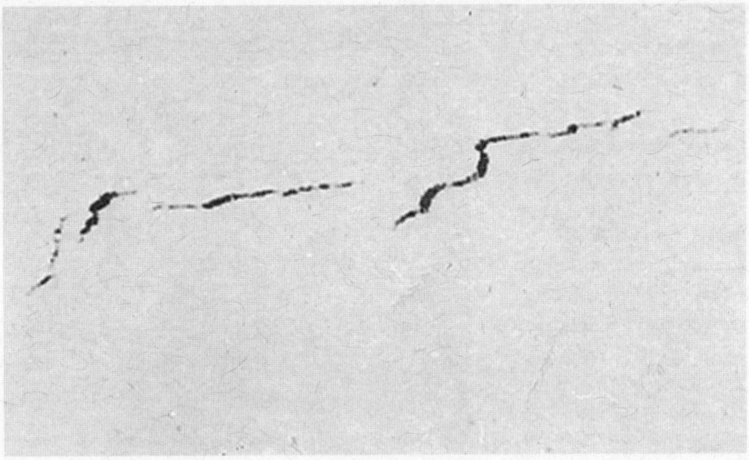

Calender cut:
A straight, sharp cut with a glazed edge, running for a relatively short distance at an angle to the direction of web travel. It is caused by a wrinkle in the web going through and being hard pressed by the calender.

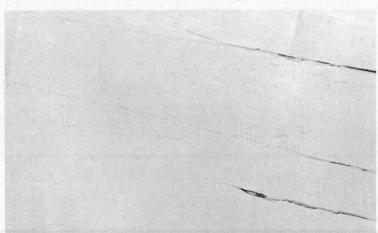

Calender spot:
A defect or imperfection in paper appearing in the form of a glazed or indented spot, often transparent. It is caused by a small flake or piece of paper that adheres to the calender rolls or is carried through the roll on the paper sheet.

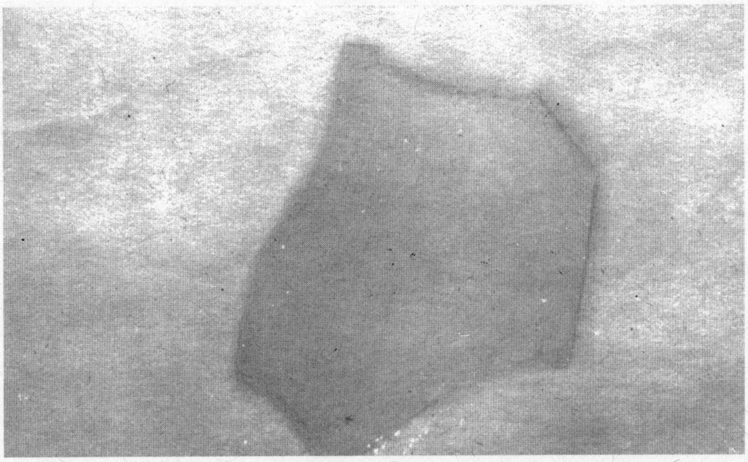

A Gallery of Paper Defects

(continued)

Corrugated roll:
A roll with bands of relatively uniform width that extend around a roll parallel to the machine direction and within which are diagonal markings resembling a rope or tire-like pattern.

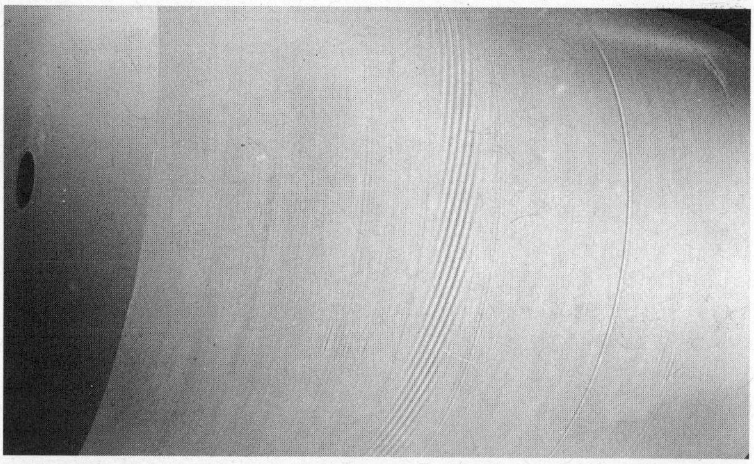

Damaged edge:
The outer portion of the roll that has been rendered useless due to mishandling. The damaged layers must be slabbed off the roll so that this paper does not enter the press.

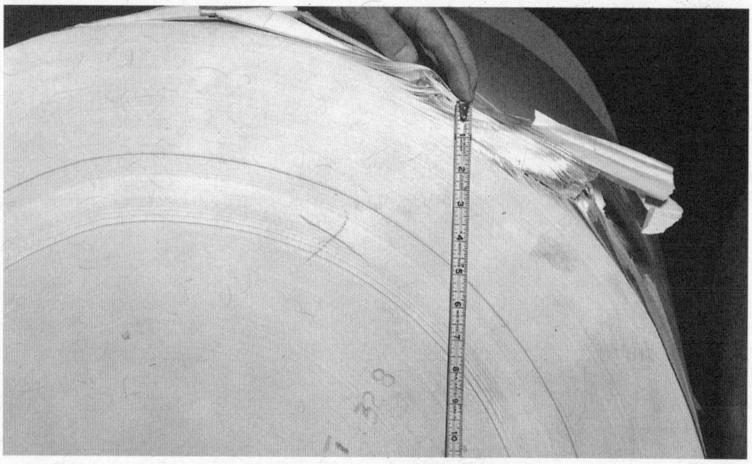

Fiber cut:
A short, straight, fairly smooth, randomly located cut caused by passage through the calender of a fiber or shive embedded in the web of paper.

A Gallery of Paper Defects

(continued)

Hair cut:
A sharp, smooth curved cut having no characteristic length or direction, which is caused by hair or some synthetic fiber getting into the web.

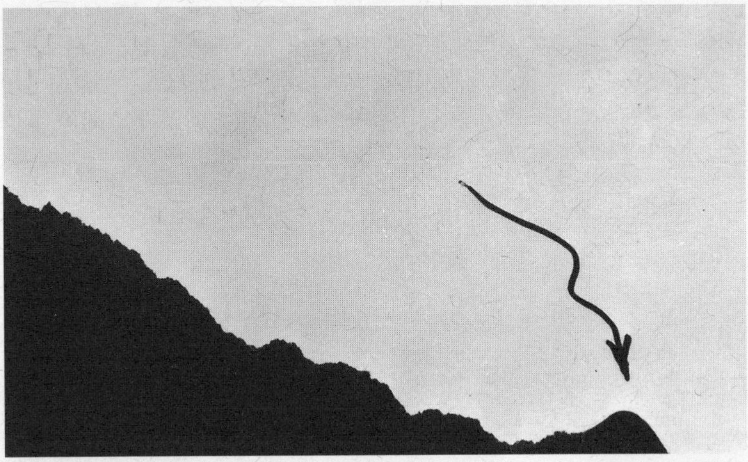

Out-of-round roll:
A roll with an irregular shape caused by storage on its side, excessive roll clamp pressure, or dropping or bumping the roll.

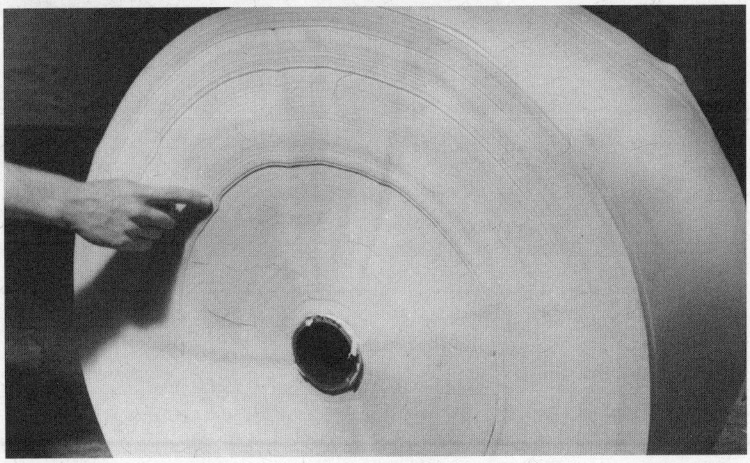

Telescoped roll:
A roll with progressive edge misalignment, concave or convex, due to slippage of its inner layers in the direction of its axis as a result of a thrust force on or within its body after being wound.

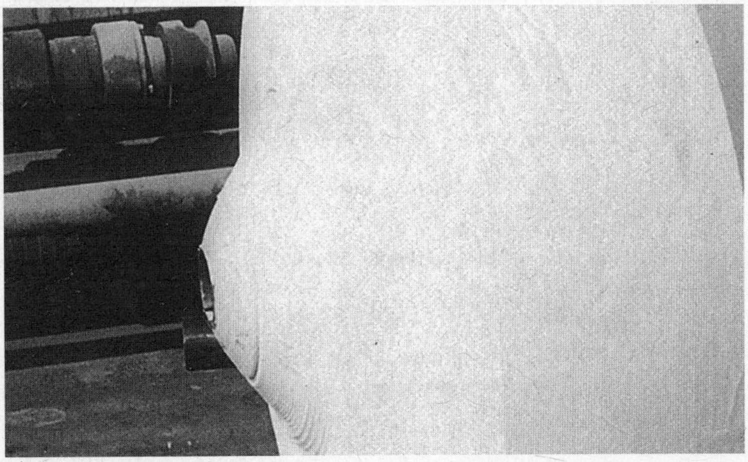

substances from the fountain solution. Coated and uncoated papers can generate piling. With uncoated papers, mineral filler can accumulate on the blanket, forming an abrasive layer. This wears the desensitizing film off the nonimage areas of the plate and may cause scumming.

Coated papers cause piling if the coating adhesive is too water-soluble. Starch-coated letterpress papers are most likely to cause piling in lithography. To be free from piling tendency, coated papers must have enough moisture resistance to prevent separation of any pigment from their coatings during printing, even in four-color presswork.

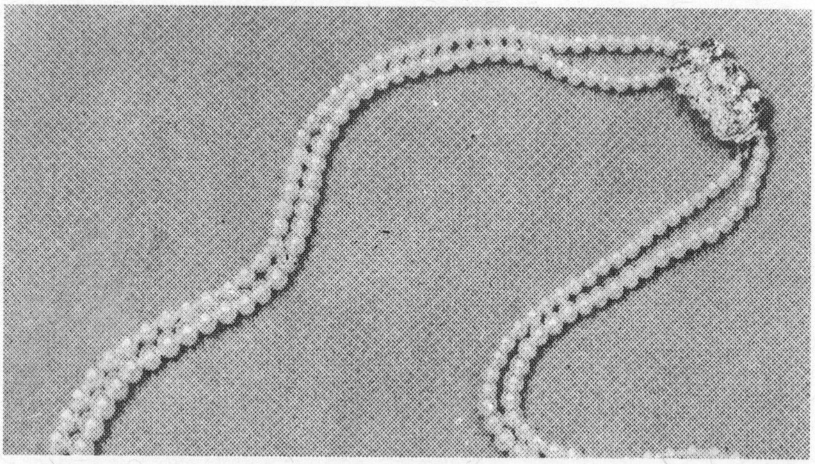

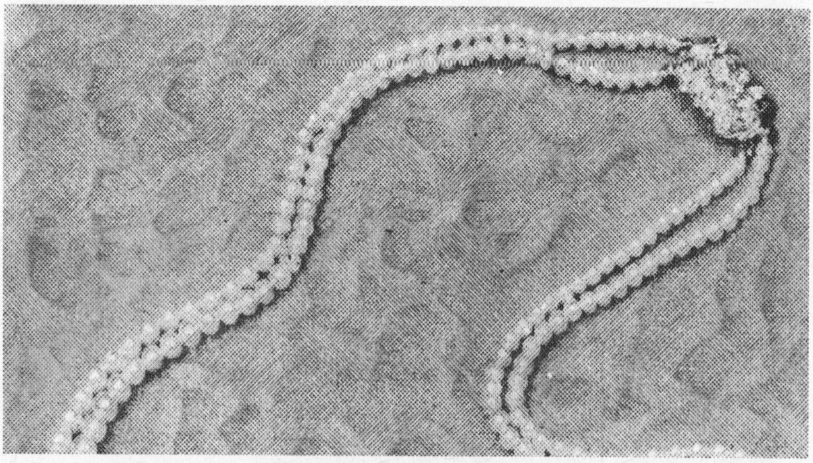

Paper coating piling: an enlargement of a print taken at the start of the run *(top)* and the same subject after 2,300 impressions, showing the effects of coating piling in the halftone printing areas

Linting

Linting is the transfer of loosely bonded paper surface fibers to the blanket. It differs from picking in that the sheet may have adequate pick resistance, but widely scattered individual fibers are picked up by the blanket. Each impression may

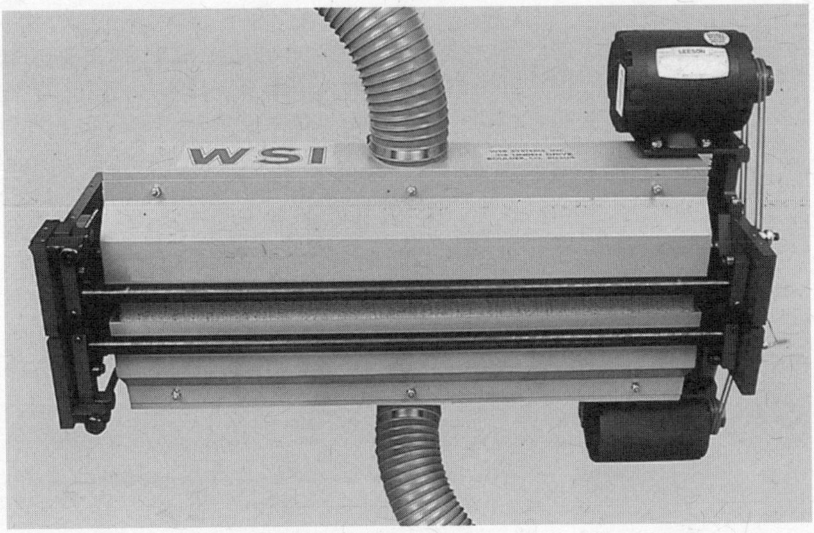

Turbo™ web cleaner, which incorporates a patented 3,000 RPM rotating buff and vacuum system to remove particles 40 μm or smaller
Courtesy Web Systems, Inc.

carry only a few of these fibers. After a few thousand impressions, the blanket, plate, and inking system can become so contaminated with fibers that the press has to be stopped and washed up. Linting is a prevalent problem with newsprint and uncoated groundwood papers. Linting is usually worse on the wire side than on the felt side of the paper. Sometimes linting occurs on the second, third, or fourth units of a multicolor press with no sign of it on the first unit. This happens because the starch surface size holds the fibers on the web during one or more impressions. After the first unit, the sizing becomes softened and the surface fibers are released and picked up by the tacky ink.

Picking

Picking is the separation of a paper's surface and its adhesion to inked blankets. Picking occurs when the ink tack (pulling force) exceeds the surface strength. Counteract picking by reducing the ink tack, the press speed, or both. Reducing ink tack is often an unsatisfactory remedy, because it affects print quality. Wash picked paper fibers from the blanket to maintain print quality on subsequent impressions.

Picking appears in various forms that always involve rupturing of the paper, and it occurs principally in solid areas.

Uncoated papers may yield small clumps of fibers that stick to the blanket and mar the printing on succeeding impressions until they are removed. The fibers quickly soak up water and reject ink, thus producing white spots in the printing. Similar spots are caused by slitter dust. To find the specific cause, select a typical spot and trace its origin to the signature where it first appeared. Examine the spot with a magnifying glass or microscope. A ruptured paper surface indicates picking. Otherwise, a loose paper particle probably generated the defect. Coated papers pick when improperly bonded coating separates from the base stock.

Offset papers must resist the force of thin ink films, which have relatively high tack. Furthermore, the resilient surfaces of offset blankets conform to paper and pull on printing and nonprinting areas.

Blistering

A combination of a heavy, tightly sealed coating, high basis weight, and high moisture content can be especially troublesome in web offset. When such a stock is printed with heavy ink coverage on both sides, internal moisture that is vaporized by the dryer cannot escape through the surface. Small bubble-like formations called blisters appear on the web surface. Blisters are round or oval and sharply defined, and each blister occurs on both sides of the web. About the only remedy, aside from avoiding such stocks or buying a better dryer, is to run the press slower and with minimum heat.

Blistering

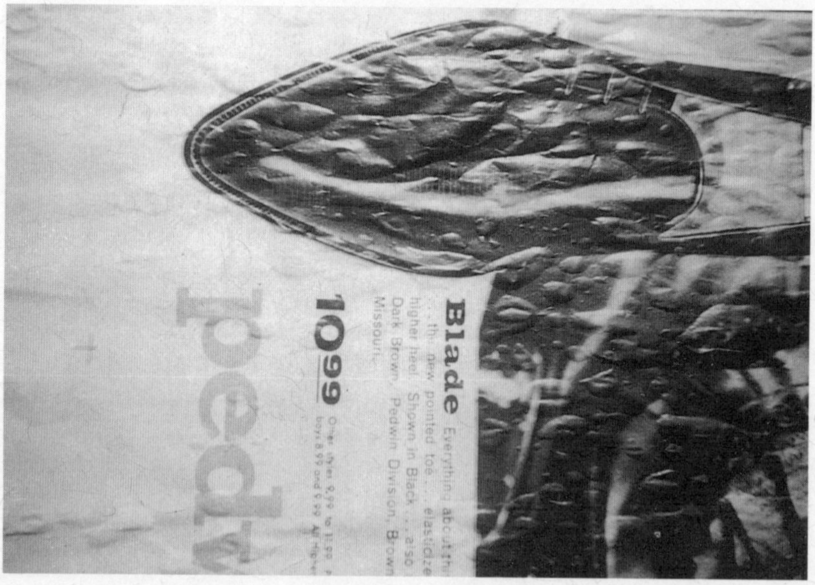

Ordering Paper in Rolls

Paper must be appropriate for the job. Selection of paper should be determined by speed of the press, number of colors to be overprinted, area of coverage, whether printing one or two sides of the sheet, and quality of results desired. The job to be printed is therefore an important consideration when selecting paper. The web offset printer can reduce paper and paper/ink performance variations by limiting the number of stocks in use.

Web Strength

Paper runs off a reel and delivers as signatures, sheets, or rolls. When paper is running at high speed, its strength and printing qualities are tried severely. Paper may be punched, numbered, perforated, slitted, and folded. It is often subjected to several post-press binding and finishing operations. The paper must endure the stresses applied by these operations.

Ordering Tips

The following tips provide guidelines to increase productivity and reduce waste.

- Order rolls made to maximum diameter. Fewer roll changes during a run reduce the number of press adjustments required, thus maintaining efficient, profitable operation.
- Limit the number of splices in rolls. This also reduces the number of press adjustments.
- Mark all splices so that the signatures containing them may be removed from the delivery.
- Specify the maximum basis weight required. The operator buys yardage, not pounds of paper. Most mills, on the other hand, sell paper in pounds, not yardage. When ordering 17×22 in. – 20-lb. (75 g/m^2) bond paper without stipulating *not heavier than,* buyers may receive 21-lb. or even 23-lb. paper. Consequently, yardage is cut down, yielding less product.
- Allow for about 3–5% spoilage for transit, wrapper, and core waste when estimating. (The weight of the roll includes the outside wrapper and the core.) The last few feet of paper nearest the core are unusable.
- Specify *free from slitter dust.* Slitter dust causes printing defects during the pressrun. Dust often piles up on the blanket of offset presses, resulting in spoilage and lost time for washups.
- Provide the proper core information. Although there is no standard size for cores, the 3.5-in. (88.9-mm) size is generally used. Roll chucks dictate the proper core size. Specify returnable or nonreturnable core. Request slotted cores if the press requires them. Large, heavy rolls may be shipped on returnable iron cores.
- Stipulate *rewound* when rolls are a narrow width. Narrow gauge equipment is high-precision equipment.

Slitting must be exact, and winding must be hard and firm.

- Specify *wire side out* or *felt side out*. Some splicers allow the roll to be unwound in one direction only. If it is desirable to run one side or the other up, winding must be specified.
- Specify *directional arrows to appear on wrappers*. These are an aid in proper orientation of the roll when it is delivered to the pressroom.
- Give handling instructions to shippers. Shipping and storing rolls on their ends is recommended.
- Stipulate weight of shipment, and show roll weights on wrappers. Since no two rolls in your order will be identical in weight, instruct your paper suppliers to number rolls and prominently mark the weight of each roll. Then as you receive, inventory, and select rolls for the press, you can identify them and fit their contents into each job requirement.
- Ask the paper manufacturers for shipping papers that identify all rolls by number and list their weights. Your shipping, stock, and accounting departments need this information.
- Keep roll cards with their respective rolls. The lot number, roll number, roll weight, and manufacturer's code are listed on these cards.
- Remember that roll weight includes outside wrapper and nonreturnable core. The weight of a returnable core is not charged.
- When estimating, allow for spoilage. The supplier will show the number and weight of each roll on the roll card and on shipping and billing papers.
- Indicate when printing is to be produced with inks other than those normally used.

Roll Handling

Inspect paper carefully before the shipper unloads it from the car or truck. Photograph any damage using an instant camera, and report it to the common carrier at once. Otherwise, the printer pays for the damage. Some printers equip their paper handlers with instant cameras and instructions to routinely take pictures of the condition of all shipments. This practice helps greatly in documenting shipping problems. If concealed damage is discovered while the shipment is being unloaded, the paper handlers should take another picture showing the extent and nature of the problem.

Powered roll-handling lift truck with side-shift feature to facilitate roll pickup and placement
Courtesy Cascade Corporation

Once rolls are received in good condition, they should be handled carefully to prevent damage. Each roll should be inspected before being placed in storage. If a wrapper is torn when a roll is handled, it should be repaired immediately to protect the paper from dirt or moisture damage.

All roll handling equipment must be in good condition. Roll clamp trucks should be equipped with pressure-regulated jaw pads.

In the pressroom, where rolls are handled manually, all areas should be kept immaculately clean. A great deal of damage can be avoided if all areas of the floor where paper is rolled are kept free of any debris that could punch holes in the surface of the roll.

Do not remove the outer wrap from a roll until the splice is to be prepared; this minimizes the chances for moisture pickup or loss on the roll surface and keeps running waste to a minimum.

17 Ink

Lithography employs planographic plates as image carriers to effect ink transfer. The image and nonimage areas are differentiated chemically. The image area of the plate receives ink, and the nonimage area is wet by fountain solution. Unlike other inks, lithographic ink must be formulated to work with water, which is the principal ingredient of fountain solution.

Ink film thickness applied to paper by the major printing processes

Offset litho	0.00008 in.
Letterpress	0.00020 in.
Gravure	0.00050 in.
Screen	0.00125 in.

Ink is a complex mixture of pigment, varnish or vehicle, and modifiers or additives. Additives include waxes to provide slip and surfactants to improve pigment dispersion. The most important properties of ink are color, color strength, opacity or transparency, body or working properties, and drying properties. All of these properties must be selected to suit the particular job; most importantly, they must suit the paper or substrate.

Although there are many classifications of printing inks, web offset printing principally employs six: news, nonheatset, heatset, waterless, ultraviolet (UV), and electron-beam (EB). Web offset inks are made from a pigment or from a blend of pigments dispersed in a viscous liquid called a vehicle.

News inks consist of a pigment and a hydrocarbon oil. When the oil soaks into the paper, the pigment remains on the surface. Thus, these inks never really dry, and the pigment is easily rubbed from the paper. Adding a modified drying oil to these *low-rub* news inks improves their rub resistance by forming a film that retains the pigment.

Nonheatset web offset inks for printing on uncoated groundwood exhibit qualities that are similar to news inks.

Heatset inks consist of a pigment, a modified rosin or hydrocarbon resin, a hydrocarbon solvent, and additives. After the solvent evaporates in the dryer, the remaining resin is set on the chill rolls and the chilled resin binds the pigment to the sheet.

Inkmaking

Ink manufacturing is relatively simple, but formulation is complex and depends largely on experience. Most inks are formulated for specific applications and are, therefore, manufactured in batches. The ingredients are premixed in a large vat and then milled. A three-roll mill shears the ink as it passes between the rolls, which rotate at different speeds.

This shearing breaks up the pigment agglomerates into microscopic particles so that each becomes completely surrounded and wet by the varnish. The mill also *classifies* the pigment, permitting finely dispersed pigment to flow through the mill and retaining coarser pigment particles. The ground ink is taken off the high-speed roll by a doctor blade. A thorough job of grinding may require as many as three passes through the mill, depending on whether the pigment is soft or hard and how easily it is wet by the varnish.

The grinding action of a three-roll ink mill

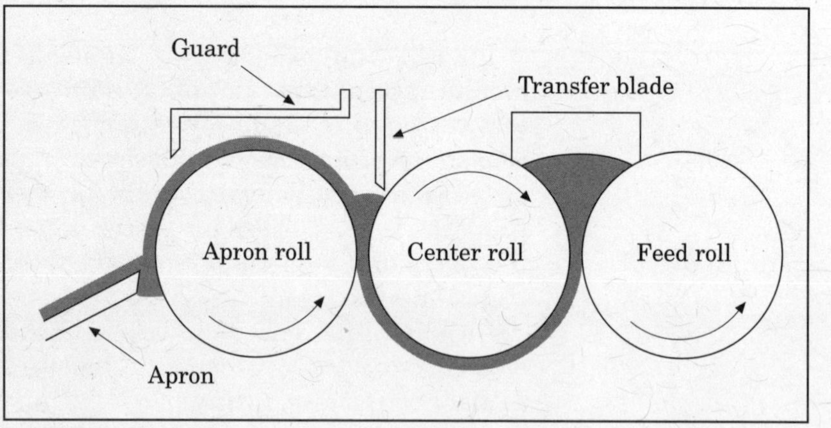

Milling is costly, and inks can be made less expensive by reducing the amount of milling. This, however, causes several problems including reduced color strength and coarser pigment. Large pigment particles in the ink may cause plate wear. Since the pigment is the most expensive part of the ink, and uniform dispersion is accomplished by extensive milling, high-quality inks cost more.

Web Offset Ink

Several different inks are used in web offset printing. Heatset inks predominate in general commercial work. News inks are used in web offset printing of newspapers, newspaper inserts, business forms, directories, and direct mail.

Heatset Inks

Heatset ink vehicles consist of resin dissolved in a solvent, and drying takes place principally by evaporation.

In printing with heatset inks, the printed web is passed through one or two dryers. The dryer must raise the temperature of the ink enough to evaporate the solvent, leaving the resin to bind the pigment to the paper. From the dryer, the web passes over chill rolls to cool it; subsequently, it can be cut, folded, and delivered. The cooling hardens the ink and is necessary to prevent setoff or marking in the delivery.

Heatset resins usually contain thermoplastic resins with no oxidizing properties, in which case no metallic driers are used. These inks lack rub and scuff resistance but are suitable for numerous jobs. Heatset inks may incorporate drying resins to produce tough, rub- and scuff-resistant films.

The solvents used in heatset inks are usually narrow-cut petroleum fractions. Their boiling points range from about 450°F to 600°F (230°C to 315°C), and the solvent selected depends on printing conditions. Solvent with a high boiling point resists evaporation under the heat of the press rollers. Solvent with a low boiling point requires less heat to burn off in the dryer. The solvent selected should be varied depending on the characteristics of the dryer, speed of the press, ink coverage on the job, and the ink receptivity of the stock. The printer should discuss these characteristics with the inkmaker when ordering the ink.

Quickset Inks

The vehicles in quickset inks are dispersions of high-molecular-weight resins in a drying oil and a solvent. When printed, part of the solvent and oil quickly penetrate the paper, leaving the resin concentrated in the ink film. The loss of only a fraction of the solvent and oil greatly increases the viscosity of the ink, so that the printing becomes relatively setoff-free in a very short time.

Offset News Inks

Web offset is the leading method for printing newspapers. Inks for this purpose are composed of pigment (usually carbon black), mineral oil, resin, and sometimes drying oil. News inks may contain a solvent. They contain no drier, because they dry by absorption, which requires no heat.

Waterless Offset Inks

Waterless offset inks contain many of the same ingredients that conventional lithographic inks contain. The difference between them is that waterless inks have vehicles that allow them to have higher initial viscosities than those of the conventional inks. Waterless offset inks also may have slightly lower tacks than those of conventional offset inks. The viscosity and tack differences between the two inks have to do with the differences between the two plates. Conventional offset lithographic plates operate on the principle that oil and water do not mix. They have a hydrophilic nonimage area that attracts water or dampening solution and an oleophilic image area that repels water and attracts oily ink. Waterless offset plates use a silicone material for nonimage areas of the plate. This silicone material has a low surface energy that resists ink if the ink's viscosity is high enough for it to be more attracted to itself than to the silicone material.

The viscosity of a liquid changes rapidly with the temperature. In conventional lithography, the presence of water in the dampening solution on press cools the ink and helps it to maintain a viscosity that does not compromise its physical characteristics while it is being worked. The viscosity of waterless offset inks is maintained on press by a press temperature control system, either a plate cylinder cooling or ink oscillator (vibrator) cooling system. Waterless offset inks are formulated at varied viscosities in order to be adaptable to the geographic temperature environment of any press.

Zone controls for each printing unit helps to extend the printing length and reduces the printing problems that will occur from one ink color to another color because of the requirements necessary for certain inks to run cooler and certain inks to run warmer.

Ink Drying Systems

Inkmakers constantly strive to improve inks and the methods by which they dry. Research has been stimulated by legal mandates to reduce the emission of solvent fumes into the air by heatset ink drying systems. Furthermore, the dryers and afterburners required to burn off heatset ink solvents consume excessive energy.

Ultraviolet (UV) inks. The UV ink drying system involves specially formulated inks and special equipment. When UV inks are exposed to ultraviolet radiation, polymerization occurs almost instantaneously. These inks contain no solvent, so solvent-fume emission from the press is eliminated. The system employs a series of lamps that emit ultraviolet radiation to cure the ink.

Many UV ink users are purchasing equipment with interstation drying, so that they can accomplish dry-trap printing. The process of interstation drying has tremendously increased the trap reading numbers on the offset sheet.

Electron beam (EB) inks. Electron beam inks are similar to UV inks, except that they do not require photoinitiators. The source for the polymerization is a stream of electrons that bombard the ink film. EB inks have all of the advantages of UV inks; they cure rapidly, dry hard, and present no emission control problems. Because they lack photoinitiators, these inks are more stable and more easily handled.

Ink Components

Pigments

Pigments are finely divided solid materials that give inks color. *Flushed* (wet) pigments can be added directly to the vehicle before they dry; this improves pigment dispersion. Pigments can be either opaque or transparent. Transparent pigments are required for process color printing.

The body and working properties of an ink depend on the vehicle and its viscosity, and on the nature and amount of pigment it contains.

Vehicles

The solid pigment particles are suspended in a complex chemical mixture known as the **vehicle.** The nature of the vehicle determines most of the working properties of the ink and some of its optical qualities. The vehicle contains the binding agent that bonds the pigment particles to the paper; it also determines the conditions required to dry the ink.

Heatset inks dry when the solvent evaporates and the hot, resinous binder is chilled. Conventional heatset vehicles contain a solvent that maintains the ink in a semiliquid state. The solvent evaporates rapidly when heated, making high press speeds possible. The nature and amount of solvent used in the vehicle directly influence the body, viscosity, tack, and length of the ink.

In addition to solvents, ink vehicle contains one or more synthetic resins and modified natural rosin that bond the pigment particles to the paper. Heatset resins are melted by the heat from the dryer and then set and hardened by the chill rolls. Without the cooling action of chill rolls, the resins remain soft and mark and smear as the web passes through the folder.

Gellants added to varnishes make them more thixotropic — stiff when not being worked. The advantage of using a gelled ink is that although it is difficult to get from the can into the fountain, as long as it remains in the inking system and is being worked by the ink agitators or rollers, it remains fluid.

The printed ink film sets immediately, which enhances the trapping of subsequently printed ink films. Printed images resist back-trapping — the contamination of subsequent printing units by a wet printed ink film. This gives much sharper printing.

Heatset inks often contain a small amount of drying oil like those found in conventional lithographic inks. These oils dry for several hours after the printed paper comes off the press. They also increase the hardness of the ink film and determine the duration of the curing stage.

The last main element found in most vehicles is a slip compound that improves scuff resistance of the printed ink film and reduces friction as the web slides across rollers and around cylinders. Waxes and polyethylene are commonly used as slip compounds.

Optical Properties of Ink

Color perception is determined by psychological, physiological, and environmental factors. Light is reflected, transmitted, or radiated from an object to the eye. Light stimulates the nerve cells that identify color. Color identification varies between individuals. The eye is basically sensitive to red, green, and blue light. All other perceivable colors are combinations of these three frequencies of light. In printing, the reflections of these three colors (red, green, and blue) from the surface of the paper are respectively controlled by application of the transparent inks known as cyan, magenta, and yellow.

Color

Objects appear colored when they either reflect or transmit light. Pigments appear colored in white light because they absorb certain wavelengths and reflect or transmit others. They appear to change color if the spectral composition of the light is varied. The three process color inks — cyan, yellow, and magenta — are transparent. Ideally each absorbs light from one-third of the spectrum and transmits light from the remaining two-thirds. Cyan has its characteristic color because it transmits blue and green light while absorbing (or filtering out) red light. Yellow transmits red and green light and absorbs the blue. Magenta absorbs green light and transmits the red and blue. Because process inks are transparent, one

The difference between how process inks work in theory and in practice

The top diagram shows how a printed surface with an ideal set of inks would reflect light over the visible spectrum. The lower diagram represents the light reflectance pattern of such a surface printed with an "average" set of process inks. The discrepancy between the two is made up through color correction techniques carried out in prepress.

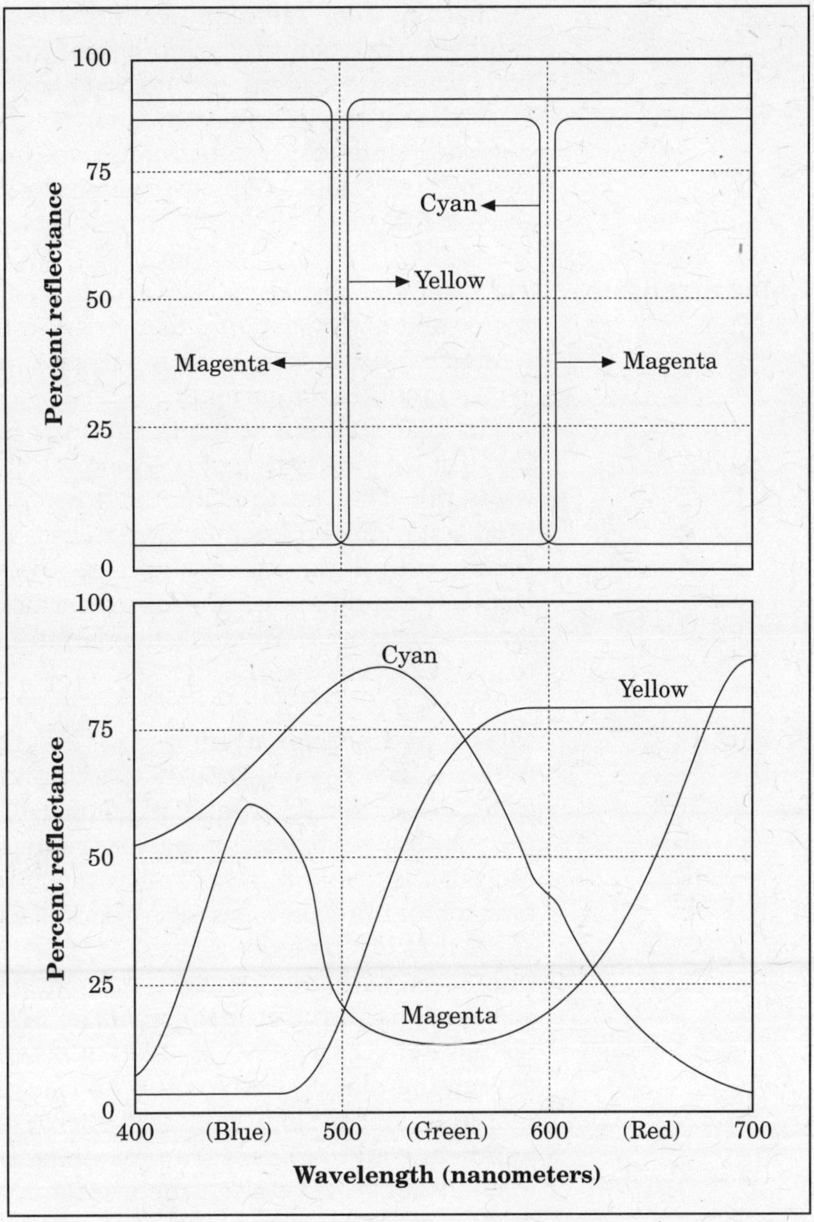

process color can be overprinted by another without changing the way each absorbs or transmits light. For example, magenta overprinted by cyan produces blue, because magenta filters out green light and cyan filters out the red.

Ordinary nonprocess inks are opaque and work in a slightly different manner. An opaque yellow ink, for example, reflects (rather than transmits) red and green light and absorbs blue light. When opaque inks are overprinted, the top color hides the bottom color, making them unsuitable for process color printing. The color of a printed ink film is a combination of both masstone and undertone. Masstone is the color of a thick film of the ink. It is the color of light reflected by the pigment. Undertone is the color of a thin film of ink. It is the color of light reflected by the paper and transmitted through the ink film.

Color Strength

The color strength (tinctorial strength) of an ink is its coloring power and is proportional to pigment concentration. Color strength must be sufficient to produce the desired color in a printed ink film of normal thickness.

The relative color strength of an ink is measured by reducing it in the proportion of one part ink to fifty parts of opaque white ink. The tint thus formed is compared with that made from a standard ink similarly reduced.

Inks with high color strength may be printed as thin films, thus increasing ink mileage. Furthermore, a thin ink film is less likely to emulsify, since less fountain solution is required to maintain ink/water balance.

The web printing industry has accepted the SWOP specifications for ink color strength. GATF is the verification center to test inks to ensure that they conform to SWOP specifications. When ink strengths fall below SWOP specifications, the ink film thickness increases, the dot gain increases, and the print contrast numbers decrease. These are all indications of an ink that is possibly too weak to be used on a web offset press. A matched series of inks is not difficult to obtain from an ink supplier. The correct pigmented load and an accurate ink film thickness from the first printing unit to the last all helps to achieve the trap numbers and the trapping of each ink placed down on the web. To achieve high density readings, low dot gain numbers, increased print contrast numbers, and increased trap readings, a partnership needs to be established between the printer and ink supplier to develop a custom series of inks for the printer.

Opacity

Opacity is the covering power of an ink — the ability of its printed film to hide what is underneath. Some pigments have high opacity while others, particularly process ink pigments, are transparent. Opacity can be measured by making drawdowns over black or a contrasting color.

Even minor opacity in a process ink can considerably affect color reproduction. An opaque yellow run on the third unit can blank out cyan and magenta. For this reason, if an opaque ink must be run, it should be run in the first unit.

Gloss

Gloss is the ability of an ink film to reflect light. High gloss is obtained when the resins in the ink film dry in a smooth, unbroken surface. Coarsely ground pigment particles protrude from the dried film surface and reduce gloss. An ink that is so highly pigmented that the pigments cannot be thoroughly covered by the vehicle will have reduced gloss. Highly porous paper can absorb and drain off enough resin to allow pigment particles to protrude above the surface. The highest gloss is obtained on the more tightly coated stocks.

Working Properties

Offset inks are basically viscous fluid materials. They are called *viscoelastic* because they behave both like fluids and like elastic solids.

Body, length, and thixotropy are three ink properties that strongly affect how the ink feeds and how it transfers and distributes on the rollers. These three properties characterize viscosity or fluid behavior. A fourth property — tack — is also related to viscosity. It is the pulling force required to split an ink film between two surfaces. The tack of a thin ink film exceeds the tack of a thick ink film.

Body

Body is the consistency of an ink, determined by its stiffness or softness. Other properties including length and thixotropy affect body.

Length

The length of an ink is a measure of its fluidity. Length is measurable by several methods.

Measuring ink flow down an inclined slab indicates length under the force of gravity. Long ink flows further than short ink. Fluidity depends on viscosity and thixotropy.

The flow test indicates how the ink will behave in the ink fountain. A short ink flows poorly and tends to back away from the fountain roller. A short ink may require steady agitation. A long ink forms a flat-surfaced puddle in the fountain, indicating low viscosity and low thixotropy.

The tapout test measures length by applying sudden pulling force to two different inks. A long ink forms a long string; the string of short ink breaks under the pulling force. In the flow test, viscosity and thixotropy are tested by applying a weak force to the ink. In the tapout test for ink length, strong forces are applied to test viscosity and elasticity.

Comparison of long ink *(left)* and short ink

Lithographic inks are usually formulated to be long, because emulsification with fountain solution reduces ink length. Elastic flow, as measured by the tapout test, remains relatively constant on the press. The most common problem is that short inks are sensitive to water pickup and tend to become waterlogged.

Thixotropy

Offset ink in a can may act like a solid, exhibiting no flow even if the container is turned upside down. However, after being worked on a slab, the same ink may flow quite freely. On standing, the ink gradually *sets up* and eventually regains its original solid consistency. Ink becomes more fluid as a result of working and less fluid on standing.

During printing, thixotropic ink is in a fluid state when applied to the paper as a result of working by the press rollers. Viscosity soon increases, producing sharp images.

Performance Characteristics

Ink interacts with press components, fountain solution, paper, and other ink during the course of a pressrun — all of which affect its performance. This section analyzes three aspects of ink performance: tack, drying, and press stability. Each is critical in diagnosing ink-related problems.

Tack

Tack is the pulling force required to split an ink film between two surfaces. Tack determines whether or not an ink will pick the paper surface or trap properly in multicolor printing. Furthermore, it partially determines the sharpness of the printed image. Multicolor work involving the successive overprinting of wet ink films requires that the tack of ink films on the web be higher than the tack of ink on the blanket. The tack of fresh ink is not the same as its tack at the printing nip of a lithographic press. Several on-press factors can either increase or decrease ink tack.

Two factors that affect tack and may be controlled by the press operator are press speed and ink film thickness. Tack equals viscosity times the speed under which the ink film is being split. Thus, tack increases with press speed. A high-viscosity ink run on a high-speed press has high tack; picking may result under such conditions. In this case, the picking may disappear by reducing press speed. Inkmakers formulate low-viscosity inks to accommodate high-speed presses.

Tack and color strength are inversely proportional to ink film thickness; that is, thick ink film has low tack but high color strength and vice versa. The press crew adjusts ink film thickness to produce the correct color or optical density. Variations in color strength from one ink to another require the press operator to adjust ink film thickness. Tack should successively decrease from unit to unit to effect proper ink trapping and paper performance.

Excessively increasing ink film thickness to achieve a specific optical density lowers tack; an ink film of higher tack on the blanket of the succeeding unit may lift the previously printed ink film from the paper. Excessively decreasing an ink film to reduce its color strength to a specified optical density increases tack; the ink may pick the paper or lift the previously printed ink film from the paper. Specify color strength when ordering ink, so that the ink may be printed at the appropriate thickness.

Emulsification also affects ink tack. Fountain solution works its way back into the roller train in the form of droplets, which are milled into the ink films on the roller surfaces. Inks can sometimes pick up 20% or more water in this way and run with no problems; however, a 20% pickup significantly lowers tack. An emulsified ink has a much lower tack than a dry ink film. The amount of water picked up by the ink depends on the nature of the ink and the condition of the ink/water balance in the printing couple.

Thixotropy also affects ink tack. Thixotropic setting can increase tack when the ink is left undisturbed in the fountain or on the rollers, plate, and blanket during a shutdown, and during the fraction of a second that the printed ink film spends traveling from one unit to the next.

Finally, solvent evaporation can also increase ink tack. Heat generated by friction in the printing units, pressroom temperature, and air flow can evaporate the solvents in heatset inks before they reach the dryer. The ink sets, and the tack increases. A temperature increase without a loss of solvent greatly lowers tack.

The tack numbers displayed on the ink can by the manufacturer are based on Inkometer readings taken under specified laboratory conditions. Therefore, these numbers are relative. The press system exerts a strong effect on these ratings. A new ink having the same tack number as the old ink performs roughly the same if the press system is not changed. Tack number should not be relied on as an indicator of ink performance in cases involving changes in press, speed, plates, and paper.

Drying

Heatset ink must dry quickly and dependably. Drying is vital in the overall performance of the ink. The boiling point of the solvents must be neither too high nor too low. A low-boiling solvent excessively evaporates on press. A high-boiling solvent requires excessive dryer heat, generating a whole series of dryer-related paper problems: low moisture content, cracking in the folder, blistering, and loss of strength.

The resins in the ink must have the proper melting point. If dryer temperature is too high, gloss will be reduced because the liquefied resins will seep into even the most tightly sealed stocks. In extreme cases, too much resin is absorbed by the paper and dry, loose pigment particles remain on the web surface (chalking).

Some heatset inks contain some metallic driers to aid in the final drying stage, which occurs off the press. If the ratio of drying compound to resins is too high, the resins will not properly combine and solidify into an ideal ink film.

Press Stability

Heatset inks do not always behave consistently or predictably on the press. Several factors contribute to ink stability. An ink should be neither too long nor too short. A short ink cakes on the rollers or piles on the blanket. A long ink tends to mist and loses its ability to print sharply.

Good moisture resistance prevents excessive emulsification if the dampening system is properly set. The ink should resist waterlogging. The ink solvent should be of the proper boiling point. If it is too low, the ink will dry on the rollers. If it is too high, excessive dryer heat is required.

18 Plates and Blankets

Plates

Lithography demonstrates the principle that oil and water, generally, do not mix. A conventional lithographic plate consists of image areas, which accept ink and repel water; and the nonimage areas, which accept water and, when wet, repel ink. Image and nonimage areas are distinguished by differences in surface chemistry. These image and nonimage areas exist on essentially the same plane; thus, lithography is a planographic process.

Today, most lithographic plates are thin metal sheets. Aluminum is the most commonly used metal, although plates can also be made of stainless steel, mild steel, or brass. Plates are usually the full size of the press cylinder and must be thin and flexible enough to wrap snugly around the cylinder. On web presses, plate cracking results when the plate does not conform to the press cylinder. Benders must be accurate; a properly bent and mounted plate conforms precisely to the cylinder and does not flex during printing.

Plates are carefully inspected to ensure that (1) they meet the required gauge tolerance; (2) they are flat; and (3) any side to be used as a printing surface is free from scratches, dents, and other surface defects.

The thickness of aluminum used varies with the press size. Standard thicknesses range from 0.0055 in. (0.14 mm) to 0.020 in. (0.51 mm), and sizes go up to 59×78 in. (1,499×1,981 mm). Plate thickness should relate to the cylinder undercut so that minimal packing is required. Several layers of packing are more likely to creep than a single sheet.

Uniform plate thickness is important. Plates up to 22×34 in. (559×864 mm) should not vary more than 0.001 in. (0.025 mm) in thickness. For example, a 0.012-in. (0.305-mm) plate should not be more than 0.0125 in. (0.318 mm) nor less than 0.0115 in. (0.292 mm) thick in any area. This is called *gauge tolerance.* In this example, it is expressed as ±0.0005 in. (±0.013 mm).

Photolithographic Plates

The majority of today's commercial printing plates are made photographically using either negative or positive film. To make a photolithographic plate, a metal plate must first be covered with a light-sensitive coating that changes its solubility when exposed to light. A plate may be exposed through a negative (negative-working plate) or positive (positive-working plate) litho film. The light that penetrates the transparent areas changes the solubility of the plate coating. After this light exposure, the plate is developed or processed to remove coating from nonimage areas. The plates are then desensitized to make the nonimage areas water-receptive.

Negative-working presensitized plates. Negative-working plates have soluble coatings that become insoluble upon exposure to light. The image (clear) areas of the negative allow light to penetrate and form the image areas of the plate. The unexposed coating remains soluble and is removed during development.

Positive-working presensitized plates. Positive-working presensitized plates are completely covered with an ink-receptive, light-sensitive coating. They are exposed through positives. The *unexposed* areas (image areas) are insoluble in the developer. The exposed areas are solubilized by exposure to light and removed during development, leaving the water-receptive metal as the nonimage areas.

Surface plates—presensitized and wipe-on. Presensitized plates are sensitized (coated) by the manufacturer; wipe-on plates are sensitized by the platemaker. Presensitized plates generally remain sensitive for one year or more. Presensitized plates consist of a thin film of light-sensitive material, usually a diazo compound or a photopolymer, that is coated on a specially treated aluminum, plastic, or paper base material. Photopolymer coatings consist of polymers and photosensitizers that react (crosslink) during exposure to light to produce a tough, long-wearing image area. Diazo coatings also react with light to produce a tough, long-wearing image area. After exposure, the plates require special organic or aqueous solvents for processing. Negative and positive plates are available with diazo or photopolymer coatings.

Presensitized plates are sometimes designated as being either *additive* or *subtractive.* These terms describe the differences in processing procedures. A presensitized plate is additive when the platemaker adds image-reinforcing materials to the image areas during processing. The coating over nonimage areas must be removed during development. A presensitized plate is subtractive if it comes to the platemaker with a durable, long-run coating applied by the manufacturer. During processing, the developer removes the unexposed coating and renders the nonimage area water-receptive.

Wipe-on plates are chemically similar to presensitized plates, but they are coated with aqueous diazo coatings in the plateroom in a simple roller coater. A specially treated aluminum or anodized aluminum plate is used. Wipe-on coatings are thin and lack durability on press, so special developers are required that contain lacquer or plastic that builds up on the image to greatly increase durability.

Multimetal Plates

Bimetal plates consist of a base metal, usually aluminum or stainless steel, on which a thin layer of copper has been electroplated. Copper forms the ink-receptive image areas and is removed from nonimage areas. The base metal thus exposed is easily desensitized and forms the nonimage area. Bimetal plates are supplied in smooth and grained form.

A special bimetal plate is made by electroplating a thin layer of chromium over a base metal of copper or brass. The chromium is etched away during processing, exposing the base metal in the image areas. Chromium remains on the plate in the nonimage areas.

Trimetal plates are made by electroplating two metals on a third base metal. The base metal is usually aluminum, mild steel, or stainless steel. A layer of copper is first electrodeposited on the base metal, followed by a thin layer of chromium. Chromium forms the nonimage areas and is etched away to bare the copper in the image areas. If grained plates are desired, the base metal sheet is grained before the other metals are plated on it. The films of these metals are so thin that they have little effect on the grain.

Laser-Imaged Plates

Laser-imaged plates are directly imaged by exposure to lasers. Because no film is used, this process completely bypasses the normal operations involved with camera and image assembly.

With advances in imaging technology, a number of lithographic printing plates are now exposed in an imagesetter or

General processing sequence for a bimetal plate

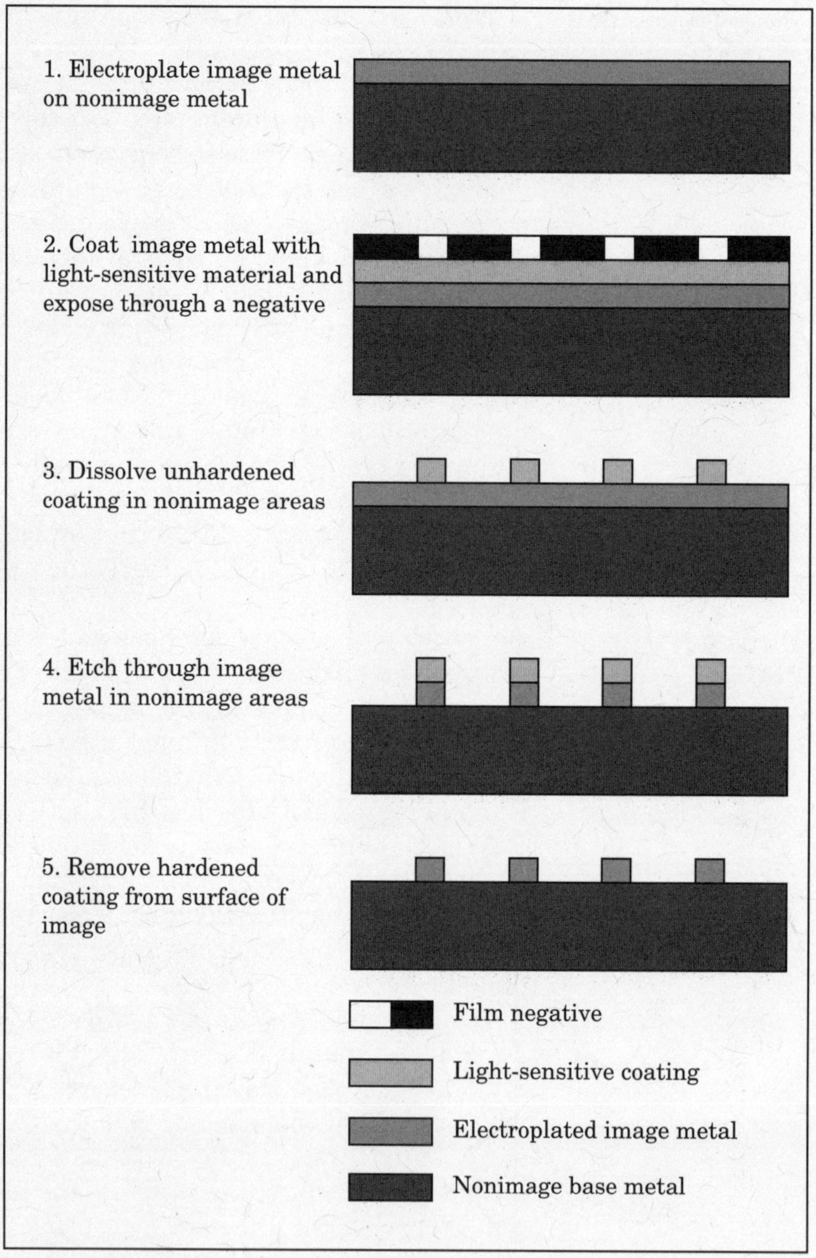
1. Electroplate image metal on nonimage metal
2. Coat image metal with light-sensitive material and expose through a negative
3. Dissolve unhardened coating in nonimage areas
4. Etch through image metal in nonimage areas
5. Remove hardened coating from surface of image
Film negative
Light-sensitive coating
Electroplated image metal
Nonimage base metal

platesetter using digitally driven, low-power lasers. This class of plate is called a *direct-digital plate* because it is exposed directly from digital data, instead of being exposed through a film intermediate. This technology is usually referred to as *direct-to-plate* or *computer-to-plate* (CTP) technology.

When a plate is exposed with a laser beam, the light scans across the plate rapidly while the plate moves slowly under

General processing sequence for a trimetal plate

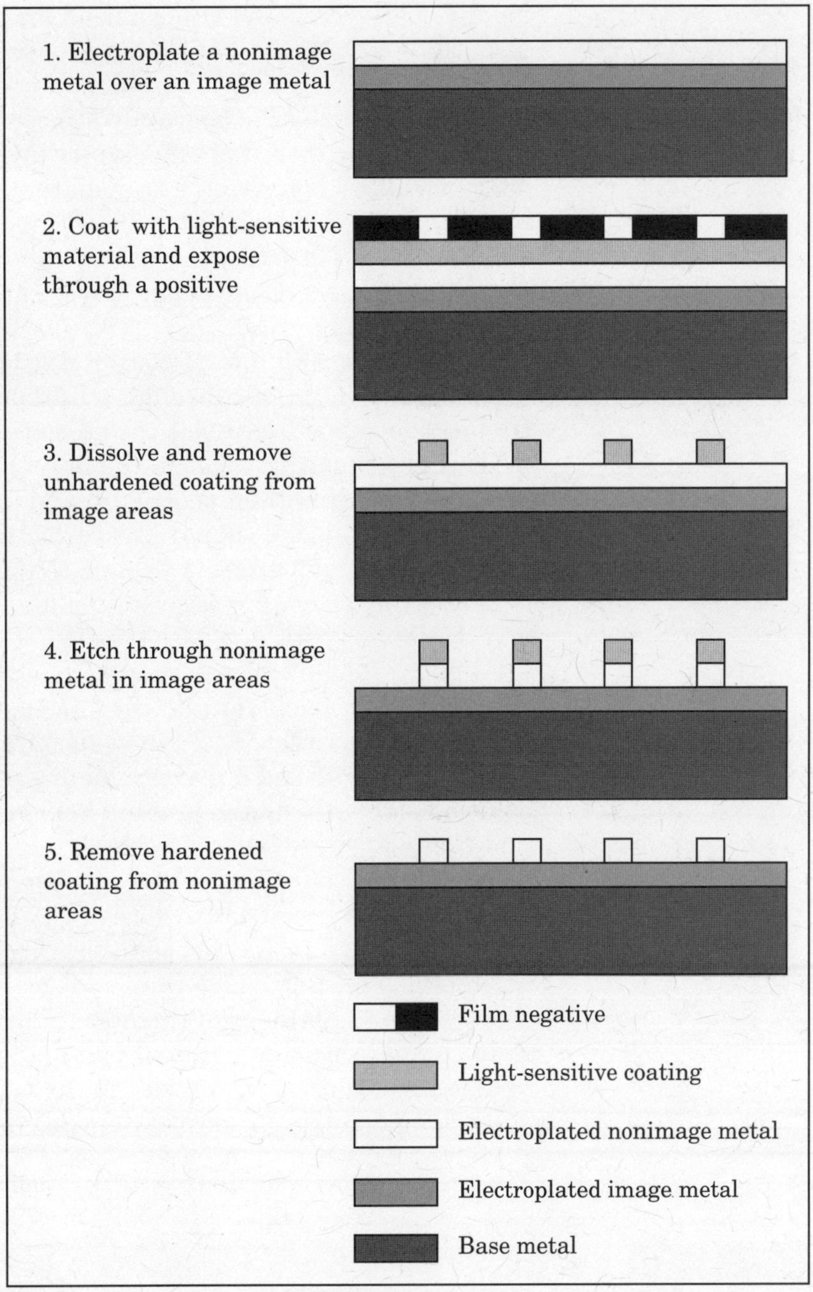
1. Electroplate a nonimage metal over an image metal
2. Coat with light-sensitive material and expose through a positive
3. Dissolve and remove unhardened coating from image areas
4. Etch through nonimage metal in image areas
5. Remove hardened coating from nonimage areas
Film negative
Light-sensitive coating
Electroplated nonimage metal
Electroplated image metal
Base metal

the beam. With a laser, each tiny printing spot may receive an exposure of only microseconds in duration.

Several different approaches to CTP technology have been announced including silver-based, electrophotographic-based, and photopolymer coatings that can be sensitized to the three dominant lasers in use today (laser diode for infrared, argon ion for blue-green, and helium neon for red) with coating sensitivities that satisfy graphic arts imaging speeds.

Waterless Plates

Plates for waterless lithography are constructed of an aluminum base, a primer, a photopolymer layer, an ink-repellent silicone rubber layer, and a transparent protective film on top. The plate can be hand- or machine-developed in a special processor. Care must be taken handling the plates; any scratches in the silicone rubber layer can become an unwanted image area.

A positive-working waterless plate is processed by first exposing it to UV light through a film positive in a vacuum frame. The exposure causes the silicone rubber layer to bind to the light-sensitive layer in the nonimage area. The top protective layer is then peeled off, and a developer that removes the silicone rubber layer from the light-sensitive layer in the image areas is applied to the plate surface.

Processing of negative-working plates begins in the same way. However, with a negative-working plate, exposure to UV light through a film negative *weakens* the bonds between the light-sensitive layer and the silicone rubber layer in the exposed image areas. After the exposure, the protective cover film is peeled off and a pretreatment solution is applied. This solution strengthens the binding between the silicone rubber and light-sensitive layers in the plate's unexposed nonimage areas. The silicone rubber layer is then removed from the light-sensitive image layer in the plate's exposed areas.

Testing at GATF has proven that the waterless process produces a sharper image than conventional web offset does. The waterless plate, as of the present, has a shorter run life than comparable conventional plates. Runs exceeding 50,000 impressions is uncommon with many waterless plates, which is not long enough for most web pressruns.

The Toray Waterless Plate
Courtesy Toray Marketing & Sales (America), Inc.

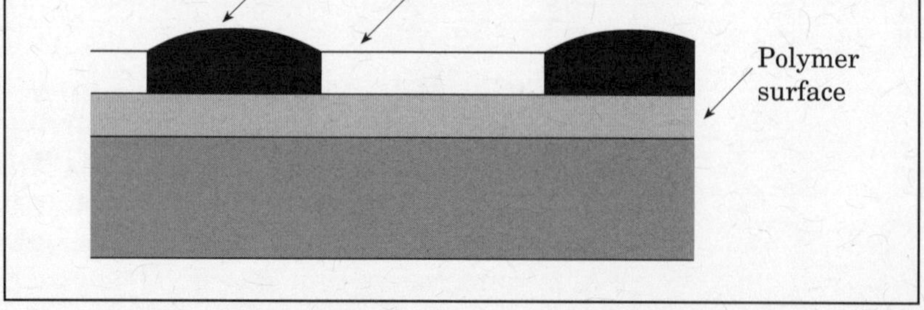

Selection of the Printing Plate

Numerous printing plates are available to the web offset printer. Since web pressruns often exceed 100,000 impressions, long-run plates are required. Less expensive short-run plates produce the same required printing quality on shorter pressruns; however, each plate has its own ink/water balance characteristics. Therefore, the savings realized by using less expensive plates for short runs may be negated by the additional makeready time required for the press crew to adjust to a change in plates. Furthermore, a printer can often save money by purchasing a large quantity of a single class of printing plate.

Various plates exhibit diverse performance characteristics. Presensitized plates resist image blinding because their image coatings are specially designed to offer a high degree of ink affinity and water-gum resistance. Presensitized plates are especially susceptible to wear caused by excessive pressures between form rollers and plate, and plate and blanket.

Multimetal plates are much more durable and wear better on press. They offer more latitude in roller and cylinder pressures. Properly treated copper has more of an affinity for ink than the image lacquers used on wipe-on plates; however, copper can also acquire an affinity for gum and water under certain press conditions. The use of specially formulated fountain solutions eliminates blinding during the pressrun. The ink film helps to protect the copper image; however, a thin ink film may allow the copper image area to pick up gum and then blind. Copper-imaged plates tend to be sensitive to excessive gum in the fountain solution.

Presensitized plates print exceptionally high quality and have the advantage of convenience. These plates are relatively susceptible to excessive pressure on the press and the composition of fountain solutions. On a properly adjusted press, presensitized plates can print 50,000 impressions or more. Negative- and positive-working presensitized plates that can print in excess of 1,000,000 impressions are available.

Wipe-on plates cost much less than presensitized plates, because they have to be coated by the platemaker prior to exposure. Coating is easily applied by hand or with a roller coater. With proper handling, they can effectively print 200,000 impressions.

Bimetal and trimetal plates, being electroplated with copper or copper and chromium, are the most expensive. However, they produce high-quality printing and are usually good for over 1,000,000 impressions.

Graining or Surface Preparation

Before a metal can be used as a base for a lithographic plate, its surface must be properly prepared. This is accomplished either by roughening the surface mechanically or treating it chemically or electrolytically. This mechanical or chemical *graining* process significantly improves press latitude, reduces drawdown time in the vacuum frame, and helps to eliminate halation. The only ungrained plates are either multimetal or chemically treated short-run presensitized plates.

Slurry Brush Graining

Most plates in the United States are grained on a machine in which a continuous web of aluminum is passed under a series of rotating nylon brushes and grained with a mixture of abrasives and water. Uniform grain is dark in color. This brush grain is very fine and is satisfactory for presensitized and wipe-on plates. Using a chemical etch after brush graining produces a much lighter, cleaner, and slightly rougher grain.

Chemical Graining

Several methods of cleaning and slightly roughening plates chemically are currently in commercial use. They are used primarily for treating relatively smooth, short-run plates prior to coating in the manufacture of presensitized plates. These plates are usually double-sided plates for use on small presses. Most bimetal aluminum plates are also chemically grained, but they are much rougher than the presensitized chemically grained plates. Stainless-steel bimetal plates are smooth without grain.

Rougher-grained plates provide better latitude on press, faster drawdown in the vacuum frame, less trouble with dirt and hickeys, better durability on press, and less tendency to slur. Some premium long-run presensitized plates are electrochemically grained to produce a uniform, relatively rough grain.

Chemical Treatments

In addition to roughening the surface, chemical treatments are also needed for some processes, especially wipe-on and negative-working diazo presensitized plates. The diazo compounds, which are ink-receptive when exposed, can react with untreated metals. Therefore, the aluminum is usually treated in a hot sodium silicate solution to create a barrier layer that prevents a reaction between the diazo and the aluminum. This treatment desensitizes the plate so that it will be more water-receptive, and bonds the diazo to the aluminum.

When positive-working diazo presensitized plates are made, surface treatments may not be necessary; fine graining and/or cleaning usually precede the application of positive-working diazos. Most premium surface plates (wipe-on and presensitized) are anodized after graining.

Aluminum Anodizing

Aluminum anodizing is a process by which a thin, uniform layer of extremely hard aluminum oxide is produced electrolytically on the grained aluminum. This anodic layer has many extremely small pores, similar to a honeycomb, that must be *sealed* before the photosensitive coating is applied. Usually, hot solutions of sodium silicate are used to treat the anodized layer, making it highly water-receptive. This process also prepares the plate surface to receive the light-sensitive coating. Furthermore, the anodic layer is hard, abrasion-resistant, and highly durable.

Coating Materials

Diazo

Diazo sensitizers are used for both presensitized and wipe-on plate coatings. Both water- and solvent-soluble diazos are used. Some diazo oxides or quinone diazides are also used, especially for positive plates. Exposure to UV light converts negative diazos directly to insoluble resins that have good ink receptivity and durability for printing. Positive diazos decompose upon exposure to light and become soluble in the developer; the unexposed diazo remains on the plate, forming the image areas.

Photopolymer Coatings

A number of different reactive polymers can be sensitized with a suitable photoinitiator for use as a presensitized plate coating. On exposure to light, the exposed parts of the coating crosslink to become insoluble in the solvents that dissolve the unexposed portions of the coating. The resultant images are tough, and the plates generally withstand long runs. Photopolymer coatings are used extensively for making printed circuits for electronic components. Some photopolymer coatings are water-developable.

Plate Packing and Mounting

The procedure for packing and mounting a printing plate is simple, but requires care on the part of the press operator. First, the plate is bent on a plate bending device, which bends the leading and trailing edges of the plate so that the bends conform exactly to the leading edge and trailing edge lockup on the plate cylinder. Inaccurate plate bending deforms a plate so that it fails to register with the other plates or fits loosely around the plate cylinder. Improper fit results in plate cracking.

Packing sheets are materials that are placed beneath the plate and blanket to raise each above bearer height, thus creating squeeze pressure. Packing problems occur when press operators deviate from standard procedures or fail to accurately calculate the amount of packing required to achieve the recommended squeeze pressure.

Packing sheets should possess dimensional stability and uniformity of thickness to raise a plate or blanket to proper height and keep it there. Probably the most common material now in use is specially manufactured kraft paper. Kraft paper is a highly compacted paper that compresses very little under roller pressure. It is made in a variety of thicknesses within close tolerance. A single sheet or several sheets can create nearly any packed height on the press. Packing comes in treated and untreated forms. The treated form is waxed to make it more resistant to the chemicals used in lithography; however, untreated packing is less likely to slip while the press is running.

Kraft paper, however, does not offer the ultimate in dimensional stability on the press. Frosted polyester (e.g., Mylar) is

Press operator measuring the combined thickness of the plate and its packing using a deadweight bench micrometer from E. J. Cady & Co.

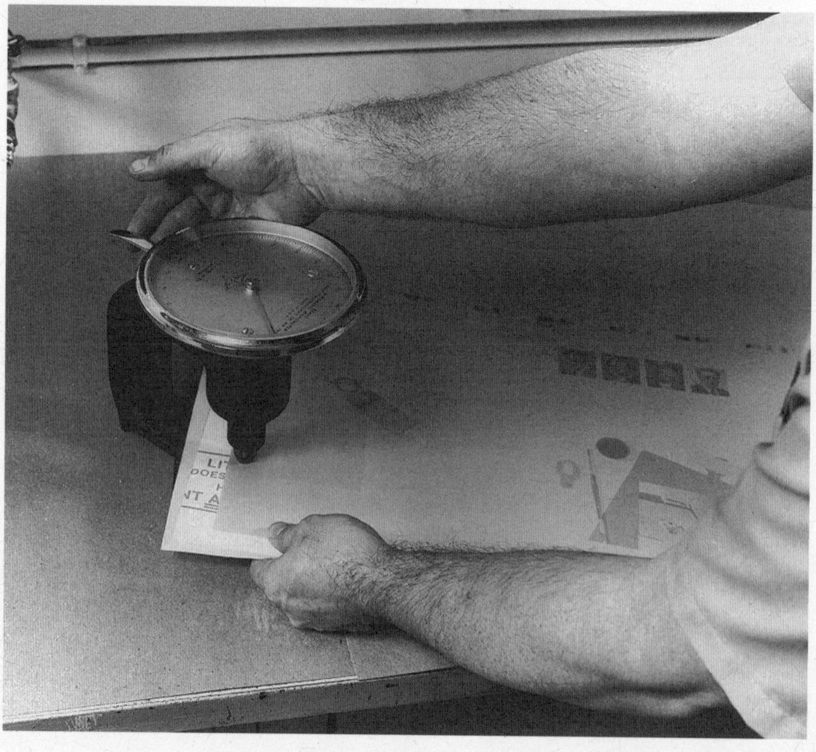

a durable packing material that effectively resists lithographic chemicals. It costs more than kraft paper, but it provides repeated use with reasonable care. Press sheets or any other papers not designed for packing purposes perform poorly as packing materials. The variable thickness and compressibility of press sheets precludes their use as packing.

Packing is usually attached to the back of the plate. Tape or glue may be used to fasten the packing to the plate at the leading edge. Oil or grease serve the same function, and they protect the cylinder from corrosive moisture by preventing seepage under the edges of the plate. The packing is trimmed so that it aligns with the bends in the plate.

The plate, with packing attached, is then inserted in the leading edge of the lockup. The trailing edge of the plate is pulled tightly as the inch button is pressed, turning the cylinders of the printing unit by small increments. The pressure between plate and blanket cylinder should be *on* to help roll out the plate as it goes around the cylinder. The primary objective is to fit the plate *snugly* against the cylinder. A bulge in the plate flexes during running and causes the plate to crack; dirty cylinders also contribute to this problem. When the gap of the cylinder comes around, the plate is inserted and the clamps tightened. It is common practice to turn the plate cylinder over a few revolutions with pressure on, to ensure a tight fit.

Plate Handling

Plates on press require protection during prolonged shutdowns to maintain the ink- and water-receptivity of their respective image and nonimage areas. The duration of the stoppage dictates the proper treatment of the plates.

Gumming a Plate

Most plates need not be gummed up for stops of up to 30 min. For stops from one-half hour to four hours, they should be gummed up and the image areas left inked. Follow the manufacturer's instructions for longer stops and overnight shutdowns. Most plates can be gummed and then washed out with the proper solvent; otherwise, the ink is likely to dry and blind image areas.

Asphaltum gum etch (AGE) is a commonly used one-step finisher that deposits asphaltum on the image areas and gum on the nonimage areas, protecting both areas almost indefinitely. Be sure to use finishers that are recommended by the manufacturer. AGE, for example, could cause gum blinding in image areas of certain brands of plates.

To gum a plate on press, first protect the printing image with just enough ink to resist gum blinding. To do this, lift the dampening and ink form rollers and run a few sheets to remove some of the ink and water. This should leave a thin charge of ink on the image areas. If the ink is too thick, it may smear into nonimage areas; if too thin, image areas may be gum blinded and not accept ink during the subsequent start-up.

Gum the plate using the recommended finisher or an 8° Baumé gum. Rub the finisher down thin; then, buff it with clean, dry cheesecloth. Gum left on the image causes gum blinding, and streaks result when the plate is reused. If necessary, the image areas should be lightly rubbed with a clean, slightly damp cloth to remove any overlying gum. The gum, however, must cover all nonimage areas, especially those immediately adjacent to the image. Gum tends to back away from the image, and these areas scum or give the appearance of image gain if left unprotected.

Desensitizing a Plate

Nonimage areas sometimes lose their desensitization on press (scumming) and must be cleaned and desensitized to restore their water-receptivity. Some proprietary plate cleaners are designed to be squirted on the plate while the press is running. The cleaner should also desensitize the nonimage areas and remove ink and piling from the image areas. Most plate cleaners are somewhat abrasive; excessive use can reduce plate life.

Plate cleaners are also used to eliminate scumming. If a plate continues to scum in the same pattern after cleaning, the plate is probably defective and should be replaced.

Aluminum plates sometimes develop an oxidation scum often referred to as *ink dot* scum. This results during shutdowns when residual fountain solution corrodes the aluminum, forming small pits. To avoid ink dot scumming, lift the inking and dampening form rollers for several impressions prior to stopping the press.

Blankets

Offset printing blankets are rubber-surfaced, fabric-backed coverings that are clamped around the blanket cylinder of a printing press. They receive images from the plates and transfer them to the substrate (paper). Blankets are capable of receiving and transferring very fine images, up to 600-line/in. halftones. Combining the lithographic process with the offset method provides a superb printing technique.

Compressible and **noncompressible (conventional) blankets** are available to the press operator. A variety of blanket surface formulations are also available to meet the special requirements of ink formulations and solvents.

The terms *compressible* and *noncompressible* describe how the blanket behaves under the squeezing action of the printing nips — plate/blanket nip and blanket/substrate nip. The noncompressible blanket when squeezed in a nip bulges out on either one or both sides of the nip. The materials cannot be compressed; therefore, they are displaced. Excessive plate/blanket squeeze causes a rubbing action against the plate as the blanket tries to recover its original shape. This rubbing action generally increases dot gain and shortens plate life. In the blanket/substrate nip, excessive squeeze slurs the print.

The displacement of conventional *(top)* and compressible blankets *(bottom)* at impact point

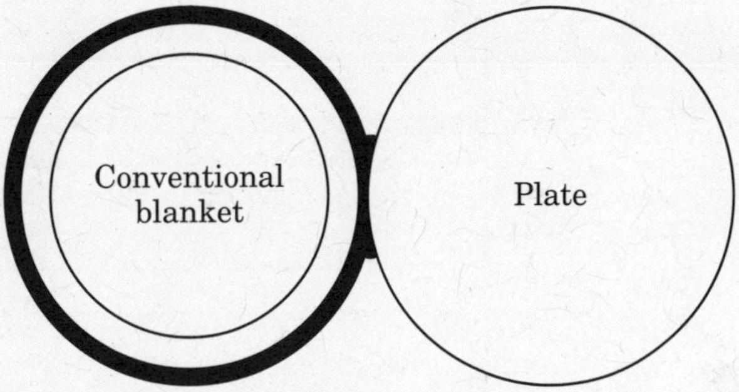

The conventional blanket bulges at impact point. Rubber displaces rather than compresses and will bulge when subjected to pressure. Because of this displacement, the surface speed of the conventional blanket is slightly different than the surface speed of the plate. One possible result is slurring.

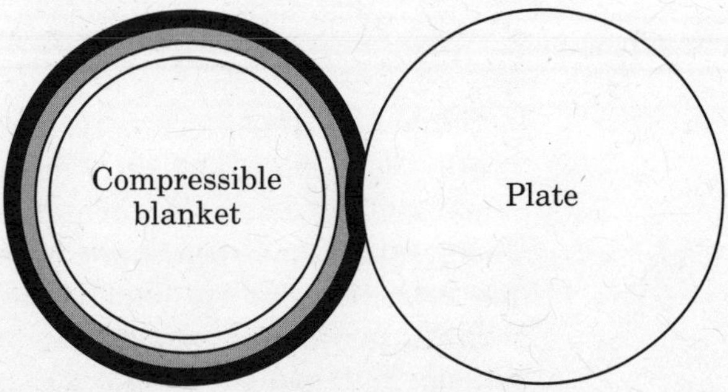

With a compressible blanket, slight bulges do form, but to a lesser extent than with a conventional blanket.

The core of a compressible blanket compresses in the printing nips. This design accommodates greater interference (within reason) that usually improves ink transfer without excessive dot gain. In some cases, noncompressible blankets print better solids, while compressible blankets print better halftones.

The reaction of a compressible blanket when out of contact with the plate *(top)* and when in contact with the plate *(bottom)*

The thickness of the rubber surface does not change. Rather, the effects of pressure are absorbed by the compressible layer.

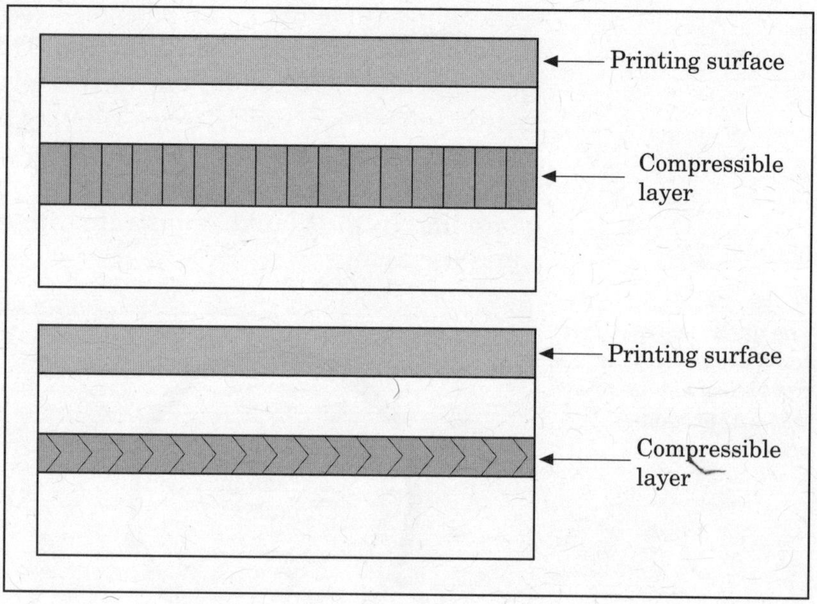

Cross section of compressible blanket *(left)* and conventional blanket *(right)*

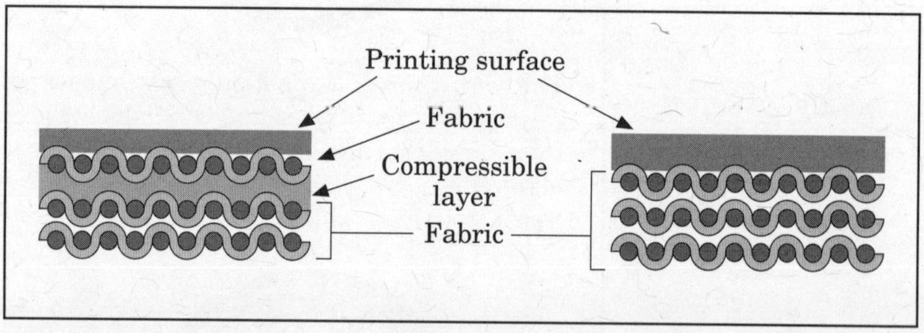

Some blankets work better with coated papers. Some inks require the use of specially formulated blankets; UV inks are one example. Specially formulated blankets are available in either compressible or noncompressible construction; it is the material (usually rubber) in the face of the blanket that is formulated to meet special requirements. Most UV inks have a tendency to swell rubber. Quick-release blankets may have a ground or roughened surface to reduce the pulling force of the ink in the nip; however a ground surface may reduce print quality. These blankets accommodate papers with low

A photomicrograph showing the printing surface, compressible layer, and carcass of a compressible blanket *Courtesy DAY International Printing Products Co.*

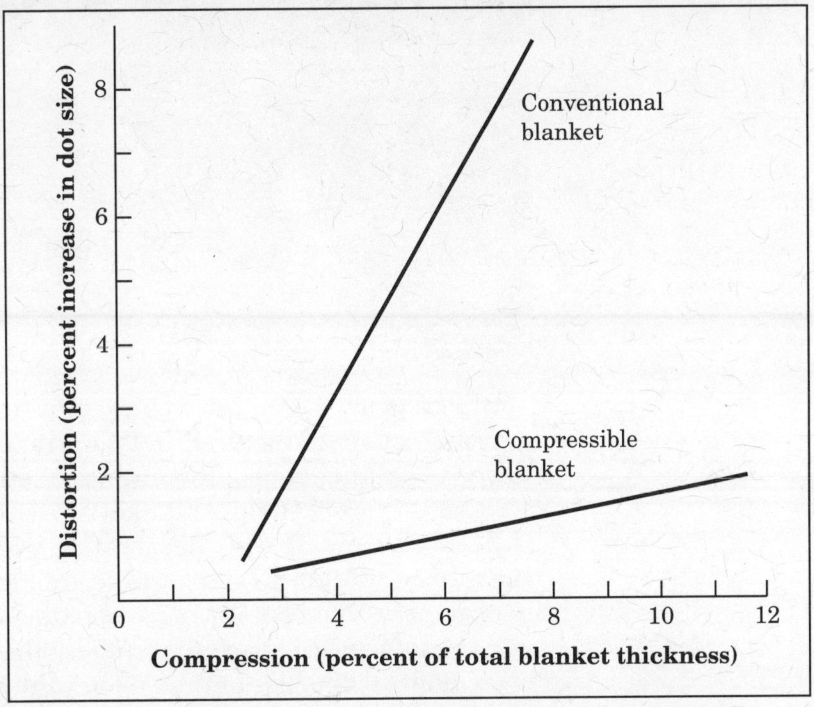

Compressible versus conventional blankets

surface strength. Adequate nip pressures are required to properly transfer ink, print dense solids, and reduce slippage.

Maintaining the recommended squeeze pressure is essential to ensure quality printing. Inadequate pressure causes uneven ink transfer and produces broken images. Excessive pressure distorts images, causes *dot gain,* and prematurely wears plates and blankets. Furthermore, excessive pressure may interfere with web feed and cause web breaks.

Performance Requirements

Evaluate a new blanket before mounting it. Measure the blanket with the warp lines or directional arrows (on the back of the blanket) in the around-the-cylinder dimension to determine if it is the correct size. Make sure that the across-the-cylinder edges are square with the warp lines. Inspect both sides of the blanket for any obvious defects. Check the caliper with a blanket thickness gauge. Randomly measure the entire surface of the blanket to determine the lowest caliper by which to calculate the proper amount of packing.

The back of a blanket showing the warp lines, which run in the around-the-cylinder direction

Blankets used on most web presses (excluding newspaper presses) are manufactured in two primary thickness ranges. Three-ply blankets usually measure 0.064–0.070 in. (1.63–1.78 mm) thick. Four-ply blankets measure 0.075–0.080 in. (1.91–2.03 mm). The *ply* designation was initially based on the number of fabric layers that comprised the carcass of a noncompressible blanket. The introduction of better fabrics and the additional space required by the compressible layer of a compressible blanket have led to the manufacture of blankets that do not have three- or four-ply carcasses. Currently, ply ratings simply refer to the two thickness ranges.

Three-ply blankets generally are not run on cylinders with undercuts designed to accommodate a four-ply blanket. A three-ply blanket mounted on such a cylinder would require an extra 0.010 in. (0.25 mm) of packing. Using a four-ply blanket on the deeper undercut cylinders reduces the amount of required packing, thus minimizing the chance of packing creep.

Thicker and heavier blankets are made for special web applications. For example, high-speed newspaper presses may require blankets that are 0.081–0.086 in. (2.06–2.18 mm) thick.

Standard tolerance on blanket thickness is about ±0.0005 in. (±0.013 mm). If the caliper varies by more than a predetermined tolerance, return the blanket to the supplier. Blanket thickness will decrease slightly, due to running compaction; retighten each blanket with a torque wrench after the first 3,000–4,000 impressions. Consult the blanket manufacturer's recommended torque.

Blanket Mounting

Blanket mounting is more difficult than plate mounting, due to the elasticity of the blankets. Mounting tension is critical, because excessively tightening the lockup can slightly decrease the blanket thickness. Blanket characteristics and varying strength among press operators make it more difficult to pack a blanket properly. Experience may tell a press operator when a blanket is adequately tensioned; however, mechanical aids ensure repeatable results to exact torque. A micrometer-adjustable torque wrench can be used to apply a prescribed tension to the mounted blanket. The torque wrench can be set to a specific torque value, and the wrench will click when the press operator tightens the blanket to that value.

Micrometer-adjustable torque-sensing wrench

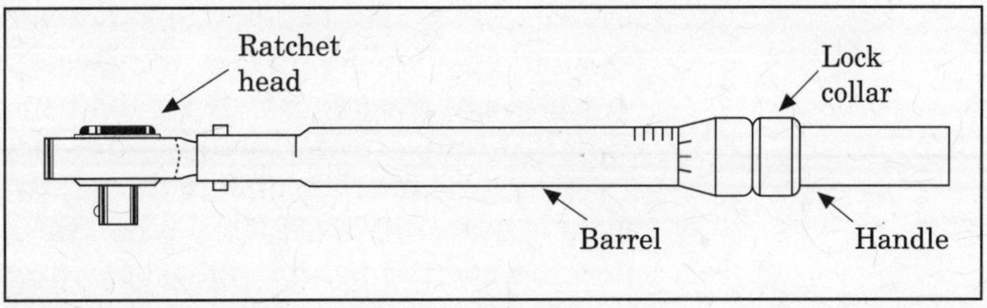

Most web offset presses require blankets that have some form of a metal bar mounted on each end. These bars are the means by which the blanket is locked into the blanket cylinder gap. There are approximately 30 bar styles available for use on different makes and models of presses. The blanket manufacturer should be able to premount the appropriate bars for use on a specific press.

A few modern web offset presses are equipped to lock blankets without premounted bars into blanket clamps that are built into the blanket reel bars.

Prepunched blankets have holes that match the bolt pattern of specific mounting bars. Unless otherwise specified, the holes in a prepunched blanket fall on a straight line across both ends of the blanket, at a right angle to the warp lines. The two rows of holes are parallel to each other. Bars for prepunched blankets consist of two metal bands with interlocking surfaces that grip the edge of the blanket from each side. Bolts connect the metal bands through holes in the blanket's edge. Prepunched blankets are not typically used on larger presses.

Determining Proper Packing

Proper packing for plate and blanket cylinders is typically recommended by the press manufacturer to achieve a specified *squeeze pressure,* which is required to transfer ink from the plate to the blanket. Squeeze pressure is variable within ±0.002 in. (±0.051 mm); several factors may contribute to such variation. A plate is commonly packed to 0.002 in. (0.051 mm) above bearer height. The blanket cylinder is packed to compensate for the difference between the packed plate and recommended squeeze pressure.

Blankets are *compressible* or *noncompressible;* that is, they compress or displace under pressure. Squeeze pressure for compressible blankets measures 0.004–0.006 in. (0.107–0.152 mm). Noncompressible (conventional) blankets require 0.002–0.004 in. (0.051–0.107 mm) of squeeze. When calculating the packing required to create sufficient squeeze, the press operator should add 0.002 in. (0.051 mm) to compensate for mounting tension and running compaction. All blankets on a press at the same time should be packed within ±0.002 in. (0.051 mm) of each other.

Another factor that affects the packing as measured on the press is bearer compression. When the press is put on impression and the bearers have been properly set, there is considerable pressure between them. These relationships can change, especially when press cylinders are small in diameter. Hard steel bearers do not remain perfectly circular, but deform under pressure. This changes the amount of undercut on the cylinders at the nip or point of impression. Normally, web offset presses are run with a considerable amount of pressure between the bearers. This pressure is beneficial in that it provides smooth rolling contact, eliminates gear backlash, and stabilizes the cylinders. Because this pressure results in the compression of the bearers in the nip, it creates problems when trying to predict the proper packing ratio for the press. For example, assume that the recommended squeeze between plate and blanket is 0.004 in. (0.10 mm). Assume also that the bearers compress 0.0005 in. (0.013 mm) each. If the plate is packed exactly 0.002 in. (0.05 mm) over bearer and the blanket is packed exactly 0.002 in. (0.05 mm) over bearer, then the actual compression between plate and blanket will be 0.005 in. (0.13 mm) rather than 0.004 in. The extra 0.001 in. (0.025 mm) of squeeze is due to the fact that the packing measurements are made relative to the uncompressed bearers. Bearer compression on newer presses is not excessive and probably runs in the range of 0.001 in. (0.025 mm) total compression for the two bearers involved. On older presses, however, bearer compression can run considerably higher, even as much as 0.002 in. (0.05 mm) compression per bearer. This would mean a total of 0.004 in. (0.10 mm) impression squeeze gained in a printing nip due to bearer compression.

Maintaining the recommended squeeze pressure is essential to ensure quality printing. Inadequate pressure causes uneven ink transfer and produces broken images. Excessive pressure distorts images, causes *dot gain,* and prematurely wears plates and blankets.

Proper Care of Blankets

Blankets are required to perform under the great stress and pressure to which they are subjected on press. They must also withstand the materials applied to their surfaces: ink, solvent, water, acids, gums, and salts.

Handle and store blankets as recommended by the manufacturer. Avoid prolonged exposure to light; continuous direct sunlight will crack blanket rubber, rendering it useless. Fluorescent light can have a similar effect. Blankets should be stored in a dark, dry, cool place.

The tubes in which the blankets are packed is a good place to store them. Never attempt to put too many blankets in a single tube, however. The innermost blanket will be very tightly wound, and prolonged storage under high stress may ruin the fabric backing.

Blankets can be stored flat. Rubber should contact rubber; fabric should contact fabric. Prolonged contact between a rubber surface and a fabric backing can cause the fabric pattern to emboss on the adjacent surface.

Blanket Washing

The blanket washes must match the ink *and* blankets. Repeated use of a solvent easily absorbed by the rubber will cause deterioration. Washes with high kauri-butanol (KB) solvents should be avoided. A low KB number indicates low solvency power. A high KB solvent will be absorbed by the rubber more easily and evaporate more slowly. Rate of evaporation is important. A low rate forces delays in reinking after a blanket wash. Retained solvent increases the tackiness and frictional coefficient of the blanket. If possible, washes for heatset blankets should have a KB number of 30 or less.

Some substances should not be used to wash blankets because they will swell the rubber. Among these are chlorinated and coal tar solvents, ketones, and ester. Aromatic solvents like toluene, xylol, turpentine, and pine oil will also cause swelling. Benzene, carbon disulfide, and carbon tetrachloride should not be used because of their high toxicity and ability to dissolve rubber. All chlorinated solvents are toxic.

Wash the surface of a new blanket with solvent and water, using a soft cloth. Be careful not to splash the solvent and water along the blanket edges, because these may not be sealed. Such soaking causes the edges of the fabric to swell. The top layer of the blanket resists solvent; the under layers probably do not. Excess solvent attacks the adhesive that bonds the rubber and carcass together.

The KB of the ink solvent must also be considered. Heatset ink vehicles also contain a hydrocarbon solvent, the most common one being No. 535 Magie oil with a KB of 27.5. When ordering blankets, some shops send samples of the inks or coatings to be used. This ensures that the blankets received from the manufacturer are compatible.

19 Maintenance

Web offset presses are complex mechanical systems that are required to run with precision at high speeds. Each component of a web offset press performs a specialized function, interrelated to the functions of other press parts. Press manufacturers prescribe operating procedures that should efficiently produce optimum results.

The initial investment in a web offset press is extremely high; therefore, the equipment is expected to run continuously for a long time. Printers must implement the manufacturer's established preventive-maintenance program to keep equipment in top running condition. The pressroom, too, must be kept as clean as possible, and regular cleaning should be scheduled. A reliable press is productive and profit-generating; regular maintenance contributes to dependability. Income is not realized during downtime; however, a breakdown may require much longer downtime than a scheduled shutdown for maintenance. Excessive repair costs and overtime pay may also be incurred as the result of a breakdown. Furthermore, jobs fall behind schedule and fewer are printed as a result of lost press time.

Identifying and servicing press components that require regular attention help to eliminate major repairs. Timely, continuous maintenance is essential, because the diverse pieces of equipment need to be serviced at different intervals. Stocking spare parts contributes to more efficient operation by reducing downtime. Management should compile a central file of press manufacturers' manuals. These manuals can be used to develop a preventive-maintenance checklist from the manufacturers' recommendations. A malfunction report allows the press crew to itemize press problems that require service. Furthermore, the job planning board should be used to post scheduled maintenance.

The preventive-maintenance program should be structured according to the frequency at which specific items require service. *Daily* maintenance operations must be performed every day. *Weekly* functions may be divided among the days of the week but should be performed on designated days. *Monthly* service includes items that must be checked after every 500 hours of operation. The frequency at which these operations are performed varies, depending upon the number of shifts that a press is run each day. A two-shift schedule accumulates 500 operating hours every 8–9 weeks; single shift, 16–18 weeks; and a three-shift operation, 4–5 weeks. Using an hour meter to record running time assures accurate, timely maintenance. *Semiannual* procedures are to be performed after every 1,500 operating hours; add them to the 500-hour list every third time. *Annual* maintenance is performed after every 3,000 hours in addition to all other procedures. The frequency at which the semiannual and annual operations are performed also varies, depending upon the number of shifts that a press is run each day.

Maintenance checklists help to ensure that all equipment is serviced as required. The person who performs a procedure should initial and date the appropriate checklist accordingly.

To enhance the efficiency of the preventive-maintenance program, some press manufacturers color-code lubrication points that need to be lubricated at the same interval. Furthermore, special lubricants for specific functions should be clearly identified, and the location for their use should be clearly marked. Preventive maintenance should be treated like a job — placed in the schedule and completed on time.

Lubrication

The principal function of lubricating oil and grease is to minimize friction wear on moving parts and to prevent rust. Lubricants should have sufficient body to resist pressure and a high enough boiling point to prevent evaporation under the heat generated by the press. Lubricants must be clean and free of grit, which abrades and prematurely wears bushings, bearings, and cams. They must remain stable under a wide range of temperatures.

Equipment manufacturers specify the precise lubricant to be used on each designated lubrication point. Never substitute one lubricant for another, unless the manufacturer has approved such a substitution. Improper lubrication may result in serious damage to the equipment.

(Text continues on page 289)

Printing unit lubrication and service points
Courtesy Heidelberg Harris, Inc.

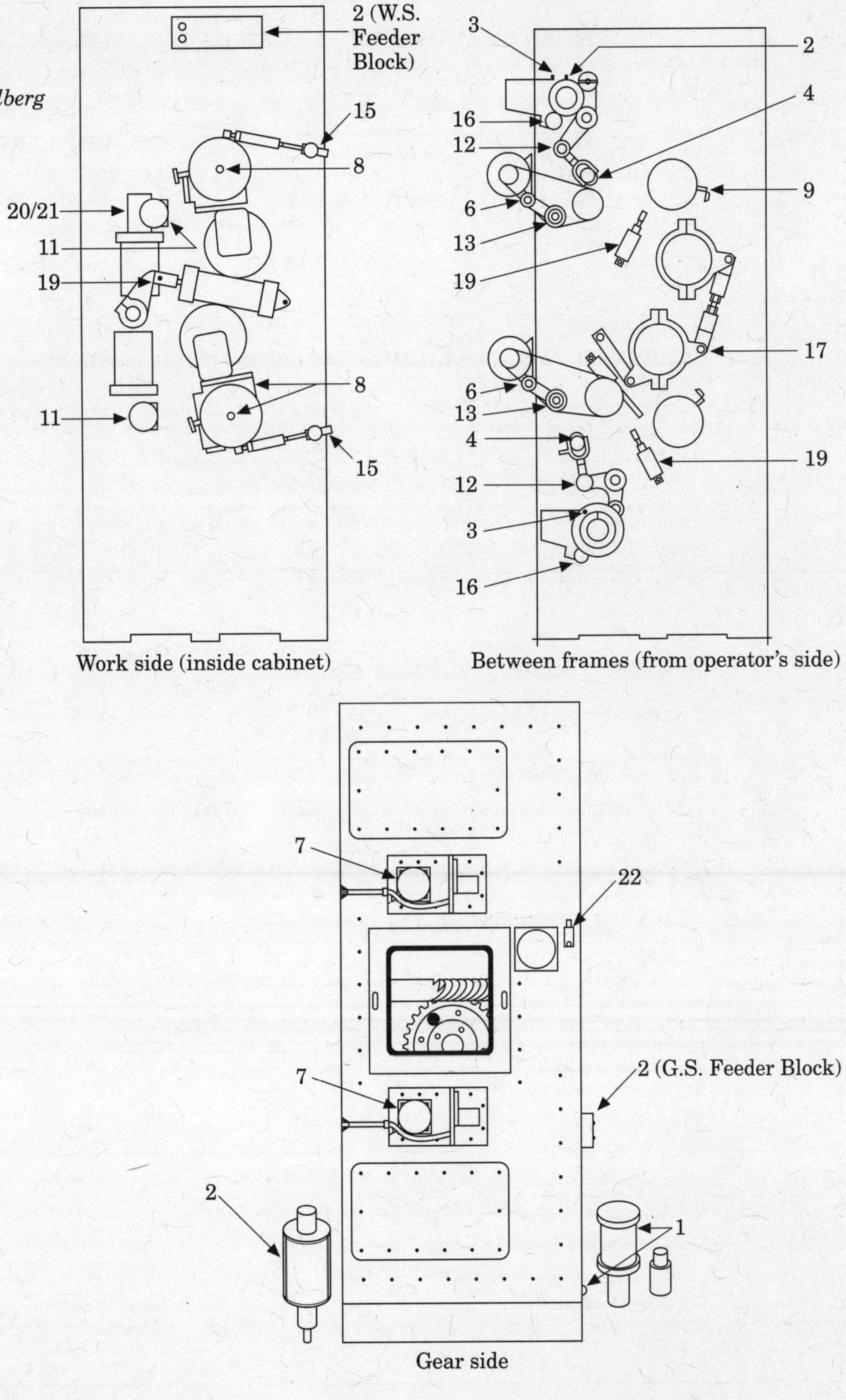

LUBRICANT MANUFACTURER RECOMMENDATIONS

LUBRICANT LETTER	A*	B*	C	D
	Mobil SHC 630 (Synthetic Oil)	Mobiletemp SHC-32 (Synthetic Grease)	600W Cylinder Oil	DTE Light
	Mobilegear 630 (Natural Oil)			

PRINTING UNIT LUBRICATION AND SERVICE POINTS

This chart covers the printing units only. Most of the points are shown in the illustration on page 285.

Item	Component	Procedure	Lubricant
		DAILY	
1	Circulating oil system behind pump, fill as necessary	Check sump oil level in window	A
2	Trabon automatic greasing system	Check reservoir level, fill as necessary	B
3	Ink fountain shoes	Grease	B
4	Inker cams (4 per unit)	Oil	A
		WEEKLY	
6	Dampener brush roller drive belts	Check tension and wear	–
7, 8	Circumferential (7) and lateral (8) register systems	Check for freedom of movement	–
9	Bearer wiper felts	Remove, check for wear and dirt, replace as necessary	–
10	DUO-TROL pan and slip roller gears	Grease	B
11	DUO-TROL pan roller drive brake	Clean by squirting with alcohol	–
		EVERY TWO WEEKS	
12	Ink ductor linkage (1 fitting on each side)	Grease	B
13	Brush dampener drive belt idler	Grease	B
		MONTHLY	
1	Circulating oil system	Replace external filter	–
8	Lateral register (4 fittings each)	Grease	B
15	Plate cylinder cocking devices (operator's side)	Oil	–

Item	Component	Procedure	Lubricant
		MONTHLY *(continued)*	
16	Fountain pivots (2 per fountain)	Grease	B
17	Impression linkage (4 fittings each side)	Grease	B
18	Plate and blanket cylinder eccentric boxes (4 remote fittings on edge of operator's side frame, 2 inside gear side frame)	Grease	B
19	Air cylinder pivots (all)	Oil	—
20	Brush dampener pan roller drive gearboxes	Remove level plug on side, fill as necessary	C
21	DUO-TROL roller drive gearboxes	Remove level plug on side, fill as necessary	C
22	Phaser	Grease	B
		EVERY SIX MONTHS	
1	Circulating oil system	Drain, remove, and clean strainer replace external filter, refill, clean pump cooling fan	A
20	Brush dampener pan roller drive gearboxes	Drain and refill to level plug on side	C
21	DUO-TROL roller drive gearboxes	Drain and refill to level plug on side	C
23	Dropdown drive bearings and tensioner on last unit	Grease	B
		YEARLY	
24	Check unit timing	See Section II	—
25	Check bearer pressures	See Section II	—

PRESS SYSTEM LUBRICATION AND SERVICE POINTS

This chart generally covers all components of the printing system except the printing unit. Most, but not all, of the points are shown in the illustration on page 288.

Item	Component	Procedure	Lubricant
		DAILY	
1	Automatic greasing systems	Check level, fill as necessary	*
2	Oil mist lubricating systems	Check level, fill as necessary	*
3	Circulating oil systems	Check sump oil level, fill as necessary	*
4	Air line lubricators	Check, fill as necessary	D
5	Dampener circulator filter	Clean, replace as necessary	—
6	Photoelectric web guide or break detectors	Clean senders and receivers, check lamps	—

Press system lubrication and service points

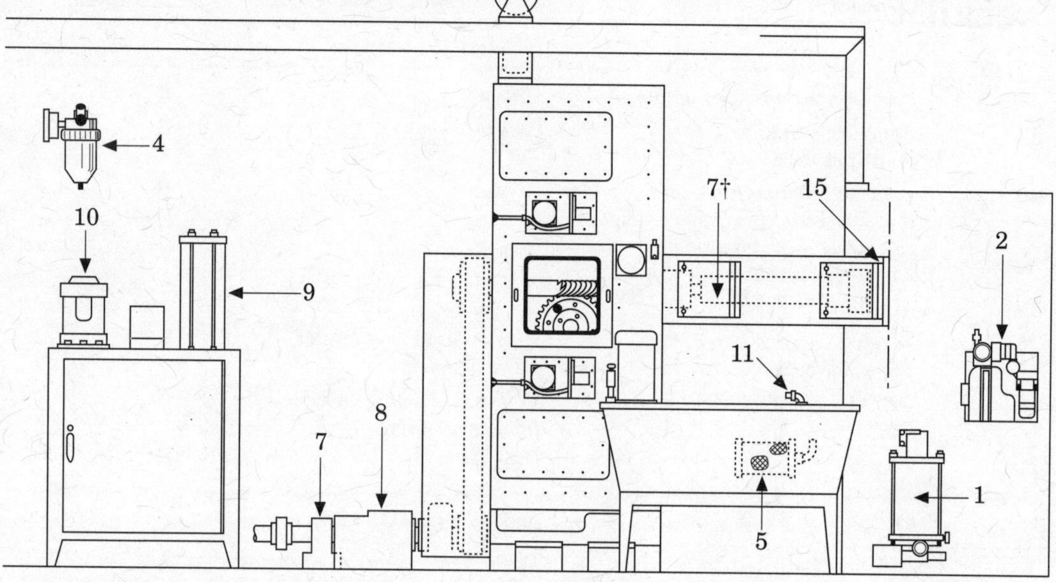

Item	Component	Procedure	Lubricant
		EVERY TWO WEEKS	
7†	Driveshaft pillow block bearings	Grease	B
8	Folder clutch	Spray lubricant sparingly onto hub splines	NEVER-SEEZ® or equivalent high-temp. antiseize lubricant
9	Dampener solution concentration reservoir	Remove and clean	–
10	Dampener solution mixer motors	Clean cooling fan	–
11	Dampener system	Flush	–
15	Unit separation clutch	Spray lubricant sparingly onto hub splines	NEVER-SEEZ®
		EVERY SIX MONTHS	
3	Circulating oil systems	Drain, remove, and clean sump strainer, replace external filter, refill	*
12	Chill roller cylinders	Flush out	–
13	Main drive motor	Cleaning cooling fan filters	–
		YEARLY	
14	Infeed, chill roller, and folder web pressure and nip rollers	Check condition, replace as necessary	–

*See Operator's Manual for recommended lubricant

†Not on all units.

Maintenance Checklist

Paster and Infeed

- Lubricate the drive on a multiarmed paster, the spindles and shafts of all rollers and cylinders, and the drive gears on the acceleration belts. If the paster has festoon rollers, each of these should be lubricated.
- Lubricate the mounting of the dancer roller. If the linkage to the roll-stand brake is mechanical, appropriate points along the linkage should be kept lubricated.
- On flying pasters, frequently inspect and clean the mechanisms that sense the roll during the paster cycle (photoelectric eyes, butt switches, or electromechanical sensing fingers).
- Periodically inspect and clean the rollers or brushes that are used to apply pressure to the splice.
- Periodically inspect the web-severing knife for sharpness and the acceleration belts for wear. Replace as needed.
- Periodically inspect and lubricate all rollers in the infeed.
- Check the roller settings of infeed metering unit. Light settings may allow slippage and reduce tension control.

Printing Units

- Lubricate the mountings of all rollers according to the manufacturer's specifications.
- Regularly check and adjust all inking and dampening rollers, especially the form rollers. Improper settings can cause ink and water distribution problems and undue plate wear, and generally impair print quality.
- Regularly perform reconditioning washups of each inking system, using multistep solvents to remove dried gum and ink, as well as to recondition roller surfaces (soft and hard). Out-of-the-way places should be thoroughly cleaned.
- Thoroughly clean each dampening system. Scrub built-up chemicals from the fountain pan. Remove grease, gum, and other materials from the roller surfaces. If a recirculating system is in use, flush the entire system with water. Replace or clean the filters as required.
- Frequently clean and inspect the cylinder bearers. Foreign particles will prevent smooth rolling contact.
- Periodically check the bearer pressures.
- Clean cylinder bodies each time plates and blankets are changed.
- Inspect and clean all gear trains; remove traces of old grease and oil. Relubricate the entire train. Inspect gear trains that are sealed in oil baths to ensure that no grit has infiltrated the system.

Dryer

- Regularly inspect and clean all nozzles in the dryer to prevent clogging. Clogged nozzles cannot evenly dry the web; subsequently, marking occurs on the folder. Remove any ink buildup from hot air orifices. These deposits are made by a fluttering web.
- Gas dryers should be inspected for leaks in the gas lines.
- Periodically check the exhaust system. Insufficient exhaust allows solvent vapors to saturate the air inside the dryer. Greater heat is required to evaporate solvent vapors, thus reducing dryer efficiency. Maintain negative air pressure inside the dryer to prevent solvent vapors from exhausting into the pressroom. Antipollution systems that recycle clean hot air back into the dryer must be maintained in top operating condition.

Chill Rolls

- Lubricate the main drive into the chill rolls, the variable-speed drive, and the chill roller mountings.
- Thoroughly clean the chill roll surfaces with a strong solvent to remove ink buildup.
- Periodically flush out the chill rollers. Systems that constantly filter and recirculate water inhibit mineral buildup. Consult the manufacturer's instructions for the proper flushing procedure.
- Check the refrigeration system to make sure that it is operating efficiently.

Folder

- Regularly and completely lubricate the entire folder. This includes the gear train from the press drive; the mountings of wheels, rollers, and cylinders; the tucker blades and folding jaws; the actuating mechanism on the chopper blade; and the drive rollers on the delivery belts.
- Regularly inspect the trolley wheels, slitter wheels, cross perforators, cutoff knives, impaling pins, tucker blades and jaws, chopper blade, and delivery belts. Replace as needed.
- Regularly inspect the mechanisms used to hold the signature and to ensure folding accuracy (e.g., cams, brushes, and wheels). Replace as required.

20 Pressroom Safety

General Presswork

Technological advancements in printing presses have led to increased press speeds. Faster presses pose additional safety problems; however, improved training methods and guarding devices have reduced potential hazards. A systematic safety approach can further reduce the number of accidents.

Press Operator

The press operator should be properly trained before attempting to operate any equipment. Follow the press manufacturer's recommended operating procedures. Develop supplemental safety procedures to ensure additional personal safety.

Avoid or cover long hair, avoid loose fitting clothing, and do not wear jewelry or ties near moving machinery. Protect yourself from all inherent dangers. Wear a hard hat and ear protection if necessary. Always wear steel-tipped safety shoes to avoid injury by heavy paper rolls or tools; the soles of the safety shoes should provide adequate traction without generating friction sparks. Wear the recommended protective gear

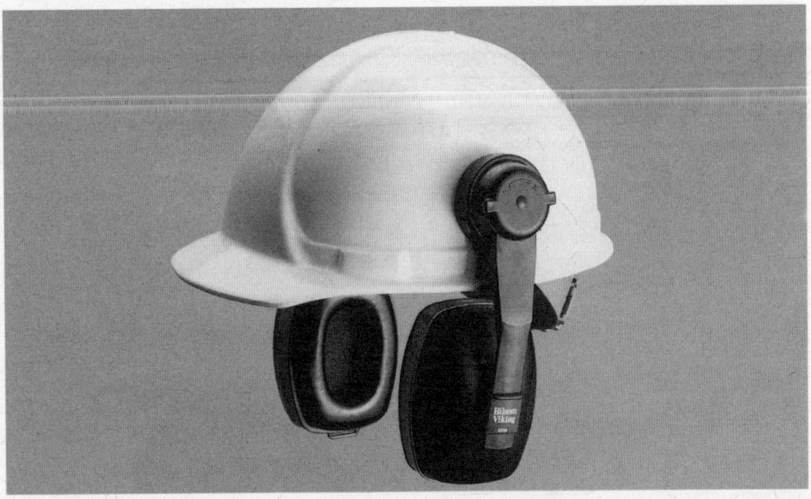

Viking heavy-duty earmuffs attached to safety helmet
Courtesy Bilsom International, Inc.

and read the Material Safety Data Sheets before handling chemicals.

Caution: *Make sure that guards, audible warning devices, flashing warning lights, and personal protection equipment are in use at all times.* Alert all crew members before the press is started. Obey all warning devices and labels.

Pressroom

Installing a new press requires careful planning. The efficient use of floor space is essential. The designated location of the press should meet the following requirements:

- The floor should be able to support the weight of the press.
- Aisle space around the press should be large enough to permit the safe transportation of materials and supplies.
- Press operators should have adequate space to safely remove the printed signatures from the delivery.
- The press should be operable and serviceable, without interfering with adjacent equipment.
- The location should have sound-absorbing devices to prevent the amplification and transmission of noise generated by the press.
- Space for auxiliary equipment and containers should be provided.
- Lighting conditions and ventilation should conform to local agency requirements.

A good press location must be accompanied, however, by good housekeeping to establish a safe working environment. All spoilage must be placed in proper waste containers that are conveniently located. Solvent-soaked rags should be placed in a closed container.

The Roll Stand

Technological changes have automated many of the rolltender's functions; however, spindle-mounted rolls that require some manual handling are widely used. The spindle is a steel shaft that runs through the core of the roll.

Running and braking increases the temperature of the spindle. The rolltender must wear gloves and handle the hot metal with caution. Furthermore, the weight of the spindle requires the rolltender to use the proper lifting technique (i.e., knees bent, back straight).

Hooks suspended by cables or chains are used to hoist the roll into sockets for running. A roll of stock usually weighs 2,000 lb. (900 kg) or more; therefore, the hooks must securely grasp the spindle before the roll is hoisted into position. The spindle must be long enough to be adequately supported at each end by the sockets. All crew members should remain clear of the area beneath a suspended roll. Rolltenders should wear leather-palmed gloves to protect their hands from injuries that may be caused by the hoisting cables or chains.

Reel-mounted rolls present fewer potential hazards; however, the rolltender must exercise care when handling and transporting a roll of paper to the infeed.

Avoid contact with the knives that cut the expired roll; make sure that they are in the "rest" position when not in use.

Rolls are usually wrapped in a heavy kraft paper to protect them prior to their use. A sharp knife or razor and a stripper are typically used to remove the wrapper. Push sharp instruments when cutting; never pull them forward.

Dampening System

Dampening solution composition varies from one manufacturer to another; most offer premixed solutions. Printers, however, may find it more economical to mix their own solutions.

Each chemical should be identified on a Material Safety Data Sheet, and the person working with the chemical must be familiar with the proper handling and mixing procedures. Furthermore, suitable protective equipment (rubber apron, rubber gloves, a face shield, and goggles) should be worn when mixing hazardous materials. Eyewash stations should be located in the vicinity.

Emergency eyewash station
Courtesy Bel-Art Products

Inking System

Many rollers comprise the ink train of an offset inking system, creating numerous pinch points wherever two rollers run in contact. These pinch points should be shielded by guards to prevent accidental contact with moving rollers. Metal grate-like guards or angle irons solidly mounted to the press frame should extend across the width of exposed roller nips.

Cylinders

The nip between the plate and blanket cylinders should be guarded to prevent personal injury and mechanical damage. New system standards require the press operator to simultaneously depress the inch and start buttons to rotate these cylinders. This eliminates the possibility of unintentionally starting the press at high speed. These systems should be operable at all times; do not electrically bypass them.

Press operators should stop the press before removing dirt or debris from the plate or blanket. A remotely operated hickey-picking device may be used to perform this job while the press is running.

When the press is initially webbed, or when it is rewebbed, the lead edge of the paper should be tapered to improve visibility of the printing nip during manual paper feeding. The press operator should grasp the paper several inches behind the lead edge.

Folders

Folders perform a variety of folding and cutting operations. The slitters should have guards that cover them as completely as possible. The exposed side that cuts the paper into ribbons is potentially dangerous during rewebbing of the press.

Rollers and cutting cylinders in the folder easily grasp fingers, loose clothing, and long hair. Pinch wheels or rolls exert tremendous pressure on the ribbons to feed them into the cutting cylinders; press crew members should avoid contact with all moving machinery.

The tapered lead edge of the paper also improves visibility of roller nips in the folder and allows the press operator to safely feed the paper. Grasping the paper several inches back from the lead edge reduces the risk of injury.

Press Decks

Large presses may include three or four levels of decks, which may be located more than 20 ft. (6 m) above the main floor. Catwalks are common on many large presses. Decks, guard rails, stairs, and ladders should conform to state and local agency standards as well as any applicable Occupational Safety and Health Administration (OSHA) standards.

Platforms with railing on a multilevel press

Repairs or maintenance procedures may require the removal of deck components, which should be reassembled before subsequently running the press. All hinged deck sections should be closed during running.

Deck materials should be sturdy and slip-resistant. Metal or wooden deck surfaces require regular cleaning to prevent dirt, oil, or grease from accumulating on them.

Decks should not be used for storage, as containers or tools could easily fall from them. Elevated decks should be furnished with toeboards to prevent objects from rolling over their edges onto people or equipment located below them.

Nonskid floor grating
Courtesy Chemgrate Corporation

Tools

Tools required for the operation and maintenance of a press should be stored on a tool rack or in a tool box. A stray wrench or screwdriver can easily fall into and damage a printing unit. Furthermore, specific tools should only be used for their intended purpose. Misuse may result in personal injury or mechanical damage. Pliers, for example, should not be used on nuts and bolts, which can easily become stripped and no longer adjustable by the proper tool. Use spark-proof tools in areas where solvents are employed.

Solvents

Small quantities of solvents are kept at most presses for routine cleaning. Most solvents are either combustible or flammable; combustible liquids have a flashpoint at or above 100°F (37.8°C). The flashpoint of flammable liquids is at or below 100°F.

Flash point of selected solvents

Liquid	Flash Point
Hexane	20°F
Textile spirits	20
Mineral spirits	105
Toluene	45
Xylene	81
Kerosene	143

Because of the danger of static charges resulting in a flash fire, containers must be grounded and bonded before transferring flammable liquids. Grounding equalizes any charge differential between the container and the ground; bonding equalizes any charge differential between two containers through an electrical conductor.

Containers for press solvents should be approved safety containers, constructed of heavy-gauge metal with lids spring-loaded to the closed position.

Potential ignition sources (faulty electrical wiring, static electricity, and friction sparks) should be eliminated. Furthermore, smoking should never be permitted in and around the pressroom.

Cleaning Rags

Presses often require hand-cleaning, especially after a web break. Cleaning rags should be kept in a designated container when not in use, so as to prevent them from accidentally being pulled into a printing unit. Dirty, solvent-soaked rags present the danger of combustion; therefore, they should be stored in a container that cannot be propped open. The container must remain closed to prevent an accumulation of chemical vapors that could result in a fire. Furthermore, exposure to chemical vapors may be hazardous to pressroom personnel.

Washup

The following procedure is recommended for cleaning blankets and applying gum or finisher to plates on multicolor presses:

- The press operator in charge should lock out all start buttons other than the one being used; all crew members should be clear of the press.
- The press operator inches the press to expose a section of the blanket and plate and then engages the stop lock button on the first unit.
- The assistant engages the stop lock button on the second unit.
- Both press operators clean the exposed segments of their respective blankets. Gum or finisher is applied to the plates.
- When both operators are clear of the cylinders, the stop lock buttons are disengaged and a signal bell or buzzer is sounded.
- The operator on the first unit inches the press until the next segments of the blanket and plate are in position.
- This procedure is repeated until all blankets have been completely cleaned and all plates have been gummed.

Chemical Handling

Most chemicals used in printing arrive from the manufacturer or distributor with warning labels that identify the chemical and its manufacturer; the labels also list hazard warnings. Material Safety Data Sheets (MSDS) that prescribe handling and storage procedures are also provided for all products containing hazardous materials.

The majority of suppliers to the printing industry have adopted the Hazardous Materials Identification System (HMIS), which uses color coding, numbers, and letters to identify health, flammability, and reactivity hazards.

The color blue and the letter "H" indicate a health hazard; 0–4 progressively indicate the severity of the hazard. Red and yellow respectively identify flammability and reactivity hazards; the letter "F" indicates flammability, "R" designates reactivity. The severity of these hazards is also expressed numerically.

The HMIS system also identifies the required personal protection equipment. Gloves, goggles, an apron, and a respirator are required in various combinations as indicated on the label by alphabetic characters (SA, SB, SC, and SF).

Employers are required to identify (label) hazardous materials, obtain the Material Safety Data Sheets, and provide training and a written program.

The Hazardous Materials Identification System

A completed label is affixed to the chemical container so that employees can be aware of the hazards associated with the chemical and wear proper personal protection gear.

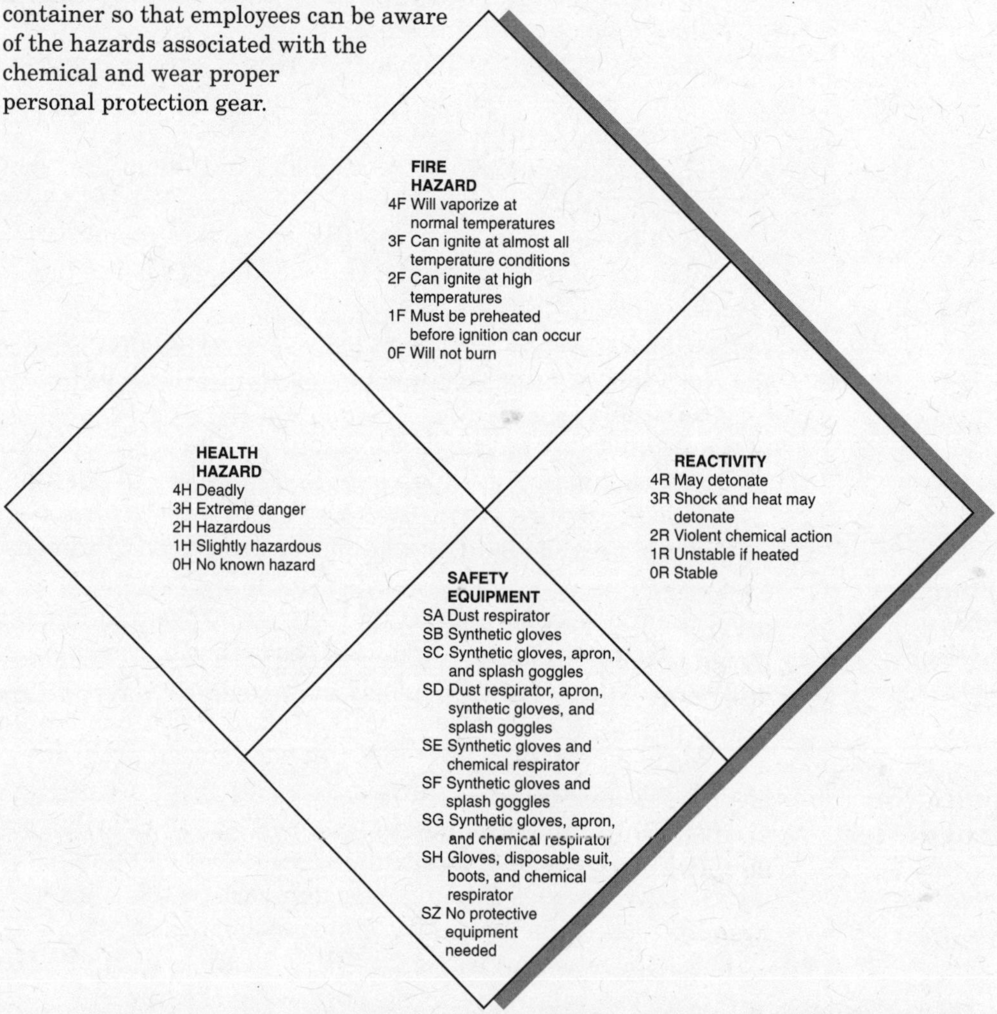

HMIS personal protection symbols

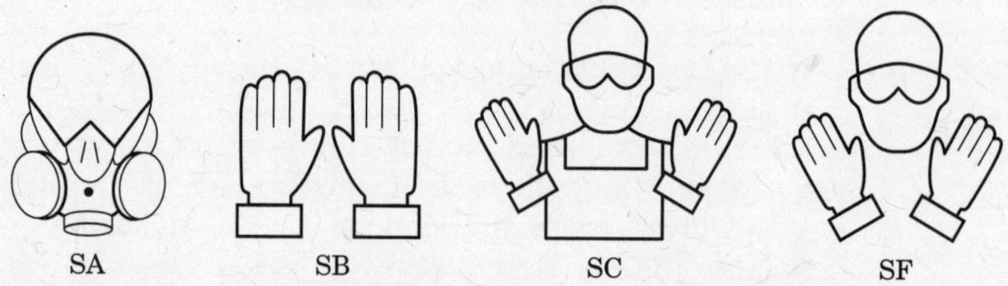

Glossary

additive (1) Any compound which, when combined with another, reduces or improves flow (workability), or otherwise changes the composition of a lubricant to a predetermined state.
(2) A substance added to another in relatively small amounts to impart or improve desirable properties or suppress undesirable properties. In printing, these substances may be added to ink, paper, and dampening solutions.

afterburner In incinerator technology (such as that found on web presses), a burner located so that the combustion gases are forced to pass through its flame in order to remove smoke and odors. It may be attached to or separated from the incinerator proper.

air pollution control device Mechanism or equipment that cleans emissions generated by an incinerator by removing pollutants that would otherwise be released to the atmosphere.

air shaft A special roller in the roll stand of a web press that uses air-actuated grippers to hold the core of the roll of paper.

alcohol, isopropyl An organic substance added to the dampening solution of a lithographic printing press to reduce the surface tension of water. *Alternative term:* isopropanol.

alcohol substitute A chemical used in a lithographic dampening solution in place of isopropyl alcohol (isopropanol).

angle bar A metal bar at a 45° angle horizontal to the direction of the printing press. It is used to turn the web when feeding from the side, or to bypass turning it in ribbon printing. The angle bar is usually filled with cooled air and perforated to reduce the friction resulting from web travel.

antifoaming agent A substance that prevents the buildup of foam in a dampening solution.

antiskinning agent A material added to ink to prevent a rubbery layer from forming on its surface when it is exposed to air.

auxiliary equipment Web guides, ink circulating systems, antistatic devices, and other such things that are not standard on presses but are often incorporated for better control of the substrate.

back cylinder See *impression cylinder.*

back pressure The force between the blanket cylinder and the impression cylinder that facilitates the transfer of the image from the blanket to the printing substrate. *Alternative term:* impression pressure.

backing away A condition in which an ink does not flow under its own weight or remain in contact with the fountain roller. It "backs away" and is not transferred to the ductor roller. Eventually, the prints become uneven, streaky, and weak. A conical ink agitator, which applies a finite amount of force to the ink, keeps it flowing or prevents it from backing away in the fountain while automatic ink leveling keeps the fountain full.

backlash gear A thin second gear bolted to the spur gear to reduce play between gears.

back-trap mottle Blotches and streaks in the solids and tones of an overprinted ink film on a press sheet due to the transfer of a printed ink film from the paper to the blanket of a subsequent printing unit. This trap problem occurs almost exclusively on sheetfed presses with four or more printing units.

backup registration Correct relative position of the printing on one side of the sheet or web and the printing on the other side.

bareback roller A form or ductor roller in a conventional dampening system that operates without cloth or paper covers.

basic size Sheet size in inches for a particular type of paper.

basis weight Weight, in pounds, of a ream of paper cut to its basic size, in inches.

Baumé scale Unit for measuring the density or specific gravity of the liquids used in the printing processes.

bearer A hardened metal ring attached to the cylinder body or journal of the plate and blanket cylinders.

bearer pressure The force with which the bearers of opposed cylinders contact each other on a sheetfed offset press.

bearer-to-bearer The cylinder arrangement in which the bearers of the plate and blanket cylinders contact each other.

belt press A printing press that uses two continuous tracks for printing books in an in-line operation from a paper roll to a delivered book, ready for its binding at the end of the press.

bending fixture See *plate bending device.*

bending jig See *plate bending device.*

bible paper A very thin, lightweight, bright, strong, opaque paper made from rag and mineral fiber pulp.

bladeless ink fountain A disposable sheet of polyester foil that is held in contact with the fountain roller by a series of small cylinders lying parallel to it.

blanket A fabric coated with synthetic or natural rubber that transfers the image from the printing plate to the substrate.

blanket, compressible A blanket with a specially manufactured layer designed to "give" or compress under pressure from the plate and impression cylinder.

blanket, conventional A hard, noncompressible blanket that bulges out on either or both sides of a nip under pressure.

blanket compressibility The extent to which blanket thickness reduces under pressure, such as during the printing impression.

blanket compression set	The permanent reduction in thickness of a blanket or any of its component parts.
blanket creep	The slight forward movement or slip of the part of the blanket surface that is in contact with the plate or paper.
blanket cylinder	The cylinder that carries the printing blanket and has two primary functions: (1) to carry the offset rubber blanket into contact with the inked image on the plate cylinder and (2) to transfer, or offset, the ink film image to the paper (or other substrate) carried by the impression cylinder.
blanket-to-blanket	A setup on a perfecting press whereby two blankets, each acting as an impression cylinder for the other, simultaneously print on both sides of the paper passing between them.
blister	In printing, an oval-shaped, sharply defined, bubblelike formation that bulges out on both sides of the web.
body	The relative term describing the consistency of an ink, referring mainly to the stiffness or softness of an ink, but implying other things including length and thixotropy.
bonding	The elimination of a difference in electrical potential between objects.
bridge roller	A roller in a combination continuous-flow dampening system that contacts the dampening form roller and the first ink form roller and transports dampening solution from the dampening system into the inking system.
buffer	A substance capable of neutralizing acids and bases in solutions and thereby maintaining the acidity or alkalinity level of the solution.
bustle wheel	A mechanical device used to compensate for paper stretching in web offset printing.
butt	The unusable portion of a roll of paper on a web press.
butt splice	The end-to-end joining of two similar materials, such as webs of paper.

caliper The thickness of a sheet of paper or other material measured under specific conditions. Caliper is usually expressed in mils or points, both ways of expressing thousandths of an inch.

catalyst A substance that alters (initiates or accelerates) the velocity of a reaction between two or more substances without changing itself in chemical composition.

catch-up The condition that occurs when insufficient dampening causes the nonimage areas of the plate to become ink-receptive and print as scum or when excessive ink reaches the plate. *Alternative term:* dry-up.

chalking Poor adhesion of ink to the printing surface. This condition results when the substrate absorbs the ink vehicle too rapidly. The ink dries slowly and rubs off as a dusty powder.

chemicals, hazardous An EPA designation for any hazardous material requiring a Material Safety Data Sheet (MSDS) under OSHA's Hazard Communication Standard. Such substances are capable of producing fires and explosions or adverse health effects like cancer and dermatitis. Hazardous chemicals are distinct from hazardous waste.

chill rolls On a web offset press, the section located after the drying oven where heatset inks are cooled below their setting temperature.

chuck The mechanism on a paper roll stand that centers and grips the roll core.

Clean Air Act U.S. federal guidelines for air quality and emission controls affecting all manufacturing concerns.

Clean Water Act U.S. federal guidelines for water quality and controls affecting all manufacturing concerns.

closed loop A process in which all control functions have been automated, including sensing output errors and correcting the input to compensate for the error.

coating (1) An unbroken, clear film applied to a substrate in layers to protect and seal it, or to make it glossy. (2) Applying waxes, adhesives, varnishes, or other protective or sealable chemicals to a substrate during the converting process. (3) The mineral substances (clay, blanc fixe, satin white, etc.) applied to the surface of a paper or board during manufacture.

collating mark A distinctive, numbered symbol printed on the folded edge of signatures to denote the correct gathering sequence.

color, HiFi A special high-fidelity color reproduction process that uses cyan, magenta, yellow, and black plus additional special colors to expand the color gamut of printing. With HiFi color based on the Küppers model, seven basic colors are used: cyan, yellow, magenta, orange, green, violet, and black. Because seven colors are used, color separations are made using stochastic screening technology to prevent moiré, which would occur if conventional halftone screening technology was used.

color bar A device printed in a trim area of a press sheet to monitor printing variables such as trapping, ink density, dot gain, and print contrast. It usually consists of overprints of two- and three-color solids and tints; solid and tint blocks of cyan, magenta, yellow, and black; and additional aids such as resolution targets and dot gain scales. *Alternative terms:* color control strip; color control bar.

color match Condition resulting when no significant difference in hue, saturation, and lightness can be detected between two color samples viewed under standard illumination.

color sequence The order in which colors are printed on a substrate as indicated by the order that the inks are supplied to the printing units of the press. Color sequence determines how well inks trap on a substrate. *Alternative term:* color rotation.

color strength An ink's color power as determined by its pigment concentration.

color temperature The degree (expressed in Kelvins) to which a blackbody must be heated to produce a certain color radiation. For example, 5,000 Kelvin is the graphic arts viewing standard.

color variation Changes that occur in the density of a color during printing as a result of deviations in the amount of ink accepted by paper or the amount of ink fed to the paper.

colorimeter An instrument that measures and compares the hue, purity, and brightness of colors in a manner that simulates how people perceive color.

common impression cylinder A drum-like cylinder that contacts several blanket cylinders, permitting multicolor printing on one side of the sheet.

compression set A permanent reduction in blanket thickness or the thickness of any of its component parts.

console The computer system workstation where operators perform specific tasks by executing commands through a keyboard. Modern presses have consoles that control inking, dampening, and plate register moves. With some systems, the results of the operator's commands can be reviewed on a nearby monitor.

corrosion inhibitor An additive to the dampening solution to prevent it from reacting with the plate.

creep (1) Movement of the blanket surface or plate packing caused by static conditions or by the squeezing action that occurs during image transfer. (2) The displacement of each page location in the layout of a book signature as a result of folding the press sheet.

cross-perforation A series of holes or slits pierced at a right angle to the direction of web travel to prevent the signature from bursting during folding. Cross-perforating also prevents gusseting.

cross-web The position at a right angle to the grain or machine direction of a web of flexible material.

crystallization The drying of an ink to form a hard, impervious surface that interferes with dry trapping.

cutoff length (1) The distance between corresponding points of repeated images on a web. (2) The circumference of the plate cylinder.

cylinder guide marks Lines on an offset press plate that match corresponding lines on the press's plate cylinder, ensuring that each plate will be positioned accurately on press.

cylinder undercut The difference between cylinder body radius and bearer radius.

dampener covers Molleton, paper, or fiber sleeves placed over dampening rollers in a conventional dampening system that aid in carrying the dampening solution.

dampening solution A mixture of water; gum arabic; an acid, neutral, or alkaline etch; and isopropyl alcohol or an alcohol substitute used to wet the nonimage areas of the lithographic printing plate before it is inked. *Alternative term:* fountain solution.

dampening system A group of rollers that moistens the nonimage areas of a printing plate with a water-based dampening solution that contains additives such as acid, gum arabic, and isopropyl alcohol or other wetting agents.

dampening system, brush A system on a lithographic press that uses a rotating brush to transfer small amounts of water from the fountain to the dampener roller train.

dampening system, continuous-feed A ductorless dampening system in which there is a continuous flow of dampening solution from the fountain roller to the form roller. *Alternative term:* continuous-flow dampening system.

dampening system, conventional A dampening system consisting of a fountain, fountain pan roller, ductor roller, oscillator roller, and one or more covered or uncovered form rollers. The ductor roller transfers dampening solution from the fountain roller to the oscillator roller. *Alternative term:* intermittent-flow dampening system.

dampening system, inker-feed An integrated, continuous-feed dampening system that delivers dampening solution to an ink form roller.

dampening system, plate-feed A continuous-feed dampening system that applies dampening solution directly to the plate using dampening form rollers, rather than indirectly using the first inking form roller.

dampening system, spray bar A variation of the inker-feed continuous-flow dampening system that applies a very fine mist of dampening solution directly to the inking system rollers.

dancer roller A weighted or spring-tensioned controlled roller positioned between a paper roll and a press unit on a web printing press. It senses and removes web slack by controlling the paper reel brake.

deadweight micrometer A device that uses the deadweight of an anvil to obtain repeatable measurements on plate, blankets, and packing. *Alternative terms:* bench micrometer, blanket thickness gauge, Cady gauge.

delamination The continuous splitting, or separation, of the paper's surface caused by the tack of the ink and the rubber blanket.

densitometer, reflection An instrument for measuring the optical density of a photographic print or press sheet.

desensitization In platemaking, the making of a nonimage area less receptive to ink by the application of a gum solution.

dimensional stability How well an object maintains it size. The extent to which a sheet maintains its dimensions with changes in its moisture content or applied stressing.

direct lithography A lithographic process in which the plate and printing surface are brought into contact.

dished roll A web of paper with progressive concave or convex edge misalignment, which is noticeable immediately after the roll is unwrapped.

dot gain The optical increase in the size of a halftone dot during prepress operations or the mechanical increase in halftone dot size that occurs as the image is transferred from plate to blanket to paper in lithography.

double-sixteen A folder that takes a thirty-two-page form and folds it as two separate or inserted sixteen-page forms.

double-thirty-two A folder that takes a sixty-four-page form and folds it as two inserted or separate thirty-two-page forms.

drier An ink additive, such as a salt of cobalt or manganese, that acts as a catalyst to convert a wet ink film to a dry ink film.

drum (1) An oscillating metal ink distribution roller. (2) A synonym for "cylinder" in many press applications.

dry dusting A preliminary pass of the sheet under pressure through the press to remove excessive spray powder, surface material, or other debris.

dry offset Printing from relief plates by transferring the ink image from the plate to a rubber surface and then from the rubber surface to the paper. Printing with this process on an offset press eliminates the need to use water. *Alternative terms:* indirect letterpress, letterset, relief offset.

dry-back An optical loss of density and color strength that may occur while an ink is setting. To achieve the proper dry density, the ink is printed with a wet density slightly higher than the projected dry density.

dryer A unit on a heatset web press that evaporates the solvent ingredient in the heatset ink.

drying agent An ink additive, such as a salt of cobalt or manganese, that acts as a catalyst to convert a wet ink film to a dry ink film.

drying section Section of a papermaking machine where water is removed by passing the web over hot drying cylinders.

drying stimulator A substance — e.g., cobalt chloride — that complements the drier in the ink.

dry-up The problem that occurs when ink appears in the nonimage area due to insufficient dampening of the plate. *Alternative term:* catch-up.

ductor (1) A small-diameter cylinder that alternately contacts the ink fountain roller and the first roller of the ink train. (2) In a conventional dampening system, a small-diameter cylinder that alternately contacts the dampening fountain roller and the oscillator. *Alternative term:* ductor roller.

ductor shock The vibration sent through the inking system when the ductor first contacts the oscillating roller.

duplicator Any sheetfed press smaller than 11×17 in. (279×432 mm) without bearers (hardened metal disks attached to the ends of the cylinder or to the cylinder's journal).

durometer, type-A Instrument used in printing to measure the hardness of roller compounds.

dwell The length of time that the ductor roller contacts the fountain roller.

emulsification Condition that occurs when an ink picks up too much dampening solution and prints a weak, snowflaky pattern.

endplay Undesirable lateral movement of a roller due to poor fit between roller shaft and roller bracket.

fan delivery, web A rotary unit with blades that form pockets which transfer individual folded signatures or newspapers from the folder to the conveyors that carry them to the delivery on a web press.

fan-out An expansion of the sheet near the tail edge.

feeler gauge A thin strip of steel ground to precise thickness and marked accordingly. It is used to adjust clearances between various press mechanisms.

felt side The top side of the paper formed on the paper machine wire. It is the preferred side for printing. See also: *wire side.*

festoon A method of storing a relatively large amount of paper on a series of rollers so that the press can continue to operate while a roll is spliced and accelerated to press speed.

fiber cut A short, straight, fairly smooth slice in the web caused by a fiber bundle catching as paper passes through the calender.

fiber puffing Surface roughening of a coated paper containing groundwood fibers. Condition occurs during heatset drying.

flagging (1) Indicating a web splice so that the spliced product can be removed from the press folder and discarded. (2) Marking printed matter to indicate a change or correction. (3) Inserting small strips of paper into a skid of press sheets as needed to indicate segments of defective printed sheets.

flying paster	An automatic device that attaches a new roll of paper to an expiring roll without a press stop, while the paper is running at press speed and without the use of a festoon.
folder, jaw	Three cylinders in the in-line finishing area of a web press that make one or two parallel folds at right angles to the direction of web travel. *Alternative terms:* parallel folder; tucker folder.
folder, ribbon	A folder on a web press used for publication work. It slits the web into multiple strips of the width required by the desired product size. Each ribbon is turned over an angle bar and guided into position so that all ribbons align with each other ahead of the jaw-folding section. The ribbons of paper are collated and brought down to the cutoff knives and folding jaws in either one or two streams. The press then simultaneously delivers either one or two sets of signatures of the same size.
form roller	A device, riding in contact with the printing plate, that transfers dampening solution or ink from an oscillator roller to the printing plate. Presses typically have one or two *dampening* form rollers and three to five *inking* form rollers.
form roller, oscillating	A special roller substituted for the first and, sometimes, fourth (last) form rollers of a press to reduce ghosting on a job.
former	A smooth, triangular-shaped, metal plate over which a printed web passes prior to entering an in-line folder. The former folds the moving web in half lengthwise. *Alternative term:* former board.
former fold	First fold given paper coming off a web press. The former fold is made in the direction of web travel, thus parallel to the grain.
fountain	A reservoir for the dampening solution or ink that is fed to the plate.
fountain blade	A spring steel plate, steel segment, or plastic angled against the fountain roller and forming the bottom of the ink fountain. Moving the blade closer or farther from the fountain roller controls the thickness of the ink film across the roller.

fountain cheeks Vertical metal pieces contacting the edges of the fountain roller and blade to form an ink-tight trough.

fountain height monitor A sensing device, usually mechanical or ultrasonic, that checks the height of ink moving over the agitator.

fountain keys A series of thumb screws or motor-driven screws or cams behind the blade that provide for variable ink flow across the fountain.

fountain roller A metal roller that rotates intermittently or continuously in the ink or dampening fountain and carries the ink or dampening solution on its metal surface.

fountain solution See *dampening solution*.

fountain solution concentrate A mixture of chemicals (compounded acids and gums) that, when combined with water and alcohol or another wetting agent, form dampening solution.

fountain splitter A device that divides the ink fountain so that two or more inks can be used in the same ink fountain. Each ink will print a different section of the press sheet; e.g., red on the left side and blue on the right side.

fungicide A substance that prevents the formation of mildew and the growth of fungus and bacteria in the dampening system.

furnish Mixture of fibrous and nonfibrous materials like colorants, fillers, and sizing in a water suspension from which paper or paperboard is made.

gear streaks Alternating light and dark marks that appear as bands in halftones and solids parallel to the gripper edge of the sheet. The distance between the marks is the same as the interval between the gear teeth on a cylinder.

ghosting The appearance of faint replicas of an image in undesirable places, caused by mechanical or chemical processes, other than setoff or show-through. *Mechanical ghosting* is caused by ink starvation. *Chemical ghosting* is the appearance of gloss or dull ghosts of images that are printed on the reverse side of the sheet and is caused by the chemical-activity influence that inks have on each other during their critical drying phases.

glaze A combination of oxidized roller surface, embedded ink pigment, dried ink vehicle, and gum from dampening solution on an inking roller.

gloss High reflectance of light from a smooth surface.

grain direction In papermaking, the alignment of fibers in the direction of web travel. In printing, paper is *grain-long* if the grain direction parallels the long dimension of the paper and *grain-short* if it parallels the short dimension.

grammage Weight in grams of a single sheet of paper having an area of one square meter (1 m^2).

grater rollers Textured press cylinders that support a web before drying, reducing smearing and marking.

grounding The elimination of a difference in electrical potential between an object and the ground.

groundwood Mechanical pulp used in papermaking produced by forcing bark-free logs against a revolving, abrasive grinding stone in the presence of water.

guide roller A cylinder on the roll stand between the roll of paper and the dancer roller. It is used to compensate for slight paper variations. Alternative term: *cocking roller*.

hair cut A smooth, curved slice in a paper web that usually occurs because a piece of felt from the manufacturing process is embedded in the web and passes through the calender.

hairline register A standard for accuracy in which the maximum deviation between printing colors is 0.003 in. (0.08 mm).

Hazard Communication Standard An OSHA regulation that requires chemical manufacturers, suppliers, and importers to assess the hazards of the chemicals that they make, supply, or import, and to inform employers, customers, and workers of these hazards through Material Safety Data Sheets (MSDS).

helical gear A gear that has teeth cut at an angle.

hickey An imperfection in printing due to a particle on the blanket or, sometimes, the plate. A *doughnut hickey* consists of a small, solid printed area surrounded by a white halo, or unprinted area. A *void hickey* is a white, unprinted spot surrounded by printing.

hickey-picking roller A roller that has synthetic fibers embedded in its surface to help it remove hickeys from the surface of an offset printing plate or to fill in the white ring on the plate surface. This roller replaces one of the ink form rollers.

hot-weather scumming The tendency of ink to print in nonimage areas when the dampening feed rate is too low.

hydrophilic Water-receptive, as in the nonimage areas of the printing plate.

hydrophobic Water-repellent, as in the image areas of the printing plate.

hygroscopic The ability of paper or other substrates to absorb or release moisture and, in so doing, expand or contract.

image area On a printing plate, the area that has been specially treated to receive ink.

image fit The agreement in distance between the register marks on each color from the gripper to the tail edge of the press sheet.

impaling pins Sharp pieces of metal that maintain web control within a folder. The web is punctured by the pins, just behind the web cutoff point, to control and pull the web around the folder cylinder, releasing it when the fold is started.

impression (1) The printing pressure necessary to transfer an inked image from the blanket to the substrate. (2) A single print.

impression cylinder A large-diameter cylinder that transports the press sheet and forces the paper or other substrate against the inked blanket.

impression cylinder pressure The force of the impression (or back) cylinder against the blanket cylinder.

infeed The set of rollers controlling web tension ahead of the first unit on a web press.

ink, heatset An ink used in high-speed web offset printing that dries primarily by evaporation while the job is still on the press. The inked web passes through a high-velocity, hot-air dryer, which drives the solvents out of the ink, and then over chill rolls that cool and set the ink before the substrate is transferred to the folder.

ink absorbency The extent that an ink penetrates the paper.

ink agitator A revolving cone-shaped device that moves from one end of the fountain to the other keeping the ink soft and flowing.

ink drying Process by which an ink is transformed from an original semifluid or plastic state to a solid.

ink feed The amount of ink delivered to the ink form rollers.

ink fountain The trough on a printing press that holds the ink supply to be transferred to the inking system. The operator controls ink volume from adjustment screws or keys on the fountain or from a remote console.

ink holdout The extent to which paper resists or retards the penetration of the freshly printed ink film.

ink setting (1) The increase in viscosity or body (resistance to flow) that occurs immediately after the ink is printed. (2) An adjustment that the press operator makes to the inking system to control ink volume.

ink vehicle A complex liquid mixture in which pigment particles are dispersed.

ink-dot scum On aluminum plates, oxidation characterized by scattered pits that print sharp, dense dots, or ink material trapped in the grain.

inking control console A computerized device that enables the press operator to control inking and a variety of other functions without leaving the inspection table.

inking system A series of rollers that apply a metered film of ink to a printing plate.

ink/water balance In lithography, the appropriate amounts of ink and water required to ink the image areas of the plate and keep the nonimage areas clean.

in-line converting Converting done directly from the last printing station or drying unit into the converting machinery in one continuous operation.

in-line finishing Manufacturing operations such as numbering, addressing, sorting, folding, diecutting, and converting that are performed as part of a continuous operation right after the printing section on a press.

insert, free-standing (FSI) A four-page, eight-page, etc., self-contained signature typically added to a newspaper.

interface The electronic device that enables one kind of equipment to communicate with or control another. The common boundary between systems or parts of systems.

isopropanol See *alcohol, isopropyl.*

kiss impression The minimum pressure at which proper ink transfer from the blanket to the substrate is possible.

knife rollers Small-diameter hard rollers that help to keep the ink system clean by picking up ink skin particles, lint, etc. *Alternative term:* lint roller.

lay Position of the printed image on the sheet.

lay sheet The first of several sheets run through the press to verify lineup, register, type, and nonimage areas.

lint Loosely bonded paper surface fibers and dust that accumulates on an offset plate or blanket and interferes with print quality. *Alternative terms:* linting, fluffing.

liquid drier A drier in which metal salts are suspended in liquids such as a petroleum solvent.

lithography, offset A planographic printing process that requires an image carrier in the form of a plate on which photochemically produced image and nonimage areas are receptive to ink and water, respectively.

loupe An adjustable-focus magnifier incorporating a precise measuring scale, with or without a self-contained light source. It is used to inspect fine detail.

makeready All of the operations necessary to get the press ready to print the current job.

masstone The color of ink in bulk, such as in a can, or a thick film of ink. It is the color of light reflected by the pigment and often differs from the printed color of the ink.

Material Safety Data Sheet A product specification form used to record information about the hazardous chemicals and other health and physical hazards employees face in an industrial workplace, along with guidelines covering exposure limits and other precautions. Employers are required to compile and maintain files of this information under the OSHA Hazard Communication Standard set forth by the U.S. federal government.

metering nip The line of contact between the two rollers of an inker-feed dampening system.

milking A coating buildup on the nonimage areas of the offset blanket that usually occurs when the coating softens because it does not adequately resist water.

misregister Incorrectly positioned printed images, either in reference to each other or to the sheet's edges.

misregister, random Misregister that varies from sheet to sheet.

misting Flying ink that forms fine droplets or filaments that become diffused throughout the pressroom.

moiré An undesirable, unintended interference pattern caused by the out-of-register overlap of two or more regular patterns such as dots or lines. In process-color printing, screen angles are selected to minimize this pattern. If the angles are not correct, an objectionable effect may be produced.

molleton A thick cotton fabric, similar to flannel, with a long nap and used to cover form rollers in conventional lithographic dampening systems.

mottle Irregular and unwanted variation in color or gloss caused by uneven absorbency of the paper.

multicolor printing The printing of two or more colors, often one over another.

nip The line of contact between two cylindrical objects, such as two rollers on an offset press.

nonimage area The portion of a lithographic printing plate that is treated to accept water and repel ink when the plate is on press. Only the ink-receptive areas will print an image.

offset blanket See *blanket.*

OK sheet A press sheet that closely matches the prepress proof and has been approved by the customer and/or production personnel. It is used as a guide to judge the quality of the rest of the production run.

oleophilic Oil-receptive, as in the image areas of the printing plate.

oleophobic Oil-repellent, as in the dampened nonimage areas of the printing plate.

opacity (1) The ability of a printed ink film to hide what is underneath. (2) The extend to which light transmission is obstructed.

oscillator A driven inking or dampening roller that not only rotates but also moves from side to side, distributing and smoothing out the ink film and erasing image patterns from the form roller. *Alternative terms:* oscillating drum, oscillating roller, or vibrator.

overpacking Packing the plate or blanket to a level that is excessively above the level of the cylinder bearer.

overrun — The quantity of printed copies exceeding the number ordered to be printed. Trade custom allows a certain tolerance for overruns and underruns.

packing — (1) The procedure for setting the pressure between the plate and blanket cylinders. (2) The paper or other material that is placed between the plate or blanket and its cylinder to raise the surface to printing height or to adjust cylinder diameter to obtain color register in multicolor printing.

packing gauge — A device for measuring the height of the plate or blanket in relation to its cylinder bearers.

paper conditioning — Bringing the paper's temperature to equilibrium with the temperature or atmosphere of the pressroom without removing its wrapping or exposing it to atmospheric and humidity changes.

paper sizes, international — The common paper sizes used in Europe and Japan. They are: A3 (11.7×16.5 in.); A4 (8.3×11.7 in.); A5 (5.8×8.3 in.); B4 (10.1×14.3 in.); B5 (7.2×10.1 in.); and B6 (5.1×7.2 in.). See also: *basis weight*.

paste drier — A highly viscous drier prepared by grinding the inorganic salts of manganese or other metals in linseed oil varnishes.

paster — (1) A device used to apply a fine line of paste on either or both sides of the web to produce finished booklets directly from the folder without saddle stitching. The paste is applied from a stationary nozzle as the web passes underneath it. (2) An automatic web splicer on a press. (3) The rejected web with a splice in it.

perfecting — The printing of at least one color on both sides of a sheet in a single pass through a press.

perfector — A press that can print at least one color on both sides of a sheet in a single pass. A blanket-to-blanket web offset press is an example of a perfector.

perforating — Punching a row of small holes or incisions into or through a sheet of paper to permit part of it to be detached; to guide in folding; to allow air to escape from signatures; or to prevent wrinkling when folding heavy papers. A perforation may be indicated by a series of printed lines, or it may be blind; in other words, without a printed indication on the cutline. *Alternative term:* perf.

pH A measure of a solution's acidity or alkalinity, specifically the negative logarithm of the concentration (in moles/liter) of the hydrogen ions in a solution. Measured on a scale of 0 to 14, with 7 as the neutral point.

pick resistance Ability of a paper to resist a force applied perpendicularly to its surface before picking or rupturing occurs.

picking The delamination, splitting, or tearing of the paper surface that occurs when the tack of the ink exceeds the surface strength of the paper.

pigment Finely divided solid particles derived from natural or synthetic sources and use to impart colors to inks. They have varying degrees of resistance to water, alcohol, and other chemicals and are generally insoluble in the ink vehicle.

piling A buildup of paper, ink, or coating on the offset blanket, plate, or rollers in such quantity that it interferes with print quality.

pipe rollers Small-diameter hard rollers that help to keep the ink system clean by picking up ink skin particles, lint, etc.

pitch diameter The working diameter of the gear attached to the cylinder journal.

planography A printing process that uses a flat image carrier, such as the lithographic printing plate, which has no relief images and has image and nonimage areas on the same level (or plane).

plate A flexible image carrier with ink-receptive image areas and, when moistened with a water-based solution, ink-repellent nonimage areas. A thin metal, plastic, or paper sheet serves as the image carrier in many printing processes.

plate, bimetal A negative-working multimetal printing plate that usually consists of copper electroplated on a base metal such as aluminum or stainless steel.

plate, negative-working — A printing plate that is exposed through a film negative. Plate areas exposed to light become the image areas.

plate, positive-working — A printing plate that is exposed through a film positive. Plate areas exposed to light become the nonimage areas.

plate, presensitized — A sheet of metal or paper supplied to the user with the light-sensitive material already coated on the surface and ready for exposure to a negative or positive.

plate, subtractive — A printing plate in which the light-sensitive coating also contains an image-reinforcing material.

plate, surface — A printing plate in which a light-sensitive coating applied to the plate surface is made ink-receptive in the image areas during exposure and processing, while in the nonimage areas it is removed or converted to a water-receptive layer.

plate, trimetal — A positive-working multimetal plate consisting of a top layer of chromium (the nonimage metal) and a bottom layer of copper (the image metal) electroplated to a base metal.

plate, waterless — A presensitized negative- or positive-working planographic image carrier that uses ink-repellent silicone rubber, instead of a water-based dampening solution, to keep ink from adhering to the nonimage areas of the plate.

plate bending device — A device that creases a printing plate in such a way that it fits precisely into the clamps of a press's plate cylinder. *Alternative terms:* bending fixture, bending jig.

plate blinding — The loss of ink receptivity in the image area due to an excessively acidic fountain solution.

plate clamp — A device that grips the lead and trailing edges of the plate and pulls it tight against the cylinder body.

plate cylinder — A cylinder that carries the printing plate. It has four primary functions: (1) to hold the lithographic printing plate tightly and in register, (2) to carry the plate into contact with the dampening rollers that wet the nonimage area, (3) to bring the plate into contact with the inking rollers that ink the image area, and (4) to transfer the inked image to the blanket carried by the blanket cylinder.

plate scanner A device that measures all of the various densities in a plate's image area at selected increments across the printing plate before it is mounted on the press. The press operator then sets the ink fountain keys to match the ink densities indicated by the plate scanner's measurements before beginning to print the job.

plate scumming The pickup of ink in nonimage areas of the plate.

polymerization A chemical reaction — usually carried out with a catalyst, heat, or water, and often under high pressure — in which a large number of relatively simple molecules combine to form a chain-like macro-molecule. Some printing inks dry by polymerization (a chemical reaction between the binder and solvent leaves a tough and hard ink deposit on the substrate).

preloaded pressure The amount of force required to hold the plate and blanket cylinder in firm contact when the cylinders are overpacked to create the recommended squeeze pressure.

press, blanket-to-blanket A perfecting press in which the blankets from two printing units are in contact, with the paper passing between the two blankets. Since each blanket acts as the impression cylinder for the other, no impression cylinder is needed.

press, offset lithographic A mechanical device that dampens and inks a planographic printing plate and transfers the inked image to the blanket and then to the printing substrate.

press, perfecting A press that can print at least one color on both sides of a sheet in a single pass.

press, sheetfed offset A printing press that feeds and prints on individual sheets of paper (or other substrate) using the offset lithographic printing method. Some sheetfed presses employ a rollfed system in which rolls of paper are cut into sheets before they enter the feeder; however most sheetfed presses forward individual sheets directly to the feeder.

press, single-color A press consisting of a single printing unit, with its integral inking and dampening systems, a feeder, a sheet transfer system, and a delivery. It can also be used for multicolor printing by changing the ink and plate and running the paper through the press again.

press, small offset Any press smaller than 11×17 in. (279×432 mm) without bearers (hardened metal disks attached to the ends of the cylinder or to the cylinder's journal).

press, web offset A offset lithographic press that prints on a continuous web, or ribbon, of paper fed from a roll and threaded through the press.

press section Section of papermaking machine where water is removed from the web by suction and applied pressure.

press sheet A single sheet of paper selected for the job to be printed on the press.

pressrun (1) The total of acceptable copies from a single printing. (2) Operating the press during an actual job.

presswork All operations performed on or by a printing press that lead to the transfer of inked images from the image carrier to the paper or other substrate. Presswork includes makeready.

print contrast The ratio of the difference in the density of a 75% (three-quarter) tone and a solid print to the density of the saturated solids on the press sheet.

printing pressure The force, in pounds per square inch, required to transfer the printed image to the substrate. In lithography, this includes the pressure between the plate and blanket, the blanket and the impression cylinder, and the impression cylinder and the substrate.

printing unit The section of the offset lithographic press that houses the components for reproducing an image on the substrate. With an in-line web offset press, a printing unit includes the inking and dampening systems and the plate and blanket cylinders.

proof A prototype of the printed job made photomechanically from plates (a press proof), photochemically from film, or digitally from electronic data (prepress proofs). Prepress proofs serve as samples for the customer and guides for the press operators.

Press proofs are approved by the customer and/or plant supervisor before the actual pressrun.

proof, direct digital color A type of prepress proof in which digital information is used to directly image the color proofing material. Various technologies, such as ink jet and dye sublimation, are used to image the color proofing material. No film intermediates are required.

proof, overlay A type of photochemical prepress proof used in multicolor or process-color printing where pigmented or dyed sheets of plastic (for each process color and black) are exposed to a halftone negative or positive from a set of color separation films, processed, registered to each other, and taped or pin-registered to a base.

proof, prepress A simulation of the printed piece that is made digitally from electronic data or photochemically using light-sensitive papers (principally to proof single-color printing), colored films, or photopolymers. *Alternative term:* off-press proof.

proof, single-sheet A type of photochemical prepress proof used for multicolor or process-color proofing where the printing colors are built up on a base through lamination, exposure to a halftone negative or positive from a set of color separation films, and toning or other processing.

proof press A printing machine used to produce photomechanical proofs. It has most of the features of a true production machine but is not meant for long pressruns.

proofing Producing simulated versions of the final reproduction from films and dyes or digitized data (prepress proofing) or production trial images directly from the plate (press proofing).

pull A group of inspection sheets removed from the delivery of the press.

quality control Systematically planning, measuring, testing, and evaluating the combination of staff resources, materials, and machines during (and directly after) manufacture with the objective of producing a product that will satisfy established standards and profitability of an enterprise.

ream	With a few exceptions, 500 sheets of paper.
reducer	An ink additive that softens the ink and reduces its tack.
reelroom	At a web printer, newspaper printers in particular, the separate area where roll stands are sometimes housed.
refiner mechanical pulp	Papermaking pulp produced by passing wood chips through a disk refiner instead of pressing the wood against an abrasive grinding stone.
refractive index	Measure of the ability of a material, such as a pigment particle, to bend or refract light rays. The result is expressed as the ratio of the speed of light in one medium to the speed of light in another medium (usually air or a vacuum).
register	The accurate positioning of images — either in relation to images on other press sheets or in relation to an image already printed on that press sheet.
register, circumferential	The alignment of successive ink films on top of each other on the printed sheets, usually accomplished on a rotary printing press by moving the plate cylinder toward the gripper or tail.
register marks	Small reference patterns, guides, or crosses that aid in color registration and correct alignment of overprinted colors on press sheets.
release	The readiness of the blanket to give up the paper after it leaves the nip.
remote control console	A computerized device that enables the press operator to control a variety of functions without leaving the inspection table. Among the functions controlled are inking, dampening, and lateral and circumferential image register.
resilience	The ability of a blanket to regain its thickness after pressure on its surface has been removed.
reverse slip nip	The point of contact where two rollers are rotating in opposite directions in a dampening system.
rewind	Rerolling a web onto a new core after printing.

roll Paper or cardboard produced in a continuous strip and wound uniformly around a central shaft or hollow core.

roll set curl Paper curl that occurs because the web has been stored in roll form long enough to cause its curved condition to become permanent. *Alternative term:* wrap curl.

roll stand The mechanism that supports the roll of paper as it unwinds and feeds into the press.

roll stand, auxiliary An extra roll stand mounted on top of another roll stand. This reduces downtime by permitting one stand to be reloaded while the other is still unwinding. The auxiliary roll stand cannot be used to feed two webs at the same time unless it is converted to a dual roll stand.

roll stand, dual A support for two rolls of paper, one stacked above the other, to feed two webs at the same time, or to reduce reloading time if a single web is used.

roller, intermediate A friction- or gravity-driven roller between the ductor and form roller that transfers and conditions the ink. It is called a *distributor* if it contacts two rollers and a *rider* if it contacts a single oscillating drum.

roller cover Absorbent cloth or paper that covers the rollers and helps to provide more continuous dampening by increasing the solution-carrying and solution-storing capacity of the rollers.

roller stripping Condition that occurs in lithography when ink oscillators fail to accept ink because they have been desensitized by dampening solution.

roller-setting gauge A device that shows the amount of pressure exerted when the press operator pulls a metal feeler strip between the two rollers being set.

roller-stripe gauge A device that is marked with stripes of specified widths and used to visually determine the width of an ink stripe on a roller or plate.

roll-fed A printing press or converting machine that receives paper as continuous webs from rolls, instead of as sheets. See also: *press, web*.

roll-to-roll printing — Printing webs of substrates and then rewinding them directly onto another roll core after printing.

scanning densitometer — A computerized quality control table that measures and analyzes press-sheet color bars using a densitometer.

scumming — The problem that occurs when a permanent ink image — usually dots — appears in the nonimage area.

sensitization — In platemaking, the making of an image area more ink-receptive.

sequestering agent — A substance that prevents the calcium and magnesium compounds in the dampening solution from precipitating.

setoff — Condition that results when wet ink on the surface of the press sheets transfers or sticks to the backs of other sheets in the delivery pile. Sometimes referred to as "offset," a term that is reserved for the offset method of printing.

sheeter — A specific web press delivery unit that cuts the printed web into individual sheets.

shortening compound — An ink additive that reduces ink flying, or misting.

showthrough — A term used to describe the visibility of printed material from the opposite side of the sheet. This characteristic is proportional to transparency of the substrate and the oiliness of the ink.

signature — One or more printed sheets folded to form a section of a book or pamphlet.

slabbing — The practice of removing several layers of paper from the outside of a new roll prior to inspection. *Alternative term:* stripping.

slip compound — An ink additive that improves scuff resistance of the printed ink film.

slip sheet — A sheet of paper placed between freshly printed sheets to prevent setoff or blocking.

smash-resistance The ability of a blanket to recover from being momentarily subjected to excessively high pressure.

smoother A device that helps to keep the sheet flat on the feedboard.

snowflaking The tiny, white, unprinted specks that appear in type and solids if the ink is excessively emulsified.

specific gravity Ratio of the weight of one material to the weight of an equal volume of water.

Specifications for Nonheatset Advertising Printing (SNAP) A set of standards for color separations and proofing developed for those printing with uncoated paper and newsprint stock in the United States.

Specifications for Web Offset Publications (SWOP) A set of standards for color separation films and color proofing developed for those involved in publications printing. The SWOP standards help magazine printers achieve accuracy when color separations from many different sources are printed on one sheet.

spectrophotometer An instrument used to measure the relative intensity of radiation throughout the spectrum as reflected or transmitted by a sample.

spectrophotometry The science of measuring color by analyzing the reflection or transmission of samples at specified points across the electromagnetic spectrum. The spectrophotometric curve is the most precise means for specifying colors since metameric pairs can be distinguished.

splice The area where two paper rolls are joined to form a continuous roll.

split fountain A divided ink fountain, or the use of dividers, to provide separate sections capable of holding two or more colors of ink, to permit the printing of two or more colors, side by side, in one pass through the press.

spur gear A gear that has teeth cut straight across.

squeeze Printing pressure between the plate and blanket cylinders. It is expressed as the combined height of the plate and blanket over their respective bearers on a *bearer-contact press* and as the combined height of the plate and blanket over their respective bearers minus the distance between the bearers on a *non–bearer-contact press.*

stacker A device attached to the delivery conveyor of a web press that collects, compresses, and bundles printed signatures.

stacker, compensating/counter A machine that alternates the layering of a stack of printed products by turning them 180° to offset the uneven thickness between face and spine.

standard viewing conditions A set of American National Standards Institute (ANSI) specifications that dictate the conditions under which originals (transparencies and reflection prints), proofs, and reproductions are viewed. For the graphic arts, the standard specifies a color temperature of 5000 K, a light level of approximately 200 footcandles, a color-rendering index of ninety, and, for viewing transparencies, a neutral gray surround. Large format transparencies must be viewed with 2–4 in. of white surround and should never be viewed with a dark surround. It is also necessary to view the original or reproduction at an angle to reduce glare.

start-of-print line A horizontal line that indicates the limit of the printing area. It is often engraved in the gutters about an inch behind the plate cylinder's leading edge.

static eliminator A printing press attachment that attempts to reduce the amount of static developing on a press because of low relative humidity and the movement of paper over metal surfaces. It can also be helpful in eliminating ink setoff or paper feeding problems. *Alternative term:* antistatic device.

substrate Any base material with a surface that can be printed or coated.

supercalendering Finishing operation in papermaking where the web of paper passes between a series of hard metal rollers and soft, resilient rollers that impart varying degrees of smoothness and gloss to the paper.

surface strength Ability of a paper to resist a force applied perpendicularly to its surface before picking or rupturing occurs.

tack Resistance of a liquid to splitting. It is measured by determining the force required to split an ink film between two surfaces.

tail-end hook A curl in the paper that develops at the back edge of the sheet away from the printed side.

temperature conditioning Process of allowing paper to reach pressroom temperature before unwrapping the paper.

thermo-mechanical pulp Papermaking pulp produced by preheating wood chips with steam prior to passing them through a disk refiner.

thixotropy Characteristic of a material that causes it to change consistency on being worked.

through drier A slow-acting drier that solidifies the ink film throughout and does not form a hard surface.

tight-edged paper A paper whose exposed edges have given up moisture to the atmosphere and shrunk.

tinting The bleeding of ink pigment particles into the dampening solution. *Alternative term:* toning.

top drier Drier that gives a very hard surface to the ink.

trapping (1) Printing a wet ink over a previously printed dry or wet ink film. (2) How well one color overlaps another without leaving a white space between the two or generating a third color where they overprint.

trapping, dry (1) The ability of a dry, printed ink film to accept a wet ink film over it. (2) Printing overprints, or one color on top of another, when the first color is already dry. Printing multicolor work on a single-color press is an example of dry trapping.

trapping, wet (1) The ability of a wet, printed ink film to accept another wet ink film printed over it. (2) Printing overprints, or one color on top of another, when the first color is not dry. Printing multicolor work on a web press is an example of wet trapping.

true rolling A term often used to describe the condition when there is no slip in the printing nip.

tucker blade A reciprocating knife used to force signatures into jaws to produce a jaw fold, or between rollers to produce a chopper fold.

undercut The difference between the radius of the cylinder body and the radius of the cylinder bearers.

undertone The color of a thin film of ink. It is the color of light reflected by the paper and transmitted through the ink film.

unitack A series of printing inks that have the same tack rating.

viscoelastic A material, like an offset ink, that behaves as both a fluid and an elastic solid.

warp The direction of maximum strength on a blanket.

washup The process of cleaning the inking systems and blankets of a press with specially formulated cleaning solutions to remove all ink as required at the end of the operating day or whenever an ink color change is necessary.

water pan A device that holds the dampening solution to be fed to the plate. *Alternative term:* water fountain.

water stop One of a series of devices that are set against the surface of the dampening fountain roller; commonly used to reduce the amount of solution reaching heavily inked areas of the printing plate.

waterless lithography A planographic printing process that does not require the use of a water-based dampening solution to prevent ink from adhering to nonimage areas of the printing plate. It requires special inks, presensitized waterless plates, and temperature-controlled inking systems.

wavy-edged paper A paper whose exposed edges have absorbed moisture and become wavy.

web A roll of any substrate that passes continuously through a printing press or converting or finishing equipment.

web lead The continuous strip of paper passing from supply roll, over various rollers, through press units, to the folder.

web lead rollers Any of the rollers used to support the paper web as it is fed through a web press.

web offset A lithographic printing process in which a press prints on a continuous roll of paper instead of individual sheets.

webfed A printing press that prints on a continuous roll of paper instead of individual sheets.

weft The direction of minimum strength on a blanket.

wet printing See *trapping, wet.*

wettability The ease with which a pigment can be completely wet by the ink vehicle.

wetting agent (1) In inkmaking, an additive that promotes the dispersion of pigments in the vehicle. (2) A substance, such as isopropanol or an alcohol substitute, found in a dampening solution, that decreases the surface tension of water and water-based solutions.

wire side Side of the paper that is in contact with the paper machine's wire during papermaking.

zero-speed splicer An automatic device that attaches a new roll of paper to an expiring roll without a press stop. The device is used in conjunction with a festoon to permit the expiring roll to come to a complete stop just before the splice is made and then to accelerate the new roll up to press speed.

Index